Paul Mason AIRK

Longman Guide to World Science and Technology

Longman Guide to World Science and Technology

Science and Technology in the Middle East
by Ziauddin Sardar

Science and Technology in Latin America
by Latin American Newsletters Limited

Science and Technology in China
by Tong B. Tang

Science and Technology in the USA
by Albert H. Teich and Jill H. Pace

Science and Technology in the USSR
by Michael J. Berry

Science and Technology in France and Belgium
by E. Walter Kellermann

Science and Technology in Eastern Europe
by György Darvas

Science and Technology in Scandinavia
by Georges Ferné

Science and Technology in Africa
by John W. Forje

Science and Technology in Australasia, Antarctica and the Pacific Islands
by Jarlath Ronayne and Campbell Boag

Science and Technology in the Federal Republic of Germany
by Frieder Meyer-Krahmer

Science and Technology in India, Pakistan, Bangladesh and Sri Lanka
by Abdur Rahman

Science and Technology in Japan (2nd edition)
by Jon Sigurdson and Alun M. Anderson

Science and Technology in the UK
by Sir Robin Nicholson, C.M. Cunningham and P. Gummett

Science and Technology in Japan

by Jon Sigurdson and Alun M. Anderson

LONGMAN

Longman Group UK Limited, Longman Industry and Public Service
Management Publishing Division, Westgate House, The High, Harlow, Essex
CM20 1YR, UK
Telephone: (0279) 442601

Typesetting by The Setting Studio, Newcastle upon Tyne.

Printed and bound in Great Britain by
Mackays of Chatham PLC, Chatham, Kent

First edition published 1984
Second edition published 1991

Distributed exclusively in the USA, its possessions, and Canada
by Gale Research Inc., Penobscot Building, Detroit, MI 48226, USA

British Library Cataloguing in Publication Data
Sigurdson, Jon
Science and technology in Japan.-2nd ed.
1. Japan. Science 2. Japan. Technology
I. Title II. Anderson, Alun M. III. Anderson, Alun M.
Science and technology in Japan
509.52

ISBN 0-582-03684-4 (Longman)

Contents

Acknowledgements

This book is a major revision of the Longman Guide Science and Technology in Japan, 1984, which was prepared by Dr Alun Anderson. The basic structure and the factual character have been retained. I have kept lengthy passages from the earlier version in areas where structural changes have been less rapid, which is true for the educational system. Many other parts have been basically rewritten and shortened by excluding detailed information on specific research institutes. The reader should, when looking for brief and up-to-date information on research institutes, consult the Longman directory Pacific Research Centres, or English and Japanese-language reference works listed in the References.

In preparing the book I have been helped by numerous people in government ministries and agencies in Tokyo. In particular I want to thank Mr Masahiro Kawasaki, Director General of The National Institute for Science and Technology and Mr Chihiro Watanabe, former visiting professor at Saitama University and currently Director-General for the Industrial Technology Department of the New Energy and Industrial Technology Development Organisation (NEDO). Their generous transfer of material and identification of information sources proved very useful. I want to express my thanks to Nihon Keizai Shimbun, Inc. (Nikkei) which has generously offered the Research Policy Institute, in Sweden, use of their excellent database "Nikkei Telecom Japan News/Retrieval" for research purposes, making it possible to check the recent situation on many research themes.

I also want to thank the many research managers in Japanese companies whom I have troubled on many occasions to obtain more specific information about their R&D activities. However, it has only been possible to superficially cover the industrial research scene which is a very significant part of the science and technology system in Japan.

A number of people have read and commented on various parts of the manuscript, identified shortcomings and also suggested considerable improvements. I am grateful for their interest and patience in my endeavour. I am in particular thankful to Professor Toru Yoshimura of Saitama University who appraised me of the historical background to technological modernisation in Japan.

A substantial amount of work has gone into the preparation of the lengthy, and it is to be hoped useful, appendices. I am very grateful to Ms Mieko Nishitani who prepared this part of the book at very short notice. Very useful suggestions for source material were made by Ms Junko Kurita, Librarian of the International House of Japan. I also want to thank my research assistant, Ms Yael Tagerud, at the Research Policy Institute at the University of Lund, who carefully prepared an electronic manuscript of the appendices and also xii

provided much needed assistance during the final days of completing the manuscript. In expanding and proofreading the appendices I was greatly helped by my wife, Akiko Yamamoto, who throughout inspired me in this endeavour.

Finally, I want to thank the direct sponsors for making this book possible. An early and generous grant from the Bank of Sweden Tercentenary Fund enabled me in 1983-84 to get familiar with the science and technology system in Japan. A grant from the Salen Foundation in Stockholm enabled me to further my specific studies on technological progress in Japan. Furthermore I am very grateful to the Institute for Policy Science of Saitama University for inviting me to Japan in January 1990 as guest researcher. Without this generous offer in time and money I would not have been able to prepare the manuscript. I want to thank Dr Anderson for his interest in and support for my revision of the earlier work. Standing on his shoulders I feel that I have been able, in certain ways, to prepare an improved reference tool for understanding the science and technology system in Japan.

The observant reader will notice that the transcription has certain flaws as long vowels are not marked. In spite of careful proofreading the transcriptions of the many names appearing in the appendices may still contain mistakes. The reader should also be mindful of the fact that the Japanese currency - yen - is throughout the book usually given only as Y - preceding the amount.

The reader should, when consulting the appendices, be aware of the introduction, on 1 January 1991, of eight digits, instead of seven, for all telephone and fax numbers in Tokyo. The principle is that the old seven digit numbers are now preceded by 3. Thus, all Tokyo numbers in the appendices have the additional 3 added. In rare cases this may be incorrect, as the approaching printing deadline made it impossible to check the numbers.

It is my expectation that this book meets a need among those with an established or potential interest in Japan's science and technology. Therefore I would appreciate to receive information on mistakes, omissions and suggestions for improvements which could be sent either directly or through the publisher. This could then serve as a preparation for a future edition of the present volume.

Jon Sigurdson
January 1991

Institute for Policy Science
Saitama University
and
Research Policy Institute
University of Lund
Box 2017
S-220 02 Lund
Sweden

About the authors

Alun M. Anderson is currently Washington Editor of *Nature*, the international science journal. Before moving to the United States he spent three years in Japan writing about science and science policy for *Nature* and over a year carying out research at Kyoto University on a fellowship provided by the Royal Society. He is the author of the first edition of *Science and Technology in Japa*n and of numerous articles about Japan

Jon S. Sigurdson is Professor of Research Policy, and Director of the Research Policy Institute at the University of Lund in Sweden. He specialises in science and industrial technology development in East Asia with a focus on information technologies. He has spent seven years in the region with three years in Japan. He spent most of 1990 in Japan, one endeavour being the major revision of *Science and Technology in Japan*. He is author of numerous articles on science and technology policy, more recently with an emphasis on company technology strategy.

Abbreviations

ABWR	advanced boiling water reactor
AI	artificial intelligence
AIST	Agency of Industrial Science and Technology
AMSTIC	advanced mobile traffic information and communication system
ATR	Advanced Telecommunications Research Institute
ATR	advanced thermal reactor
BIDEC	Bio-industry Development Centre
BRAIN	Bio-oriented Technology Research Advancement Institution
CST	Council for Science and Technology
DIGSUCC	driver information and guidance system using car communication
EA	Environment Agency
ELNET	Electronic Library Inc.
EPA	Economic Planning Agency
ERA	Engineering Research Association
ERATO	Exploratory Research for Advanced Technologies Organisation
ESPRIT	European Strategic Programme for Research and Development in Information Technologies (EC)
ETL	Electrotechnical Laboratory
FBR	fast breeder reactor
FGC	fifth generation computer
HDTV	high definition television
HFSPO	Human Frontier Science Programme Organisation
HSST	High Speed Surface Transportation Corporation
HTGR	high temperature gas-cooled reactor
HTTR	high temperature engineering test reactor
ICOT	Institute of New Generation Computer Technology
IMS	intelligent manufacturing system
ISAS	Institute of Space and Astronautical Science
ISTEC	International Superconductivity Technology Centre
JAERI	Japan Atomic Energy Research Institute

JAIF	Japanese Association for Industrial Fermentation
JAL	Japanese Air Lines
JAMIC	Japan Microgravity Centre
JAMSTEC	Japan Marine Science and Technology Centre
JAPIO	Japan Patent Information Organisation
JECC	Japan Electronic Computer Company
JEIDA	Japan Electronics Industry Development Association
JESSI	Joint European Sub-Micro Silicon Initiative (EC)
JETRO	Japan External Trade Organisation
JICST	Japan Information Centre for Science and Technology
JIPDEC	Japan Information Processing Development Centre
Jisdei	Research and Development Programme on Basic Technologies for Future Industries
JKTC	Japan Key Technology Centre
JMA	Japan Meterological Agency
JNR	Japanese National Railway (now privatised JR)
JOIS	JICST on-line information system
JRDC	Japan Research Development Corporation
JSPS	Japan Society for Promotion of Science
KDD	Kikusai Denshin Denwa Company (for international telecommunications)
Keidanren	Keizai Dantai Rengokai (Federation of Economic Organisations)
KEK	National Laboratory for High Energy Physics (Ko-enerugi Butsurigako Kenkyujo)
LDP	Liberal Democratic Party
LSP	large scale project
LWR	light water reactor
MAFF	Ministry of Agriculture, Forestry and Fisheries
MESC	Ministry of Education, Science and Culture
MHW	Ministry of Health and Welfare
MITI	Ministry of International Trade and Industry
Monbusho	Ministry of Education, Science and Culture
MoT	Ministry of Transportation
MPT	Ministry of Posts and Telecommunications
MSX	Japanese operating system for personal computers jointly developed by Microsoft and ASCII (Japan) in 1983
MT	machine translation
NACSIS	National Centre for Science Information Systems
NAL	National Aerospace Laboratory
NASDA	National Space Development Agency
NEDO	New Energy and Industrial Technology Development Organisation
NEEDS	database system organised and operated by Nihon Keizai Shimbun (Japan Economic Journal)
NHK	Japan Broadcasting Corporation

NICs	newly industrialised countries
NIRA	National Institute for Research Advancement
NIRIM	National Institute for Research in Inorganic Materials
NIST	National Information System for Science and Technology
NISTEP	National Institute for Science and Technology Policy
NRIPR	National Research Institute for Pollution and Resources
NTT	Nippon Telegraph and Telephone Corporation

OBI	Osaka Bio-science Institute
OCR	optical character recognition
OECD	Organisation for Economic Cooperation and Development
OEICs	opto-electronic integrated circuits
OEM	original equipment manufacture
OTL	Opto-Electronics Technology Research Laboratory (JKTC R&D company)

PATOLIS	patent on-line information system
PERI	Protein Engineering Research Institute
PNC	Power Reactor and Nuclear Fuel Development Corporation
PSI	personal sequential inference

RCAST	Research Centre for Advanced Science and Technology (University of Tokyo)
RIKEN	Institute of Physical and Chemical Research
RIMNS	Research for Metal Surface of High Performance (JKTC R&D company)
RTRI	Railway Technical Research Institute

SAC	Space Activities Commission
SCAP	Supreme Commander of the Allied Powers
SCM	superconducting magnet
SCR	Space Communication Research Corporation (JKTC R&D company)
SDI	Strategic Defense Initiative (USA)
SIGMA	software industrialised generation and maintenance aids
Sortec	Sortec Corporation (JKTC R&D company for synchrotron orbital radiation (SOR) technology)
SSC	superconducting super collider (USA)
STA	Science and Technology Agency
STC	Space Technology Corporation (JKTC R&D company)

TOKKEN	TOKubetsu KENkyu (feature of Hitachi research system)
TRDI	Technical Research and Development Institute
TRC	Tsukuba Research Consortium
TRON	the real-time operating nucleus
TSC	Tsukuba Space Centre
TSCJ	Telecommunication Satellite Corporation of Japan

| UHV | ultra high vacuum |

Zaibatsu   industrial and financial combines of a conglomerate
                type officially dissolved during the post Second World War
                period

Chapter 1

Science and technology in Japan

Japan is today a technological superpower, and more than 10 per cent of the world's expenditure for activities in science and technology are controlled by Japanese companies and government agencies. The size of the Japanese science and technology system is considerably smaller than that of the US but bigger than that of Germany, which are the only ones offering a basis for comparison as long as a European Technological Community has not become a reality, or until the Soviet Union has established a viable economic structure.

On the global scene there has over the past decade or so been a noticeable shift in the character of national comprehensive security. Industrial prowess and economic power have partially replaced military capability as a key factor for guarding national interests. Technological capability, as well as research and development efforts, has in the past played a major role in maintaining a lead in military development. Similarly, technology is now taking on an increasingly major role in civilian spheres. Being obsessed with economic security, Japan has emerged as an economic and technological superpower – which has become more evident through the relative decline of the US and the still more drastic failure of the USSR.

Japan is, as a consequence, requested by its industrial competitors to engage in more basic and creative research and share its technological research more widely. This forces the Japanese science and technology system to become more open and more internationalised. However, it is in many ways the most integrated and comprehensive system which exists, and may remain so during most of the present decade.

Forces inside Japan are also compelling changes and are in fact more important than outside political forces in modifying the science and technology system. Japan's technological development had already in the late 1970s completed the catch-up phase and embarked on a number of new approaches in order to strengthen the technological and scientific base. These included, in the government sector, programmes such as the Future Generation Basic Technologies, The Fifth Generation Computer Project and the Exploratory Research for Advanced Technologies Organisation (ERATO), to mention some of the most widely publicised.

During the 1980s new species of research organisations and financing systems have been established which cut across ministerial and agency borders and increase mobility of researchers. The interface between universities and national research institutes on one hand and industry on the other has increased.

The changes within the private companies have been less noticed although this sector has in relative terms become increasingly important. The private sector in Japan accounts for more than 80 per cent of the country's expenditure on research and development. This dominance is likely to go on increasing until the government is able to muster more political underpinning to expand the financial support for the university system and various national and international programmes. The expenditure on basic research at the universities has already been surpassed by the expense of basic research in the private companies.

The success of the Japanese industries and the ongoing globalisation of markets are compelling the companies to move more and more of their production overseas. A logical consequence is the transfer of other activities, such as design and product development and eventually research, in order to tap more efficiently into a global pool of scientific knowledge and resources. Although R&D activities in the private sector are, in the main, still located within Japan, a rapid globalisation is expected to take place during the present decade.

In sum, the Japanese system for science and technology is rapidly changing in order to become more creative and more internationalised. Such changes take place both within the government sector and in the private sector. This book will in the main deal with the present structure for science and technology and indicate its roots in the recent and occasionally to the more distant past. However, throughout the presentation major efforts have been made to illustrate the characteristics of dynamic change in the Japanese system for science and technology.

Structure

The science and technology system has to be understood at three different levels – performing, funding and decision-making, of which the latter is the most difficult to comprehend (in any country) as it consists of both formal and informal structures.

Research and development is carried out in five different categories of institutions, all of which will be discussed in considerable detail further on in this volume. These are:

1) the university system which consist of state, local government and private institutions,

2) government research institutes, which exist both at the national and local level,

3) public corporations,

4) non-profit foundations and

5) company R&D laboratories which include development activities in divisions/companies, central research laboratories and basic research laboratories.

The university system includes, aside from the traditional departments, a number of institutes attached to specific universities or operated separately on an inter-university basis to serve the whole university system. The government research laboratories, of which there are close to 100, have in terms of staff and funding been relatively stagnant over the past ten years or more – although undergoing rapid changes to become more geared to long-term and fundamental research. Many of the institutes which are controlled by various ministries, or directly by the Science and Technology Agency (STA), are undergoing structural changes in order to make their activities more relevant to a rapidly changing situation.

The public corporations for research, which among others include New Energy Development Organisation (NEDO) which was reorganised in 1988, have increased their importance, which is partly explained by their ability to offer more flexible ways of funding research. The non-profit foundations have expanded quite significantly in recent years. These include research projects which have been established on a semi-permanent basis, to which companies and other organisations dispatch their staff on a temporary basis, which serves as an important means of enhancing researcher mobility, generally low in Japan.

Finally, there are the massive R&D activities of the private companies which today constitute more than 80 per cent of total expenditure for R&D in Japan. These activities are still almost entirely carried out inside Japan. There is a very heavy concentration in the Greater Tokyo Area, which may accommodate as much as 50 per cent of Japan's industrial R&D.

The pattern of funding is relatively simple. The private industry basically funds all its own R&D, while the government provides almost all the funds for government research institutes. The funding of the university system is shared by the government and the private sector (universities), with the major share coming from the government. The public research foundations are funded mainly by private organisations and by private industry, with the remainder of funding coming from the government.

The many linkages between government and private industry activities are not noticeable at this level of aggregation. However, an extensive network of relations exists in almost all major research projects or programmes which usually involve major companies, government research institutes and universities, or university professors in their "private capacity". Such research networks, which will be particularised further on, have had a considerable impact on the establishment of joint research organisations in Europe and the US.

The decision-making and formulation of policy will be handled only briefly in this introduction, and private industry will be discussed solely in its own context. There are a number of government organisations involved with science and technology. The Science and Technology Agency (STA) is formally responsible for the overall administrative co-ordination of all R&D activities carried out by ministries and government agencies with the exception of the Ministry of Education and Culture (Monbusho).

The highest organ for policy formulation and deliberations is the Council for Science and Technology (CST), which belongs to the Prime Minister's Office. The required secretariat services for the Council are provided by STA and Monbusho. In addition it should be noted that both nuclear energy and space science, which require national planning, have been given special commissions – the Atomic Energy Commission and Space Activities Commission respectively, which conduct overall policy planning and co-ordination for all government institutions active and concerned in these two fields. For further details the reader should consult the section of this volume which deals with the government system. The Defence Agency operates its own Technical

Research and Development Institute and co-ordinates major development projects in the private sector, which generally involves collaboration with counterparts in the US. See Chapter 13.

Despite the official views on co-ordination and policy formulation for the whole nation, it is obvious to any observer that the science and technology landscape in Japan is charged with intensive competition. This is obviously so in the large private industrial sector where such a situation is natural. However, it is equally true of many of the government agencies and ministries. Thus, it is not surprising that similar proposals surface at approximately the same time in various parts of the administration with ministries vying for control of new programmes and new funds.

So, similar joint research programmes involving private companies, government research and usually universities are to be found in several ministries like Agriculture and Fishery, Health, Post and Communications and, naturally, in the Ministry of International Trade and Industry (MITI). The competition in science and technology policy may in fact be beneficial but partly undermines the ambition of the Science and Technology Agency to achieve co-ordination.

Achievements

Evaluation of individual researchers, research groups, laboratories or sectors is continuously being carried out all over the world and quantitative indicators are generally used. There are no generally accepted ways of evaluating the national systems although this is often done both inside the country and by international organisation such as OECD.

However, this book is not primarily evaluating the system for science and technology in Japan but providing information and insights on its structure and dynamic change. This notwithstanding, I will refer to some of the commonly discussed indicators by starting at the scientific apex and ending in the market-place.

So far Japan has received only five Nobel prizes, of which two were awarded during the past decade, while US scientists received 31 during the same period. Three of Japan's Nobel awards were in Physics with the remaining two in Chemistry and Medicine. Sad as this is for the scientific community in Japan, this fact indicates that Japan has been lagging in frontline research. It also reflects the lack of an environment conducive to the creative research, which is partially a criticism of the university system, where frontline research is mainly done in most other advanced countries. This is also reflected in a recent study aimed at identifying the best research centres in the world. The major US universities figured prominently in this list, but in the local Japanese context only a couple of the universities showed up although several of the institutes attached to universities, or other government institutions were given good ratings.

The publication of scientific papers provides another tool for measuring activity and performance and shows a very different pattern. In field after field the scientists in Japan have emerged as major contributors to new scientific knowledge. This is particularly true in areas such as various disciplines relating to electronics, life sciences and new materials, which will all be illustrated in the relevant sections of this book. Aside from the broad aim of gaining new scientific knowledge the publication of scientific papers reveals two other important patterns. First, scientific research in almost any particular field, as revealed in scientific publications, usually starts considerably later than in the US but usually expands very rapidly. Second, the involvement of researchers from private company laboratories is very prominent in many scientific fields and usually remains at a high level year after year.

Measuring patent activity provides a tool for gauging potential achievements which are closer to the market place. Japan has emerged as a major nation in filing and obtaining patents and much effort has been expended on understanding this phenomenon. It has been concluded, in one major study, that the Japanese companies have been increasing their patenting activity in areas which are much less science-based than in the US, including electronics but have undertaken less patenting activity in the more science-based areas of chemicals and pharmaceuticals.

The conclusion is that the US, in its patenting activity, is much closer to the scientific edge, while Japan has become a leader in engineering and technological innovation with, for the time being, weaker links to science. The study referred to argues that "much of the remarkable Japanese technological success observed over the last decade has in fact been due to highly innovative technology, originating from Japanese technological innovations." So Japan is not really at the frontier of technological research – in maintaining close links with present science. However, the Japanese system is extremely good on product innovation and product implementation which may also reflect the emphasis given to engineering education at the universities.

Still another measure is the balance of payment for technology imports and exports. This measure, which is very vague in its uncertain coverage, shows that Japan is still a net importer although the balance has shifted quite dramatically during the past two decades. The ratio between technology receipts and technology payments, which was 0.13 in 1971, had increased to 0.33 in 1988. However, the corresponding figure for the US which was 10.56 in 1971, still remains at 5.24 in 1988.

Finally, I want to mention the trade balance for high technology products which is also difficult to measure due to unclear definitions and rapid shifts in products which gradually include a higher technological content. The latest available figures show that share of high R&D intensity industries in total manufacturing and exports has remained the same for the aggregate Japanese industries and increased considerably for exports. The full effects of the second oil shock and the high value of the yen are likely to have rapidly increased the R&D intensity both of manufacturing output and exports.

Looking at specific products a much clearer and familiar picture emerges. Japan produced 8.2 million passenger cars in 1988 of which 54 per cent were exported. In the same year the country manufactured 28 million video cassette recorders and 2.2 million copying machines of which 79 per cent were exported. The competitive strength of Japanese companies can be exemplified for many other products for which marketing skill and financial acumen are critical factors. However, there can be no doubt that technological research geared to specific industrial objectives is a very important element for the Japanese success.

There can be no better illustration to this than the emergence of a handful or more of Japanese electronics companies to become world leaders in the manufacturing technology for generation after generation of memory chips – the integrated circuits which are needed in all types of electronic equipment. Three of the major electronics companies – Hitachi, Fujitsu and NEC – have also emerged as major contenders in the world market for super computers which was once controlled by a single company – Cray in the US. Japan has also initiated major efforts to become one of the leading nations in space exploration and in the development and manufacture of much of the needed spacecraft and other facilities.

In analysing key technologies for advanced industrial products – be they in the civilian or in the defence sector – it has become increasingly obvious that the balance is shifting and continues to shift from the US to Japan. At the same time Japanese leaders in the government and in industrial circles are formulating strategies which will enhance the creativity in science and forge closer links between technology and science. Simultaneously it is obvious that Japan expects to maintain its lead in many sectors of the electronics technology spectrum while advancing in many other fields such as chemicals and pharmaceuticals via genetic engineering and other science-based tools, and also embarking on large-scale efforts in space and ocean exploration.

Japan in the global context

The global science scene is shifting quite dramatically in four different arenas. First, defence technology and military R&D will decrease in relative importance as the Cold War situation has come an end, even if political and military changes are less noticeable in East and South East Asia. Second, global scientific issues are coming to the forefront, as is exemplified by the warming of the atmosphere due to increasing levels of carbon dioxide. Third, sharing the costs for expensive installations to advance scientific knowledge will become increasingly common. Fourth, demands for access to industrial technology are becoming stronger and stronger, both from the advancing countries in the Third World, and from the advanced countries which are losing their competitive advantage.

Japan has been accused, particularly by the United States, of having been a free rider in an open global system for science and technology. Although only partially correct, the issue has become increasingly critical as the US government and its agencies have become more and more vocal in their demands as their technological leadership is vanishing in sector after sector. The US government has, in volatile negotiations with counterparts in Japan, requested systemic changes which would give the US "symmetrical" or "comparable" access to the Japanese system for science and technology.

The government and its agencies in Japan have not been deaf to US requests – even if they will only partly meet the outlandish demands. The latest MITI vision, published in the summer of 1990, reveals most clearly the Japanese understanding of its science and technology system and its relation to the world. The new vision, which follows an earlier one which become public ten years ago, in 1980, has four pillars. These are internationalisation, "originalisa-tion", "regionalisation" and "gentlification" of research. These concepts, although originating from MITI, in the vision context, reveal the basic thinking and indicate changes in many parts of the science and technology system in Japan. The various MITI policies are presented and discussed in several chapters and the comments here will be now be limited to globalisation.

The globalisation of the Japanese science and technology proceeds along three different lines. First, the most rapid change may be seen in the globalisation of company research. Today, even the most internationalised Japanese companies like Sony and Canon only have 2 per cent of their R&D activities outside Japan. This should be compared with Philips in Holland and Ciba-Geigy in Switzerland which have roughly one half of their R&D outside their home countries – which of course reflects the needs of big global companies originating in a small country with a limited home market. However, Siemens in Germany has 15 per cent of its R&D outside Germany and IBM has around 40 per cent outside the US.

Japan has gained enormously from rebuilding and expanding its economy in an era of free trade expansion and expanding markets hungry for Japanese products. However, the value of exports constitutes little more than 10 per cent of the gross national product. Although this is almost one third of the industrial production the role of exports is much more significant in certain sectors, such as electronics. However, the Japanese exports constitute a much lower share than in countries such as Sweden, the Netherlands and Germany. Furthermore, only a very small share of Japanese companies' sales abroad is produced outside Japan – less than 5 per cent. This will change, partly due to requests from the US and EC countries, as the large Japanese companies establish global integrated networks for marketing and production. Nissan, for example, already sells half of its car production outside Japan, 50 per cent of which is produced outside the country, and the balance will continue to shift. Such a situation indicates a trend of globalisation in which science and technology play an important role.

Many of the major companies with an export orientation have indicated that they will already by 1995 have major R&D activities outside Japan. NEC and Sumitomo Electric indicate that 10 per cent of their R&D activities will be outside Japan in 1995 and Hitachi has forecast that one third of all its researches may be outside the country by the end of the century. The expansion of research abroad may mainly mean that R&D activities will be integrated into manufacturing units which are serving local or global markets from bases outside Japan. However, the expansion will also accrue from research laboratories, centres and groups which may be affiliated with universities or other foreign institutions to serve the corporation by tapping a global reservoir of talent and advanced knowledge.

The government agencies are no less active in promoting internationalisation, although hampered by the lack of funds to finance major international projects and often suffering from misunderstanding on how to prepare and implement truly international programmes. A first major attempt to launch an international science and technology scheme was the Fifth Generation Computer Project (see Chapter 9) which was initiated in 1981.

Foreign governments and companies were invited to join and a kind of founding conference was held in Tokyo in 1981. Although it has been questioned whether the offer was seriously meant, the foreigners were not rushing forward to join. The reasons were twofold. First, the project design had already basically been established with limited possibilities for foreigners to influence the orientation of the project. Second, foreigners doubted that Japan had much to contribute in the field of artificial intelligence and computer architecture, which were key pillars of the project, and expected to have their brains picked – if they were to join. However, the launching of the project triggered frantic activity in Europe and has no doubt contributed to the early and successful launching of the ESPRIT programme within the European Community, among other things.

Another major scheme to offer scientific co-operation with other advanced countries came with the launching of the Human Frontier Programme (see Chapter 19), which now has its headquarters in Strasbourg in Europe. However, the programme initially received only a lukewarm response with sniping remarks that Japan has little to contribute in life sciences. More recently Japan has offered foreign participation in other major programmes which include the International Institute for Superconductivity and more recently Joint International Research Programmes into an Intelligent Manufacturing System.

Furthermore, the national research laboratories have also been opened to the foreigners, by waiving the strict requirement that staff should be Japanese nationals. Similarly the university system has gradually become more and more open. The most innovative research scheme – ERATO – controlled by Japan Research Development Corporation under the Science and Technology Agency in fact has a very sizeable number of foreign researchers and even project leaders in some ten ongoing projects. In the past few years several companies have also made their central research laboratories open by inviting researchers – often on generous scholarships. Hitachi invites, through its HIVIPS programme which started in in the mid-1980s, a substantial number of researchers who spend a year or more with the company, usually at the Hitachi Central Research Laboratories.

In sum, science and technology in Japan is becoming increasingly internationalised through expansion outside its national borders and through making the system more open at home. Although the globalisation is so far only marginal it can be expected that changes will become more rapid and dramatic during the 1990s. Thus, we may expect Japan to become a technological superpower which could provide a major contribution for solving global problems.

However, it is not likely that this will remain a smooth process as the leaders of the past, among advanced countries, will see at least some of their earlier advantage disappear. At the same time the developing countries want to expand their access to Japanese technology – without necessarily paying the required price. A major presence of R&D controlled by Japanese companies may be resented both in Europe and the US. Such resentment may never appear if activities are perceived to be beneficial for the host country and foreigners and foreign companies are making good use of equal opportunities provided in Japan.

Chapter 2

Japan's islands and people

Although the aim of this book is to describe the science and technology system in Japan – its structure, policies and achievements – it is not possible to comprehend the situation fully without grasping some of the key features of this island country. Although the country was for a short period of time an imperial power, Japan is now confined to a densely populated area which suffers from the caprices of nature, such as earthquakes and great climatic differences, and with very limited natural resources. Traditional patterns of social relations and ethics remain an integral part of the contemporary society. Furthermore, Japan is presently experiencing the most rapid change of the age structure anywhere in the world. These natural and national characteristics have a distinct bearing on the way objectives are identified, priorities determined and policies implemented.

Japan consists of a long, narrow chain of islands, 3,800 kilometres in length if the northernmost islands, now under Soviet control, are included. Although the position of Japan is often compared to that of the British Isles, the northernmost point, at 45°33' N, actually has the same latitude as Milan in Italy, while the southernmost point, at 20°25', has the latitude of the Central Sahara desert. Tokyo sits at almost the same latitude as Athens and Los Angeles. No other country of comparable area spans such a vast difference in latitude or, as a consequence, experiences such a range of climates: in winter the Sea of Okhotsk surrounding the northern islands freezes and temperatures average −8.5°C, while at Naha, the capital of Japan's southernmost province, palm trees are growing and temperature averages 16.0°C.

Japan's total area is 378,000 square kilometres, which is approximately the same size as the re-united Germany but only one twenty-fifth that of the USA. The population is 123 million (1989), which is about half that of the USA and roughly 60 per cent more than that of the new Germany. However, the Japanese population is heavily concentrated around four huge urban areas which are Tokyo, Osaka and Nagoya on the main island of Honshu, and Kitakyushu with adjacent Fukuoka on the southern island of Kyushu. Almost 60 per cent of the total population live in these four metropolitan areas and another 15-20 per cent in other urban areas. In fact roughly one half of the population lives in the belt area or corridor stretching from Tokyo-Yokohama to Osaka-Kobe.

Geography and climate

Japan consists of four main islands – Hokkaido, Honshu, Shikoku and Kyushu – in addition to an island chain stretching to the northernmost island of Okinawa and about 3,900 adjacent smaller islands. A long chain of mountains runs through the middle of the archipelago, separating it into two, one side facing the Pacific and the other the Japan Sea (China Sea). Around 68 per cent of the country is mountainous – the highest peaks being around 3,000 metres – and covered with forest, 14.4 per cent is agricultural land, 4.1 per cent is used for dwellings, another 2.9 per cent for roads and about 0.5 per cent is used for industrial purposes.

Japan owes its extremely mountainous terrain to its position on the Circum-Pacific Orogenic Zone: a region where two of the Earth's crustal plates collide, building mountains and producing frequent volcanic eruptions and earthquakes on the mainland, and forcing the crust down in the extremely deep Japan and Izu-Ogasawara trenches off the Pacific coast. Consequently volcanoes are numerous, around 70 of which are active – one tenth of the world total. Not surprisingly, given the terrain, the rivers are short and fast-flowing and form deep gorges in the mountainous regions. The mountainous terrain is also reflected in the extremely indented coastline, particularly that of the Pacific coast where the mountains often drop straight into deep water.

The climate is extremely variable, not just because of the north-south extension of the country that puts its northern end in the arctic (sub-frigid) zone and the southern end in the the sub-tropic one, but because of the complex topography and the influence of the ocean currents.

Three major currents flow near the coasts of Japan of which two are warm currents flowing from the south. One is the Japan Current or Kuroshio ("black current", named after the purplish colour caused by its high salt content) which flows along the Pacific coast while the other warm current, Tsushima, enters the Japan Sea. From the north a cold current, the Oyashio or Kurile Current, flows down past the Eastern side of the Kurile Islands and Hokkaido. It is particularly rich in plankton and produces a very rich fishing ground off Hokkaido but is also effective in bringing about the low temperatures of the northern regions.

The mountains running through the centre of the main part of Japan clearly bring about the two main climatic regions. On the Pacific side the summers are hot and humid with prevailing winds from the south-east and winters are dry and clear. On the Japan Sea coast, north-westerly winds from the Asian continent bring the heaviest winter falls of snow in the world: in the north-west annual snowfalls of five metres are not uncommon.

The broad division into Pacific and Japan Sea climates is modified by local topography. In the inland basins very high temperatures are reached in summer, while in the coastal regions lying around the shores of the Seto Inland Sea the climate is much more moderate. All except the most northerly parts of Japan experience a hot and humid rainy season in late June and early July, and the southern and easterly regions are affected each year by typhoons from August to October.

Natural resources

Natural resources consist of three main categories – food, forestry, energy and mineral resources. Japan as an island country is well endowed with fishing grounds which are among the richest in the world. Japan's total production of fish amounts to more than 12 million metric tons (1987), ahead of the USSR and China and the largest in the world, accounting for some 15 per cent of world production. The advanced development of Japan's fishing industry is largely attributable to its offshore fishing grounds, where the meeting of the warm Kuroshio Current and the cold Oyashio Current results in an abundant supply of fish. Since the reorganisation of the economy prompted by the Dodge Plan a few years after the end of the First World War, Japan has been basically self-sufficient in food production although now importing large quantities of foodstuff for cattle, pig and chicken production. The characteristic features of the food eaten by the Japanese people can be traced back to the prehistoric era. The abundant fish as a protein source was early on supplemented by rice, for which the climate and soil of Japan were exceptionally suited. Production of rice, which is the staple food, has always been regarded as the basis for life in Japan. This partly explains the reluctance to switch to imported rice even though this is available in the world market at considerably lower costs than rice grown on the Japanese islands.

Almost 70 per cent of Japan's total area is covered by forests which play an important role in land conservation, essential because of the mountain ranges and torrential rains. However, Japan's forests account for less than 1 per cent of the world's total forested land. Although producing 33 million metric tons in 1987, Japan is a major importer of logs and wood chips, importing roughly 70 per cent of its total consumption, including important areas such as printing and packaging.

Metal mining in Japan, as represented by the copper, lead, and zinc industries, is tied directly to the refining industry, and has in the past played an important role in the domestic supply of raw materials. However, the national demand for non-ferrous ores is largely met through imports because of increased domestic labour costs, depletion of high-yield ore deposits and the difficulties in mining exploration. As a consequence, the Japanese government has sought to promote development of overseas resources through investment in projects to exploit jointly rich deposits in a number of countries.

Japan used to be rich in coal resources, although the coal industry was slow to develop and had its real beginning only after the Meiji Restoration in 1868. The coal industry entered the period of its greatest activity during the first quarter of this century and reached an annual production of 30 million metric tons in 1919. New mining methods were developed and increased coal production was adopted as a high priority policy, and annual production reached 50 million metric tons in 1957. Increasing reliance on imported oil and soaring labour costs and safety problems in deep deposits forced a drastic reduction. The production is now down to less than 15 million metric tons, which corresponds to approximately 10 per cent of the country's energy consumption in 1987.

Japan's steel industry is the world' second largest after that of the USSR, and possibly the most efficient – even if Korea has in recent years become a very strong contender for efficiency. The country is, together with West Germany, a world leading exporter of steel. However, the Japanese steel industry is almost completely dependent on foreign supplies of iron ore and coal.

There are no major inland deposits of petroleum or gas and the topography has not favoured Japan with a continental shelf with any rich oil resources to exploit. Thus, the rapid industrial expansion in 1955-1970, which focused on heavy and chemical industries, was completely dependent on large-scale imports of crude oil, iron ore and other minerals, all of which were available at low cost until the first oil shock in 1973.

Population

With a population in 1990 of 123.6 million, Japan is the seventh most populous country in the world, after the People's Republic of China, India, the Soviet Union, the United States, Indonesia and Brazil. Overall population density is high at 327 persons per square kilometre and puts Japan among such densely populated nations as the Netherlands, South Korea and Bangladesh. Naturally, the concentration of the population in the strip of flat land on the Pacific coast of the main island of Honshu, forming the Hokkaido megapolis running from Tokyo to Osaka, makes the population density very uneven.

Figure 2.1 Population and GNP density per habitable area (1988)

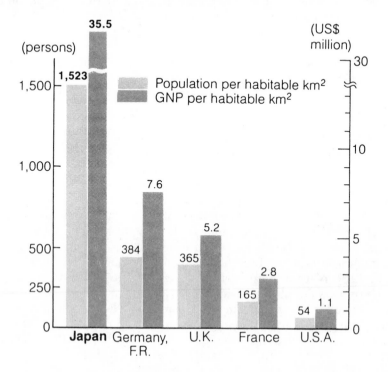

Source: Japan 1990 – An International Comparison, Keizai Koho Centre, Tokyo 1989, p. 11

Figure 2.2 Changes in the population pyramid

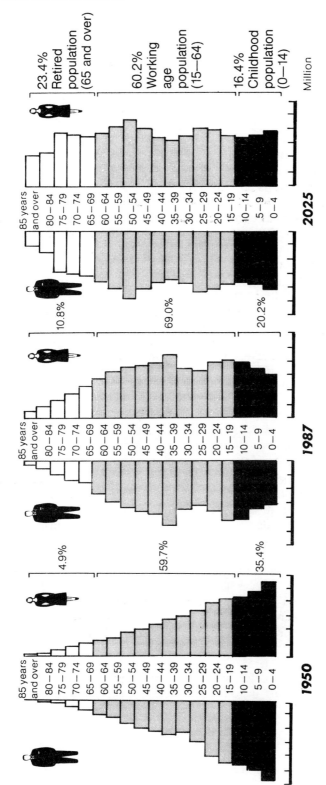

Source: Japanese Working Life Profile – Statistical Aspects, Japan Institute of Labour, Tokyo 1989, p. 10

In the many mountainous areas of Japan the population density is very low, while the industrial plains have the highest population densities of anywhere in the world. Figure 2.1 provides a comparison of population densities per habitable square kilometre. The density in Japan is 1,523 persons per square kilometre, to be compared with less than 400 in Germany and the UK and only 54 in the USA. When comparing GNP per habitable square kilometre Japan reaches 35.5 million US$ compared with 7.6 million in the Germany and only 1.1 million US$ in the US. Thus, not only the population but also industrial production and all other economic activities show an extreme degree of concentration. This situation partly explains the extremely high land prices in the urban ares in Japan but also indicates an influence on transportation and personal communications to make the Japanese industrial and economic system highly efficient.

The total population has doubled in the past fifty years and tripled over the last century but population growth is now falling and is rapidly approaching zero. A very profound change in the overall structure of the population is taking place. With the rapid slowdown in the birthrate and an increase in life expectancy the proportion of old people in the population is increasing very rapidly. The shape of the Japanese age pyramid remained almost the same until a few decades ago. Today the effects are already very noticeable, and by the year 2025 it is predicted that Japan will have an age pillar rather than an age pyramid. See Figure 2.2. The implied changes, the ageing of the Japanese society, will take place quicker than in any other country, forcing the planners and politicians and naturally the people to identify new approaches for handling many societal issues.

Society

A few brief comments about the Japanese society are made as societal relations have a considerable bearing on the way science policy is determined – the often intense competition between ministries for prestige projects, and the length of time taken to discuss projects and analyse similar projects in other countries, for example, reflect the way Japanese society is organised.

No country in the world has experienced a higher rate of economic expansion than Japan. Although with strong roots in the preceding period, the major changes started with the Meiji Restoration in 1868. By the turn of the century, a completely new social order had emerged based on modern institutions observed to be successful in Europe and America. The modernising of Japan in 1900 incorporated modern industries, public education, private stock companies, mass transportation, banks, a conscripted military, and a host of other institutions which replaced a less integrated, Confucian-inspired feudal order.

However, traditional patterns of social relations and social rightness still remain a significant part in today's Japan. It is often argued that the best examples are provided by the traditional household, village society, and Confucian morality. In the past the traditional household and village shared common characteristics of social solidarity based on common practical interests. It is usually pointed out that each was corporate in significant ways, and each combined the notion of participation in decision-making with that of a status hierarchy and formal authority. Furthermore, the morality of Confucianism was a contributing factor that helped shape a natural evolution of modern institutions.

A new social system ripened as Japan entered into this century. Having purchased companies from the government, older commercial houses and emerging entrepreneurial groups became innovative centres for continued industrial development. Conspicuous among the new creations were 'zaibatsu', or industrial and financial combines, which comprised many companies owned by a key holding company. The larger companies developed complex networks of sub-contracting and were generally exploiting the wage differentials in small companies while expanding their own seniority and welfare system. After the Second World War Japan was in fact indirectly ruled by the US occupation forces – until 1952. During this reform period the 'zaibatsu' holding companies were abolished and ownership more widely distributed – to which a high rate of inflation contributed – with a significant reduction in the gap between rich and poor.

Education also expanded during the post-war period. The government has in fact always acknowledged the significance of having a highly educated population. There can be no doubt that the Japanese system is meritocratic and education is the central source of social mobility. Thus, it is not surprising that competition to enter the universities is extremely intensive and educational accomplishments score very high in international comparisons.

The vertical – or group – organisation assumes that belonging and loyalty are connected with membership in organisations such as large companies, ministries, universities, religious organisations, etc. The form of organisation and loyalty stems from a persistence of social relations that arose earlier in Japanese history – far beyond the modernisation which started in the past century.

One consequence of the vertical structure is an almost complete lack of class-consciousness in Japan. Surveys have repeatedly shown that a majority, sometimes as much as 90 per cent of Japanese, regard themselves as middle-class, and it is true that the type of education and the interests of the Japanese do not differ greatly according to socio-economic status, as they do in the West. The Japanese are rightly proud of this. Indeed, one famous commentator has pointed out that, once one understood the significance of the division of a British pub into a lounge bar and a public bar, little more need be said to explain the failure of the British economy!

It would be quite wrong, however, to believe that because Japan lacks consciousness of class, it has a more equitable distribution of wealth or a greater social mobility than do Western nations. Four major social groups can be identified. At the top is the 10 per cent or so of society who own and control the nation's wealth. Second comes the "labour aristocracy", workers in large companies who enjoy lifetime employment, consistent wage increases according to the number of years of employment, and company health insurance. This relatively privileged group has formed the image of the Japanese worker abroad, but it contains only around 30 per cent of the labour force.

Beneath this group comes a large group working in small and medium-sized enterprises. Their wages are lower, job security is not guaranteed and the provision of health care is generally poor. The large companies generally subcontract to smaller companies, which occasionally means that the good conditions found in the large companies are bought at the expense of smaller companies. Finally there is a large class of casual workers, including a sizeable faction of the female labour force, who can be hired and fired at will. There has generally been a considerable wage differential between male and female employees, with a reluctance to provide equal career opportunities for women. The situation is slowly changing as more women enter the workforce and are determined to exploit career opportunities outside the traditional family chores.

Among the last group there are also small groups of migrant workers who come from poor farming regions to supplement the income from their farms during the off-season. More recently, Japan is experiencing the problem of illegal immigrants from developing countries, lured by high wages. Most of them come on tourist visas which are generally given for three months, or occasionally on student visas. Although the authorities are very strict many employers are quite willing to use these foreign labourers, usually at low wages.

Within groups of people sharing, for example, a common workplace, there is a greater conformity in views and degree of interdependence than is seen in the West. This is even true on a national scale and in part reflects the long period for which Japan was isolated – the country was for all practical purposes closed to all foreigners for 250 years – and the almost total absence of foreign ethnic groups with different manners and customs.

In psychological terms interdependence has its origin in the unique child-rearing practices found in Japan. Young children are at first extremely pampered by western standards, but at around the age of five suddenly enter an extremely competitive educational system which culminates in the university entrance "examination hell". The result is, according to psychologists, a remarkable initial dependence of the child on the mother which is later transferred to the adult's dependence on the family group and the workplace which sustains him.

These two characteristics – the formation of vertical groups and the high degree of dependence within a group – have important effects on the decision-making process. Decisions on policy are often made extremely slowly as all members of a group are consulted, and consulted again, until a conscensus is reached. But once a conscensus has been attained the agreed policy can be implemented very quickly. The consequence of this approach can naturally be seen even in the science and technology programmes. With only few exceptions the major science programmes, discussed in Chapter 6 and Chapter 7 took a very long time to decide and were begun well after similar programmes in the West, but they are often better integrated and have a clearer aim than the latter. The past decade has provided numerous examples of commanding technological leads in the West being rapidly eroded once a Japanese effort springs into action, and it is very likely that many more examples will emerge in the future.

The political parties

The present political system provides a considerable degree of centralisation of power – particularly compared with the pre-war period. There have in fact rarely existed any rivals to the power of the prime minister and the cabinet during the post-war period. Much of this centralising potential was realised because of the unchallenged position of the Liberal-Democratic Party since 1955. This has enabled long-term lines of communication and pressure to be established between the ruling party, the ministries, and certain pressure groups, in particular those representing large companies and agriculture. It is often pointed out that, although the bonds of this ruling elite have frequently been exaggerated, there is little doubt that the members have been able to maintain a high degree of common understanding on basic economic policies. In recent years the often outlandish demands from the USA that Japan must change its domestic policies in areas such as retail system, control of land prices, increased level of investment in public infrastructure, etc., have made the cohesion remain much stronger than it would otherwise have been. Thus, the actions of the the US can be interpreted as those of a strong opposition party acting against the domestic parties.

The present political suitability dates from 1955 when the Liberal Democratic Party came into existence through the merger of two conservative parties. The socialist parties also joined forces in the same year to become the Japan Socialist Party. A faction left in 1959 over the controversy over the revision of the United States-Japan Security Treaty to be signed in 1960, and formed the Democratic Socialist Party. A new political force, the Komeito (Clean Government Party), the political arm of the powerful religious organisation Soka Gakkai, made a dramatic entry on the political scene in the 1960s. A fifth major party is the Communist Party.

The Liberal Democratic Party, which consists of several factions and may be likened to a "United Front Party", has hardly been seriously challenged since it was established in 1955. However, in the general elections of 1967, LDP failed for the first time to win a majority of the popular vote and its share of the vote continued to fall. The emergence of a multiparty system did not materialise and LDP regained its power during the 1980s, to be challenged by the Socialist Party towards the end of the decade. LDP lost its majority in the House of Councillors (Upper House) in 1989 because of the advance of the Socialist Party but was able to keep a majority at the election for the House of Representatives. The present election system, which is neither proportional nor majority votes in one-member units, is favourable to LDP but serious discussions are under way to change the system.

The eight main regions

Japan is divided into 47 administrative prefectures and eight main regions, of which five refer to the main island of Honshu. See Figure 2.3. The population figures for regions are from the 1990 census.

Kanto
– area 32,383 square kilometres, 8.6 of total
– population 38,541,000, 31.2 per cent of the total
– population density 1190/square kilometre
The Kanto region lies at the centre of Japan and contains the capital, Tokyo.

Figure 2.3 Map of Japan with major cities

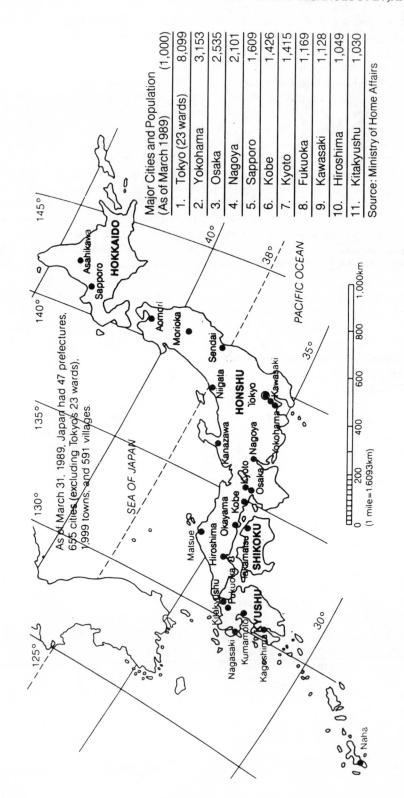

Major Cities and Population (As of March 1989)	(1,000)
1. Tokyo (23 wards)	8,099
2. Yokohama	3,153
3. Osaka	2,535
4. Nagoya	2,101
5. Sapporo	1,609
6. Kobe	1,426
7. Kyoto	1,415
8. Fukuoka	1,169
9. Kawasaki	1,128
10. Hiroshima	1,049
11. Kitakyushu	1,030

Source: Ministry of Home Affairs

As of March 31, 1989, Japan had 47 prefectures, 655 cities (excluding Tokyo's 23 wards), 1,999 towns, and 591 villages.

Source: Japan 1990 – An International Comparison, Keizai Koho Centre, Tokyo 1989, p. 11

It is the most densely populated region of the country. North-Eastern Kanto is dominated by high mountains but the Pacific side contains Japan's largest area of flat land, the Kanto plain. Around Tokyo Bay are concentrated Japan's major industrial centres of Tokyo, Yokohama, and Kawasaki: with the exception of textiles virtually every industrial sector has major production facilities in this one region.

Kinki
- area 33,074 square kilometre, 8.7 per cent of total
- population 22,207,000, 18.0 per cent of total
- population density 671/square kilometre

The Kinki region contains Kyoto, the old imperial capital, and Osaka, the second largest economic centre, The northern part of Kinki is mountainous and receives the heavy winter snows typical of the Japan Sea coast. To the south lies the Osaka plain, which has a warm, wet climate with particularly heavy summer rains. All forms of heavy and light industry are found in the Osaka-Kobe region, while Kyoto remains a centre for administration and for traditional arts and crafts.

Chubu
- area 66,777 square kilometres, 17.7 per cent of total
- population 21,022,000, 17.0 per cent of total
- population density 315/square kilometre

The northern part of Chubu region contains many of Japan's highest mountains and has numerous peaks over 3,000 metres. To the south is Mount Fuji, the highest mountain in Japan at 3,776 metres. North of the mountains, on the Japan Sea coast, very heavy snows fall in the winter, but the area is one of the major producers of rice. Industry is concentrated around Nagoya where there are highly developed textile, oil refining, automobile manufacturing and heavy industries.

Chugoku
- area 31,789 square kilometres, 8.4 per cent of total
- population 7,746,000, 6.2 per cent of total
- population density 244/square kilometre

Chugoku is the westernmost part of the main island of Honshu and because of its position to the north of the Seto Inland Sea has been an important maritime link for trade between Kinki and Kyushu. Mountain ranges run east-west through the centre of the region dividing it into two: the Japan Sea coast which, like the rest of that coast, receives heavy snows in the winter, and a region with a mild climate bordering the Seto Inland sea. Petrochemicals, textiles and other heavy industries have developed but the resulting pollution has destroyed many of the fishing grounds in the Inland Sea. The ports in the region are, however, still of major importance for fisheries further afield.

Shikoku

- area 18,828 square kilometres, 5.0 per cent of total
- population 4,195,000, 3.4 per cent of total
- population density 223/square kilometre

Shikoku is a mountainous island situated to the south of the Seto Inland Sea. Until recently it has been comparatively isolated and underdeveloped, a situation which is likely to change as the island has now been linked to Honshu by one of the world's longest bridges. Northern Shikoku has the mild climate characteristic of the Seto Inland Sea area, and supplies the urban Kinki region with vegetables from farms in the many small plains along its shoreline. In the south of the island the abundance of forests and hydroelectric power has created a large pulp and paper industry. The island is also an important base for the fishing fleet which exploits the bonito found in large numbers in the nearby Kuroshio Current.

Kyushu

- area 44,419 square kilometres, 11.8 per cent of total
- population 14,518,000, 11.7 per cent of total
- population density 327/square kilometre

The most southerly of Japan's four large islands, Kyushu is a mountainous region with numerous volcanoes including two that are still very large and active – Aso and Sakurajima. The climate is warm and wet and rice, wheat, oranges, and vegetables are grown and cattle reared. The nearby warm Kuroshio Current and the large Continental Shelf makes the area important for fishing. Northern Kyushu contains coal deposits, and iron and steel industries are highly developed in Kitakyushu area, Japan's fourth massive industrial and urban zone. To the south Nagasaki is an important shipbuilding centre. In recent years Kyushu has been an increasingly important centre for electronics, and semiconductor companies, both domestic and foreign ones, which have established plants in and around Oita in the north.

Tohoku

- area 66,912 square kilometres, 17.7 per cent of total
- population 9,738,000, 7.9 per cent of total
- population density 146/square kilometre

Tohoku, the northern part of the main island of Honshu, is in relative terms a backward region in which the development of industry and the exploitation of natural resources has lagged behind the rest of the country. The area is divided into two by three parallel ranges of mountains which run from north to south. The Japan Sea side of the region is warmed by the Tsushima Current but experiences enormous snowfalls in winter when the moisture-laden winds from the sea rise over the mountain ranges. The eastern side has generally low temperatures, influenced by the cold Oyashio (Kurile) Current. The region produces a quarter of the nation's rice and much fruit and has a large fishing industry. The main industrial centre is Sendai.

Hokkaido

- area 83,520 square kilometres, 22.1 per cent of total
- population 5,644,000, 4.6 per cent of total
- population density 68/square kilometre

Hokkaido, Japan's northernmost island, is a mountainous region with a cold climate and heavy snowfalls from November to April. The major industries are agriculture and fishing: the area is noted for its dairy farms and the surrounding Continental Shelf is one of the richest fishing grounds in the world. There is little other industry based on local raw materials, principally the production of timber, paper and wood pulp from the region's extensive forests. Hokkaido is now linked to the main island of Honshu through one of the longest tunnels in the world.

Chapter 3

A technological superpower – its economic and industrial foundation

Historical background

Japan has, since the early 1960s, been seen as an economic power on the global scene. Its very rapid economic development since the end of the Second World War can be attributed to the competent and aggressive leadership of the private companies, the greatly improved possibilities for free trade and the development role shouldered by the government agencies.

There is a long tradition of a development state in Japan which can be traced already in the decades before the Meiji Restoration. Technology has always played an important role in industrial development, and Japan was already in those early years very eager to learn about scientific and technological achievements abroad and bring the relevant knowledge to Japan in order to reduce the threatening gap in technological prowess vis-a-vis the Western powers.

In 1855 Japan imported naval ships from Holland, and Dutch instructors were active in teaching various military sciences such as shipbuilding, surveying, cartography and so on. In response to a government request Holland provided machinery and engineers to establish the Nagasaki Iron and Steel Works, which was completed in 1861.

After the Meiji Restoration the activities grew in scale and Japan became much more active in screening the industrialised world and importing the required technology. Although mistakes were made the Japanese soon identified the best sources for relevant knowledge and in the early period imported a large number of specialists. They were asked to remain for a relatively short period of time, because of their high remuneration. This, early approach established a pattern which was to be followed for almost a century – identifying sources for needed technology and building industries and institutions to realise fully the potential in Japan.

A gradual development of industries financed by private capital followed the transfer of government-operated factories to private ownership which took place around the turn of the century. By the end of the Russo-Japanese War in 1905 Japan had been able to develop heavy industries such as shipbuilding, iron- and steel-making, coal mining and power generation. By then the *zaibatsu* business groups had already emerged as major players on the industrial scene. The industrial structure greatly changed during the First World War and the focus shifted towards heavy and chemical industries. The economy benefited from being on the winning Allied side and far away from the major European arena of fighting. Japan recorded a considerable trade surplus and became for a short period of time a creditor-nation.

Throughout the early modernisation period the *zaibatsu* partook in a major way in the country's technological progress. These institutions originated in the Edo period from a wealthy class of merchants and became very prominent during the early part of the century, as the owners diversified their control over trade and finance aside from major activities in mining and manufacturing. The *zaibatsu* had easy access to capital and were aggressive entrepreneurs. Thus they imported foreign technology, adapted and improved the technology and built industrial empires in which economies of scale played an important role. In doing so the *zaibatsu* fostered a new elite of business managers which were able to match the elite bureaucrats.

A considerable strengthening of the technological and industrial base took place during the period from 1914 till the late 1920s. At the outbreak of the war Japan was stopped from importing chemicals and other important materials from Germany and embarked on a number of initiatives to remedy this situation. One such enterprise was the establishment of the Institute of Physical and Chemical Research (RIKEN) which had a primary objective of promoting basic studies in science and thereby contributing to the industrial development of the country.

A number of other institutes were also established, several of them with the expressed purpose of assisting industry. The military outlook started to colour many of these efforts, which is true for the shipbuilding industry and also for a fledgeling automobile industry which was granted subsidies to produce six officially designed types of truck, and the army strongly demanded that the automobile industry be strengthened.

Origin of a technology policy

In a policy document from 1930, issued from the Commerce and Industry Council, it is possible to identify many characteristics of present policies which included the following ideas:

1. promote communication and transfer of research results so that they may be used effectively by industry;

2. promote joint research so that similar research is handled in a co-ordinated way;

3. identify the key research topics for which relevant support/subsidy systems should be developed; and

4. establish organisations which can maintain communication for and control of research activities.

The menacing war situation created a conflict between the military and some of the *zaibatsu* combines which were opposing the military requirements. The consequence was that the war-oriented economy generated a new generation of financial combines that specialised in heavy manufacturing industries for the military sector. This military shift explains the fact that the output of heavy industries in 1938 for the first time exceeded that of light industry.

The science and technology system was increasingly influenced by military considerations. The outline for the basic national policy in 1940 included a passage which requested the promotion of science and rationalisation of industry. With an Education Ministry having a keen interest in science and technology, the Planning Board prepared a plan which aimed at national control of technology research. The document suggested the following four measures:

1. the country should have a Technology Board as the central control agency;

2. there should be a Science Board;

3. the national, public and private research institutes should be reorganised and their facilities improved; and

4. more funds should be allocated for research.

The plan encountered much opposition as private industry was not willing to give up control of its research facilities and the various ministries and agencies were not too eager to give up control of their facilities. Naturally, the university sector was also negative. However, the measures were eventually accepted and adopted by the government in May 1941. The major purpose was to establish a firm structure for the war situation – based on science and technology. It was expected that Japan would benefit from epoch-making developments in science and that its society should become scientifically-minded. The required measures in a number of areas, with the establishment of research institutes and research programmes, and the necessary administrative structure were concretely stated.

The establishment of a Technology Board, which incorporated the existing Ministry of Commerce and Industry, was officially announced in January 1942. The Technology Board became increasingly powerful and took charge of planning and realisation of research. Although the new structure for promoting science and technology had quickly been established the actual research results were slow in coming. This led the government to discuss Improvement Measures for Scientific Research in August 1943, followed in October by the Act for Establishment of Total Measures for Science and Technology Mobilisation. This resulted in the creation of the Research Mobilisation Commission and the Wartime System for Researchers. However, there were serious shortages in research equipment and supplies, co-ordination was poorly executed and many researchers and engineers had been mobilised in the military services, So the military mobilisation of research in Japan was hardly a success.

Technology policy after 1945

Naturally the Technology Board was abolished when the Allied Occupation came to Japan and its function was in the main divided between the Ministry of Education and the predecessor of the present MITI. Without the military orientation the basic principles of the support system for science and technology remained. The rapid expansion of science-oriented universities and technical colleges to meet the military requirements remained or were re-constituted under a new educational system to train a large number of engineers to serve the civilian industry.

The technological development, to serve military purposes, provided a significant corner-stone for technological progress after 1945. The optical industry benefited from the infusion of knowledge from the producers of precision military equipment. The engineers in the military aircraft industry turned to the production of engines, automobiles and railway transportation like Shinkansen. The shipbuilding industry shifted from battleships to commercial vessels and was step-wise and significantly contributed to Japan's emergence as the world's leading ship-building nation.

However, the wartime isolation also meant that Japan had been cut off from the technological development which had taken place to some extent in the UK but mainly in the USA, and technology imports became very important. This situation provided MITI, which had been re-constituted in 1949, with an important mission. The ministry immediately began to survey the frontiers of technological knowledge and keep itself well informed about the industrial possibilities of new technologies. Thus, MITI could set realistic national priorities for technological progress by choosing certain industries which were to be cultivated while others were to be phased out. The most important policy instrument was MITI's control of foreign trade, without which this cultivation of industries and technologies would not have been possible.

Until around 1965 MITI had almost total control over all imports and exports and no major transaction could be completed without its approval. The trade control, in combination with administrative guidance, enabled MITI, in partnership with private companies, to direct imported technology, finance, and natural resources to a changing set of industries – at first coal and steel, then shipbuilding and other heavy industry, to be followed by petrochemical and chemical industries and finally electronics industries.

Administrative guidance (*gyoei shido*) is employed by government agencies to secure the acceptance by individual firms of policies and practices which are judged to be desirable by the government. Such guidance may consist of directions, requests, admonitions or suggestions, originating from the ministries concerned, and often supplemented in more subtle ways. More or less formal study groups, advisory boards or councils appointed by a ministry or an agency are asked to deliberate on various issues. The subsequent reports often have the implicit character of administrative guidance. It may often come in the form of recommendations from a *shingikai* – ministerial deliberation council.

The system of administrative guidance was widely used, in particular by MITI, in the immediate post-war period, up to the mid-1960s, when it came under severe criticism from Japan's major trading partners. Its effectiveness may have been exaggerated for MITI experienced a series of failures which happened in cases where there was limited consensus between the government and private industry, or between the various ministries or agencies concerned. Most prominent among the failures are MITI's attempt to make the car manufacturers develop and produce a people's car in the 1960s and the following attempt in the early 1970s to make the major electronic companies join forces on one computer design in order to meet the challenge of IBM.

In the late 1960s and the early 1970s the role of MITI and administrative guidance declined rapidly as Japan became a free-trade nation and the private firms had become both financially and technologically strong. However, there can be little doubt that administrative guidance remains an important instrument and that efforts to promote the national interests in science and technology remain strong in Japan – as they do in all industrialised countries. However, the towering direct role of MITI has been replaced by a situation in which government initiatives are more widely shared, and are more subtle. Even more important is the dynamic emergence of world technological leadership among Japanese private companies.

Economic growth and industrial restructuring

There are a number of factors which have made this success possible and a selection has been made to highlight the following four factors:

1. economic growth and industrial restructuring;

2. the willingness, and ability, of the private sector to shoulder very large expenditure for research and development;

3. the foresight of the government in promoting relevant policies; and

4. the recent integration of the private sector to engage in long term exploratory basic research.

These factors will be discussed in varying depth before the chapter gives an international comparison. Finally follows a discussion of the new research and technology initiatives which are embedded in the visions of agencies. The R&D structures and technology strategies of individual companies are covered in the following chapter.

During 1990, twelve large companies will each allocate more than Y100 billion to research and development. See Table 3.1. Their combined outlay for

Table 3.1 Largest R&D spenders in Japan (1990)

Name	Amount (billion yen)
Hitachi	380
Toyota Motor	380
Matsushita Electric Industry	337
NEC	300
Fujitsu	298
Honda (imputed figure)	190
NTT	260
Toshiba	256
Nissan Motor	240
Mitsubishi Electric	187
Mitsubishi Heavy Industry	104
Canon	100
Total	3,032

Source: Nihon Keizai Shinbun, July 2, 1990

R&D development amounts to Y3,000 billion, which is 30 per cent of the national expenses for R&D. All these companies are today household names like Toshiba, Toyota and NEC.

It is natural to find that the five electronics companies are in the top league and that possiblly NTT, the telephone company, should be included in the same group. The ranking list also includes three of the major automobile companies and two companies from the Mitsubishi group and Canon, which has shown a phenomenal rate of growth in the past decades. All large companies in Japan, and many of the not so large companies, have rapidly increased their expenditure on research and development. The consequence is that the ratio of research to the gross national product has increased considerably. Taking 1975 as a starting point for comparison they both grew at the same rate until 1980. Since then the national expenditure for R&D – mainly in the private sector – has increased much more rapidly than GNP. See Figure 3.1.

Figure 3.1 Changes in R&D expenditure and GNP (fixed prices, 1975:100)

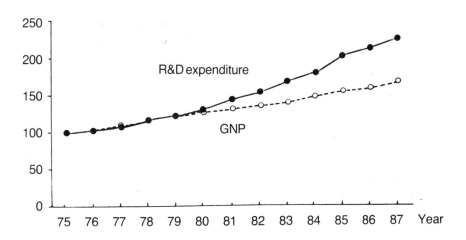

Source: Science and Technology White Paper (Kagaku Gijutsu Hakusho) 1989. Compiled by Science and Technology Agency, Tokyo. Printing Bureau, 1990, Ministry of Finance, p. 4

The rapid expansion of company R&D expenditure is caused by a number of factors of which the following three are important:

1. both the national economy and the individual companies have restructured towards knowledge-intensive high-tech industries;

2. each product or product system contains a higher level of complex functions and features which are rooted in preceding R&D; and

3. the product life-cycle has shortened, which requires more research for a certain amount of sale.

Simultaneously the manufacturing sector itself is undergoing two fundamental changes. First, many of the new products require less costly production equipment. Second, manufacturing facilities have become more and more flexible and new investment is not required for each new product generation. The consequence is that expenditure, or rather investment, in research and development equals or even surpasses investment in machinery, equipment and plant in many of the Japanese companies. This is true for Hitachi, NEC and Toshiba and these companies should increasingly be viewed as development companies and not primarily manufacturing companies. A similar trend is distinguishable for the industry as a whole. The ratio between R&D expenditure and investment in facilities has increased from about 0.3 in 1977 to roughly 0.5 in 1987 and is constantly increasing. See Figure 3.2.

Figure 3.2 Ratio between R&D expenditure and investment in plant, machinery and equipment in Japanese industry, 1977-87

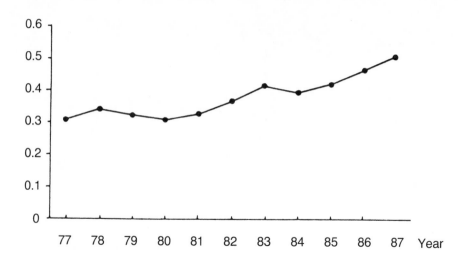

Source: Science and Technology White Paper (Kagaku Gijutsu Hakusho). Compiled by Science and Technology Agency, Tokyo. Printing Bureau, 1990, Ministry of Finance, p. 4

One would assume that this trend is concentrated in the electronic, and car industries and some others. However, this is not the case and the same trend is affecting processing and raw material industries. See Figure 3.3.

The most striking increase in research and development expenditure during the 1970s and the 1980s has been in motor vehicles. This investment in advanced, fuel-saving technology had already paid dividends when in 1980 Japan overtook the USA to become the world's largest manufacturer of automobiles. The top four companies – Toyota, Nissan Motor, Honda and Mitsubishi Motor – supply the majority of an annual production of more than 8 million vehicles, of which more than 50 per cent are exported, although the share is declining as production is reallocated overseas.

Figure 3.3 Trends in equipment investment and research and development investments

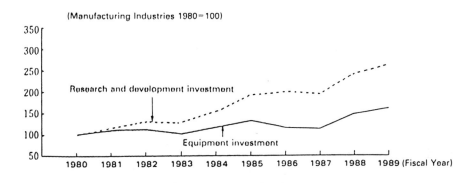

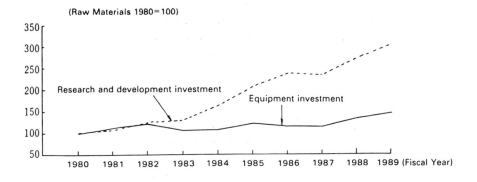

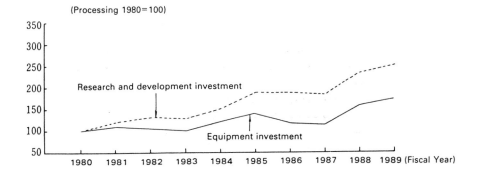

Source: Economic Survey of Japan 1988-89. Compiled by Economic Planning Agency, Tokyo: The Japan Times, 1990, p. 88

The other area in which a massive increase in research was seen throughout the 1970s, and continued throughout the 1980s, is telecommunications and electronics including semiconductors. (See Chapter 9.) An important feature of the electronics industry in Japan is that it has basically developed around comprehensive electrical manufacturers – like Toshiba, Hitachi and Mitsubishi Electric – or grown out of consumer electronics companies – Matsushita, Sharp, Sanyo – with an important part played by the telecommunications companies.

This has resulted in major changes of the industrial structure in Japan which will be illustrated with a comparison between the production of steel and semiconductors. There are five major companies in the steel industry: Nippon Steel, Kawasaki Steel, NKK, Sumitomo Steel and Kobe Steel. The five major companies active in the semiconductor field are NEC, Toshiba, Hitachi, Mitsubishi Electric and Fujitsu. By providing average figures for five major parameters – sales, employment, profits, investment and ratio of own capital it is possible to design the pentagon which is presented in Figure 3.4. This shows that the steel industry which was once the mainstay of the early industrial development in Japan after the Second World War has now been dwarfed by the emergent five major electronic companies.

Figure 3.4 Comparison of major steel and electronic companies in Japan (average figures)

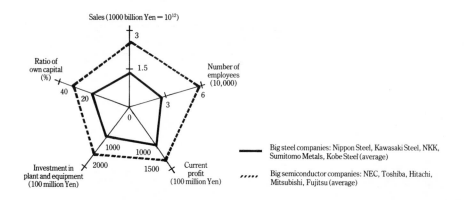

Source: Nikkei Electronics (Nikkei Erukutoronikusu), May 28, 1990

Today Japan holds the leading position in the world market for most types of advanced consumer electronics equipment. In its formative period, the Japanese electronics companies emphasised the development and manufacture of consumer electronics. During the 1980s there has been a shift of emphasis to industrial electronics such as telecommunications, semiconductors and equipment needed for the manufacture of semiconductors. See Figure 3.5.

Figure 3.5 Trends in major export items

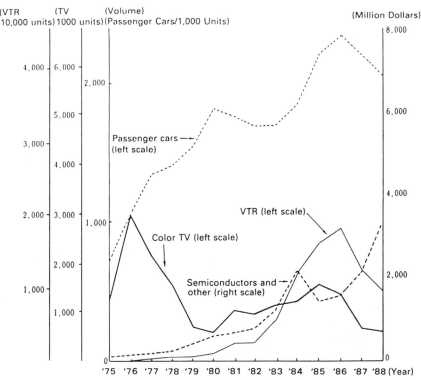

Notes:
1. Taken from "Foreign Trade Statistics", prepared by the Ministry of Finance
2. Volume is shown for passenger cars, colour TVs and VTRs and monetary values are shown for semiconductors and other electronic parts

Source: Economic Survey of Japan 1988-89. Compiled by Economic Planning Agency, Tokyo: The Japan Times, 1990, p. 142

Although there has been a drastic drop in the export of VTRs and colour TVs the industrial sector has shifted towards the production of products with a higher value added.

Chapter 4

Technology and industrial restructuring

Structure of Japanese industry

Although the image most foreigners have of Japanese industry is of vast enterprises providing guaranteed employment for their employees, and receiving loyalty and obedience in return, the reality is rather different. Japan is really the land of the small business. The giant business conglomerates whose names have become known throughout the world employ only a fraction of the workforce. Overall small businesses employ around 70 per cent of the working population.

In the small manufacturing businesses labour conditions are much poorer than in the giant concerns, productivity is lower and the future uncertain. Much of their business – in the region of 60 per cent – is the manufacture of parts subcontracted to them by larger companies. When there is a business recession production falls much more rapidly in the small enterprises than in the larger ones as subcontracts are reduced and the larger companies reduce their levels of stocks or even – during the 1980s – shift their subcontracts to foreign suppliers to reduce costs.

There has been much discussion in Japan concerning the dual structure of the economy and a special agency within MITI – Small and Medium Enterprise Agency – exists to try to improve the productivity and conditions. Nevertheless, the economic success of larger companies has partly come from this system and the supply it ensures of inexpensive components.

Research and development activities are almost entirely concentrated within the large industrial groups and other major companies. Indeed, when a small enterprise needs to improve its production processes it will often turn to the company it supplies with parts for its research and development.

Original equipment manufacturing (OEM) is becoming an increasingly important element in the technology strategy of big companies – both in domestic and overseas markets – for the following reasons. First, OEM products will expand the overall market for a specific product and provide the original manufacturer with a large income, from which the company is in the position to make larger allocations for R&D than would otherwise have been possible. Second, accepting an OEM strategy as a complement to direct sales under own brand name provides the possibility of achieving more rapid acceptance of a new technology or system which will benefit the originating company. Third, OEM expands the production base and economies of scale can be reaped. The OEM approach has been a very prominent part of Sony's strategy to receive wide and speedy acceptance of its 8 mm compact camcorder which was introduced in 1990.

In a more indirect way it may be argued that the large Japanese semiconductor companies which are leading the race into successive generations of memory circuits will be acting in the same way and may start licensing the manufacturing technology.

Chief among the massive Japanese enterprises are the industrial groups which owe their origin to the earlier *zaibatsu* groups. These were business conglomerates which had their origin in concerns set up soon after the Meiji restoration and which grew to enormous power by the Second World War. At the end of the war *zaibatsu* groups owned almost half of the heavy industry. A major feature of the *zaibatsu* was that a single holding company owned the shares of all the affiliated firms and also held absolute control over them. Almost all the power was thus concentrated in a single individual or family who was sole owner of the holding company. Close ties were maintained with particular political parties and funds were provided to further the interests of the *zaibatsu*.

Not surprisingly the *zaibatsu* were strong supporters of the pre-war right-wing government and benefited initially from the supply of military equipment during the war. They were broken up by the Allied Occupation to help prevent the resurgence of militarism. However, some of the old *zaibatsu*, like Mitsubishi, Mitsui and Sumitomo, have emerged – although with a very different structure. The new groups are not strongly consolidated under the control of single families but are united in a co-operative agreement that includes the provision of funds by a single, central bank, intercorporate stock ownership, interdependence in business transactions and joint development of new business lines.

There are eight major groups today: Mitsubishi Group, Mitsui Group, Sumitomo Group, Fuyo Group, Dai-Ichi Kangyo Bank (DKB) Group, Sanwa Group, Tokai Group and Industrial Bank of Japan Group. For example, Mitsubishi consists of some twenty companies centred around Mitsubishi Bank, Mitsubishi Heavy Industries, and Mitsubishi Corporation (Trading). Mitsui, the leading group before the war, took some time to regroup itself and now consists of some twenty companies centred on Tayo-Kobe-Mitsui Bank, Mitsui Mining, Toray Industries, Mitsui Petrochemical Industries, Toshiba Machine and Toyota Motor Company. See Figure 4.1.

Restructuring

Japan has in the past three decades constantly restructured its industries to suit its own resource base – increasingly dependent on human resources and technological prowess – and a changing pattern of global trade taking into consideration the emergence of newly industrialised countries (NICs). The consequence is that the coal industry which once dominated the energy supply in Japan has almost vanished – despite sustained and very costly government efforts to revitalise the sector. Aluminium smelting has disappeared due to increased energy prices after the two oil shocks. The petrochemical industry has also suffered serious setbacks – after its initial boom in the 1960s and 1970s. More recently the Japanese steel industry has been affected by intensifying competition from other countries and a simultaneous reduction in demand.

Figure 4.1 The Mitsubishi Group

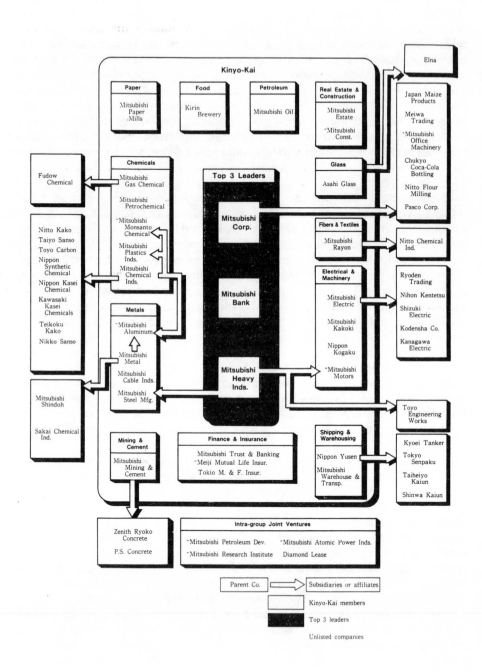

Source: Industrial Groupings in Japan 1988, 8th edition. Tokyo, Dodwell
Marketing Consultants

The problems of many declining industries have been handled under the Law on Extraordinary Measures for Specific Industries, popularly known as Structural Recession Law. The law came into effect in May 1978 and was designed to help industries trapped in structural recession after the first oil shock of 1973-74. At the time twelve industries were identified as requiring help. The issues were discussed in the Industrial Structure Council which is under the supervision of the Industrial Structure Division of MITI.

In recent years a number of measures have been introduced to ease the transition of declining industries. However, there can be little doubt that efforts and eventual success are mainly taking place inside the companies themselves. In the following sections the changes in the steel and chemical industries will be explained and the structural change will be illustrated by discussing the technology strategies of some of the major companies in each sector.

Steel industry

Japan is a world-leading exporter of steel products and its steel industry is the world's second largest and possibly most efficient – although the country is almost completely dependent on foreign supplies of iron ore and coal. Traditional steel-making was able to meet the domestic demands until the end of the Edo period. With the opening of the country in 1868 the government took initiatives to establish modern steel-making facilities which were later passed on to private ownership. The first integrated steel plant was built by the government at Yawata on Kyushu in 1901 and the first blast furnace had a capacity of 60,000 tons. Then followed the establishment of several modern steel companies which enjoyed a boom until the end of the First World War.

The government took various initiatives in the 1930s to strengthen the steel industry. One was the establishment of Nippon Steel, which was created out of the state-owned Yawata Iron and Steel Works and five private firms – some of which were controlled by *zaibatsu*. Some of the most powerful private steel companies – Nippon Kokan, Kawasaki Steel, Sumitomo Metals Industries and Kobe Steel – remained independent. The structure is basically the same today although Nippon Steel has gone through a couple of transformations to become the present privately owned company.

In 1961 Japan surpassed the UK in steel production and in the 1980s surpassed the US to become the world's second largest steel producer. The steel industry includes integrated steel makers, electric steel makers, rolling firms and specialised steel companies, but the industry is dominated by the five companies mentioned above, of which Nippon Steel is by far the biggest producer. During the 1980s Japan's steel production has been slightly above 100 million tons per year. The production was 106 million tons in 1988, which was 13.5 per cent of a world total of 780 million tons.

The steel industry has suffered from rapidly increasing energy costs. Equally dramatic have been the changes in exchange rate for yen-dollar which dived from 250 yen/dollar in 1985 to 125 yen/dollar, and returned to 150 yen/dollar in 1990. The consequences have been far-reaching for the Japanese steelmakers. All of them have pressed ahead with restructuring which includes closing a number of blast furnaces and other facilities, and transferring a substantial number of the workforce. To meet the challenge the companies are now entering such fields as urban development, and electronics and information technologies – which will be illustrated for the Nippon Steel Corporation.

Nippon Steel Corporation

Nippon Steel Corporation is the world's largest steelmaker and meets about 30 per cent of the domestic demand, and has an export share of 25 per cent. The total sales in 1990 were Y2,750 billion and the company has 57,233 employees with an average age of 43 years.

The forerunner, the Nippon Steel Company, which was established in 1934, almost monopolised steel production in Japan. In 1950 the company was divided into two companies – Yawata Seitetsu and Fuji Seitetsu – in order to reduce the economic concentration. The two companies independently expanded and became the largest steelmakers in Japan and they merged in 1970 to become the present Nippon Steel Corporation.

The research and development structure at Nippon Steel Corporation has strongly been shaped by the early history of the company and the present efforts to diversify the activities of the company. Let us first look at the historical development. At the breakup of the Nippon Steel Company in 1950 a major R&D laboratory existed at the original Yawata Works. This was further expanded and became a process technology laboratory at the merger in 1970. Before that the Yawata company had already in 1959 established a fundamental research laboratory. The Fuji company also had a central R&D laboratory which became the products R&D laboratory at the time of merger in 1970. The merger took place when the high growth era of steel production was over and the industry entered into a more mature phase during the 1970s, which has been followed by continuing restructuring and laborious attempts in diversifying the steel companies.

In 1983 the Nippon Steel Corporation carried out a reorganisation of its research structure. The steel works laboratories became specialised on steel products and production technology respectively while the fundamental research laboratories were expanded to cover research in new materials, chemicals, material characterisation and future technologies. In the meantime the construction activities had increased in importance which led to the creation of the plant engineering and technology centre in 1972. See Figure 4.2.

Another major restructuring is presently under way in 1990 through which the laboratories for product technology and process technology together with the plant engineering centre will be integrated into a single research and engineering centre located at Tokyo Bay near Kimitsu Works, one of the major steel complexes belonging to the Nippon Steel Corporation. The company states that its new Research and Engineering Centre is being established basically to reform the conventional technical development organisation and is expected to serve as a springboard for the company's diversification. The creation of the new centre, of course, requires the transfer of a large number of researchers from various locations in Japan and some of the staff may remain at the works rather than move to the new centre.

The centre will, when completed in the second half of 1991, have a total staff of 1,180, of whom 310 are classified as researchers. The staff will also include 360 engineers, of whom 70 will be engaged in development. In addition the centre will have an administrative staff of 120, and 390 technical assistants.

Figure 4.2 Evolution of R&D structure at Nippon Steel Corporation

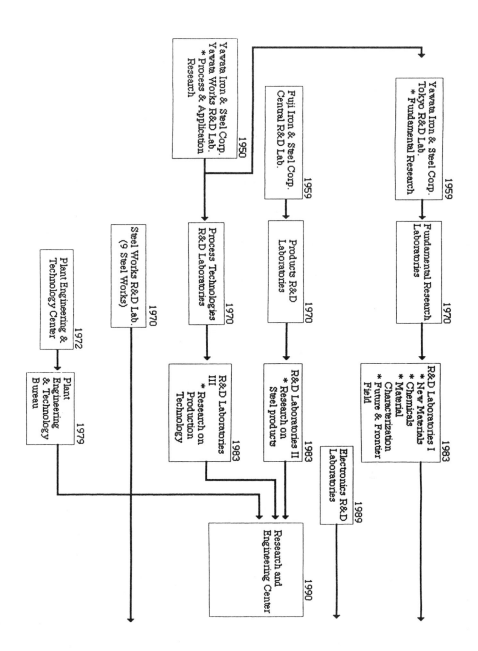

Sources: All Japan Research Institute Planning Directory (Zenkoku kenkyujo keikaku soran). Tokyo: Sango Times, 1988. *Directory of Japan's Private Technological Research Institutes (Moeru zuno shudan Nihon no minkan gijutsu kenkyujo soran).* Tokyo: Nihon Kogyo Shimbun sha, 1987; and other publications

In 1989 the company established an Electronics R&D Laboratory which reflects the belief inside the company that information technologies and electronics will continue to expand and provide business opportunities – even for newcomers. Furthermore the company also maintains the R&D Laboratory oriented towards fundamental research, with a total staff of 450 of whom 230 are researchers. In total Nippon Steel Corporation has corporate research laboratories with a total staff of close to 2,000 people.

Steel products in 1990 still constituted 90 per cent of total sales. In 1986 the company announced that it expected sales to increase from Y2,500 billion in 1986 to Y4,000 billion in 1995. The production of materials such as steel, new materials and chemicals would remain almost the same whilst sales for electronics products and systems would expand to 20 per cent and those of engineering and urban development to 10 per cent respectively. Naturally, it is still much too early to pass any judgement on the possible success of the diversification plans.

However, it is of interest to look at the shifts of allocation of R&D resources. In 1986 Nippon Steel Corporation allocated approximately 30 per cent of its R&D budget for non-steel research and development. In 1988 61 per cent of the researchers were allocated to work on problems related to steel and steel works, with another 18 per cent doing research on new materials and 8 per cent engaged on electronics research.

The share for electronics research has more than doubled and is now above 20 per cent. The rapid changes are also reflected in the overall figures and in 1990 the company says that 55 per cent of all R&D resources are used for non-steel research and indicates that this share may go on increasing. It may be estimated that the R&D budget for the Nippon Steel Corporation is of the order of 3 per cent of total sales, which would amount to approximately Y80 billion in 1990.

The diversification of activities has been concentrated in the electronics field after Nippon Steel Corporation decided to develop such businesses in 1986. In May 1986 Nippon Steel established the Concurrent Nippon Corporation, a joint venture with Concurrent Computer Corporation in the US to manufacture and market super mini computers.

In March 1987 Nippon Steel acquired an equity interest in GTX Corporation in the US and got access to advanced computerised processing technology for drawings. Nippon Steel used this technology to develop a drawing processor system – NSXPRES 5000 – which was announced towards the end of the same year.

In April 1987 Nippon Steel entered into an original equipment manufacture (OEM) with Nihon Sun Microsystems and started to market the Sun world-leading engineering workstations under the brand name of NSSUN. In the same year Nippon Steel contracted the Synergy Computer Graphics Corporation in the US for rights to manufacture and market their electrostatic colour copier. These are a few examples of new electronic ventures in which the Nippon Steel Corporation is active.

It should be noted that the company has considerable strengths in handling complex technological systems and in project management, which were developed when designing large-scale, complex steel production systems. In order to exploit this knowledge base the company has entered into joint ventures with the Itoh trading company, and with IBM Japan and Hitachi, to develop and market small to medium-sized software systems for production control, safety management, information control with electronic filing etc. Furthermore, Nippon Steel has also established its own software company – Nippon Steel Information and Communication Systems Inc. – which, drawing on the in-house expertise, has developed software packages for test support, operations control and various business applications tasks.

Naturally there has been a parallel development of research and development activities for the electronics sector. The early approaches comprised a Materials Research Laboratory and an Instrument and Control Laboratory which came into being in 1983. The latter was expanded into an Electronics and Control Laboratory in 1985. These two laboratories formed the basis for the establishment of the Nippon Steel Electronics Research Laboratories in 1989. This organisation now has two laboratories for semiconductors – Materials and Basic Technology – which both originated in the earlier Materials R&D Laboratory. In addition there are three laboratories for Computer Systems, Applied Electronics, and Instrument and Automation. Rough estimates would indicate that approximately 20 per cent of Nippon Steel researchers are engaged in the electronics sector and that the electronics sector gets, at least, the same percentage of the total company R&D budget.

In May 1990 *Nikkei Electronics* reported that Nippon Steel designs its own application specific integrated circuits (ASICs) and produces silicon wafers. The entry into the electronics businesses is also being pursued by the other four steel companies. The same magazine observes that Kawasaki Steel is going to mass-produce ICs from the summer of 1991 and already has started production of clean-room equipment for IC manufacture. The most active companies appear to be Sumitomo Metal Industries, which collaborates extensively with companies within the Sumitomo Group, and Kobe Steel which has entered into a joint agreement with Texas Instrument to mass-produce ICs starting in the summer of 1992.

External relations are important for the R&D activities of the company. The joint ventures, some of which have been mentioned, and contractual agreements with other companies number in total about 100. Nippon Steel also has special relations with approximately 30 research institutes. In addition the company has special, contractual relations with some 300 university professors/departments for which the costs amount to 0.6 per cent of the total company R&D budget. The university contacts are considered to be important for the following five reasons:

1. the professors provide connections abroad;

2. they provide windows on relevant scientific discoveries;

3. they provide broad overviews;

4. they make the company better known; and

5. the contacts facilitate recruitment of staff.

Nippon Steel does not yet have any research facilities abroad although it is studying the question and the problems which have to be solved. One reason which may possibly prompt Nippon Steel Corporation to set up research laboratories abroad is that the company faces difficulties in recruiting staff as steel industry is no longer seen as the most attractive employer.

Nippon Steel naturally participates in a number of national R&D projects, of which coal liquefaction has been one for which a pilot plant is located at its Kimitsu Works. Nippon Steel took a leadership role for the pilot plant while Sumitomo Metal Industries will shoulder a similar role for the next, bigger step. However, the project is seen as too long-term, too difficult and too dependent on the price of oil. However the national projects are generally seen as beneficial as they save money and provide results such as market identification, plant conceptualisation and technical ideas. More recently Nippon Steel Corporation has joined national projects which focus on the development of new materials, underground structures and low gravity technology for manufacture.

Chemical industry

The chemical industry in Japan saw its origin in the 1880s when the government started to import the production technologies for glass, various inorganic chemicals, cement and so on. Then followed the development of the electrochemical industry at the beginning of the century which was triggered by the surplus generated in the hydroelectric industry. The coal-based chemical industry developed in the 1930s when the government actively promoted the coal industry and the production of chemical fertiliser, rayon and various other products and many subsectors of the chemical industry had reached international standards at the time when the Second World War started.

The petrochemical industry started to be developed in the late 1950s and was supported by two important factors. First, a shift in Japanese energy balance away from coal to oil, with a declining role for hydropower, created a surplus of feedstock for the petrochemical industry – naphtha. Second, the government enacted the Foreign Investment Law to expedite the introduction of foreign technology. The rapid expansion of scale reduced the manufacturing costs, which further enhanced the development of the sector. In a short span of time a large number of huge petrochemical complexes were established.

Both petrochemicals and basic chemicals are dominated by general chemical companies belonging to the former *zaibatsu* groups while fine chemicals like pharmaceuticals, cosmetics, synthetic detergents etc. are directed by large independent enterprises. The total production value of the Japanese chemical industry was about Y20,000 billion in 1990, which amounts to approximately 60 per cent of that of the US chemical industry and is 70 per cent larger than that of West Germany. However, the Japanese companies are generally much smaller than their foreign counterparts and the country has no equivalent to Hoechst or Bayer in Germany, which in terms of sales are four to five times larger than the biggest Japanese chemical companies. Ten of the largest chemical companies in 1988 had total sales of Y5,255 billion which is approximately the same as the sales of Hitachi in the same year. The same ten companies allocated Y240 billion to research and development in 1988, which is roughly the same as for Hitachi in that year.

The ten companies referred to include include three groups of companies.

One is the three fibre makers Asahi Chemical, Toray and Teijin although the first one has almost completely shed its fibre production. Another group consists of four comprehensive chemical companies which are Mitsubishi Kasei, Sumitomo Chemical, Showa Denko and Mitsui Toatsu. A third group consist of Mitsubishi Petrochemical and Mitsui Petrochemical which are both heavily specialised in petrochemicals. Then there is Asahi Glass which has a very strong position in glass products. All these companies, with the exception of Asahi Glass, have been greatly affected by changing situations for raw materials and in markets and have been forced to restructure their operations, as will be illustrated for Mitsubishi Kasei.

Mitsubishi Kasei

Mitsubishi Kasei is Japan's largest integrated chemical company and its main lines of production consist of carbo-chemicals such as cokes and various petrochemicals which account for approximately 40 per cent of sales. Total sales were Y750 billion in 1989 and the number of employees was 8,916 with an average age of 39.

The company started as the Nippon Tar Kogyo in 1934, later changing its name to Mitsubishi Chemical and more recently it became Mitsubishi Kasei. The last two Chinese characters (for Kasei) denote "changing into better". When the company started it had three major lines of production: coal chemistry with coke and coal tar, inorganic chemistry with fertilisers and inorganic pharmaceuticals and inorganic chemistry with dyestuffs, pigments and drugs. Metallurgy with aluminium production was added in the mid-1950s, shortly to be followed by petrochemistry. Biotechnology was a new field of development which was added in the mid-1970s. The three major areas of development – functional materials, information and electronics, and life sciences, which have come into existence during the 1980s – draw heavily on the competence that the company had developed earlier.

The total expenditure on research and development was Y41 billion in 1990 – corresponding to 5.5 per cent of sales – of which 25 per cent is allocated for corporate research (with 15 per cent going to the Mitsubishi Research Centre and the other 10 per cent to the Mitsubishi Kasei Institute of Life Sciences) and the remaining 75 per cent to the business groups. The total number of researchers is approximately 2,200. The R&D organisation consists of the Research Centre in Yokohama and eight development centres attached to the various plants.

In addition the company also maintains the Mitsubishi Kasei Institute of Life Sciences, which was established in Tokyo in June 1971 and has a total staff of approximately 180. The institute, which is an incorporated company fully owned by Mitsubishi Kasei, is a comprehensive research organisation specialising in life sciences. It is engaged in scientific research into biological phenomena with a view that new advances emerging from the research can be transformed into commercial products through applications research carried out by departments of the Research Centre.

The company also owns Mitsubishi Kasei Institute of Toxicological and Environmental Sciences in Tokyo. This institute, which has a staff of 160, is basically engaged in testing various products and substances on contract from the parent company and other related companies. In addition research is being done in a number of subsidiary companies which employ 1,200 people. So the total research staff of the Mitsubishi Kasei groups is almost 3,500. The resource allocation within the Research Centre is strongly biased towards future business possibilities. Life sciences take 40 per cent, information and electronics 15 per cent and specialty materials 25 per cent. Thus, these areas which are categorised as research for functional products consume 80 per cent of the centre's research resources and an even higher percentage of researchers is allocated for such purposes. The share remains almost the same when the total research resources for Mitsubishi Kasei Corporation are included – functional products receive 79 per cent.

The Research Centre is currently organised in three research sectors: chemical science, life science and material science. The material science research sector has six laboratories: carbon and inorganic materials; thin films; imaging materials; polymers; advanced composite materials; and engineering development.

The overall R&D strategy of the company has six main components:

1. Improve petrochemical processes.

2. Expand business for carbon products.

3. Consolidate the basis for polymer and related products.

4. Establish a basis in reprographics and electronics.

5. Develop a basis in pharmaceuticals.

6. Develop a basis in biotechnology.

In implementing the strategy the company will actively pursue execution of exploratory research and collaborate with external research institutes, whenever feasible. The company has an Investigatory Committee for Advanced Science and Technology (ICAST) which identifies promising research topics worthy of long-term commitment and provides incentives to young researchers. ICAST reacts to future trends and technology to direct the activities within the Research Centre and the Mitsubishi Kasei Institute of Life Sciences.

In assisting ICAST the company can draw on more than 150 contracts with university professors/departments which provide early signals and insights. The costs for the university contracts amount to roughly 1 per cent of the total company R&D budget. In addition the company has further improved its intelligence system by instituting a company-specific science attaché system, started in 1987. Every year the company selects five researchers who are asked to independently plan and carry out global surveys of relevance to the company and remain abroad for approximately three months, and then to report back to the company.

ICAST is thus in a good position to provide guidance for the next planning stage which is carried out by the Promoting Committee for Advanced Science and Technology (PCAST). This committee is responsible for preparing the research plan for the Research Centre, discussing the plan and evaluating the results. The formal R&D management is organised in a series of conferences. The Corporate Strategy Conference is held every year at the end of November and roughly fifteen managing directors participate. Then follows, a few weeks later, the R&D Strategy Conference which deliberates both over the short and middle term projects in the business groups, and the long term projects to be carried out by the Research Centre and by the Mitsubishi Kasei Institute of Life Sciences.

In January follow separate R&D Conferences of Business Groups and an Exploratory Research Conference, and the conclusions are then consolidated in the R&D Action Program which is ready at the end of March. Included in this management structure are meetings for assessing R&D projects which deliberate on commercialization, the suspension or ending of projects.

At present Mitsubishi Kasei is involved in six basic areas of technology: carbon chemistry, inorganic chemistry, metallurgy, polymer chemistry, electronics and biotechnology. The company manufactured pharmaceuticals during the 1930s and 1940s. The production stopped in 1955 to be restarted in 1970.

Functional products today constitute 31 per cent of sales and petrochemicals 38 per cent, the remainder being carbon and inorganic products. The functional products, which in the early 1980s constituted only 10 per cent of sales, are expected to expand considerably beyond the present level – and possibly to reach 50 per cent of sales in 1995.

One example of a functional product is carbon fibre based on coal tar pitch, which equals the tensile strength of PAN-based carbon fibres and is superior in elasticity while also being very cost competitive. Another newly developed product is a conductive carbon black that provides excellent conductive properties to polymer materials. The substance is easier to form than metallic power fillers based on silver, nickel and other materials, while also having a strengthening effect.

Mitsubishi Kasei has also become a leader in liquid crystal polymers (LCPs) and has developed original technology for thermotropic LCPs with superior processability, dimensional precision and cost performance. The company has developed two types of moisture-permeable film. One is a porous polyethylene film with countless micron pores. The film has excellent vapour permeability but is highly resistant to water. The other new substance is a non-porous transparent moisture-permeable film based on a compound of poly-amino acid and urethane. Apart from its vapor-permeability, the film also has advantages that are expected to lead to medical uses, including the ability to keep out ultramicroscopic organisms such as viruses, and excellent physiological capability. Thus, it is expected that the material could be used for artificial blood vessels and skin, and as gas separation membranes.

In electronics the company has since become a leading manufacturer of organic photoconductors (OPCs) which play a major role in electro-photographic copying machines. The OPCs have been further developed for use in laser printers, liquid crystal shutter printers and other types of printer. Mitsubishi Kasei has also entered into the manufacture of improved types of rigid disks as floppy disks, in co-operation with the Verbatim company in the US, and optical disks.

The diversification efforts were triggered by the slump for petrochemical products in the early 1980s. Furthermore the low costs for oil since the mid-1980s led to a reduction in sales volume, which provided another stimulus for diversification based on a strategy that the company should move out of raw materials and engage in highly processed chemicals.

Mitsubishi Kasei participates in a number of national projects one of which is the Coal Liquefaction of the NEDO Sunshine Programme. This project is a continuation of an earlier project carried out in South Africa. At the suggestion of a vice-president of Kobe Steel a new coal liquefaction project was launched which involves research collaboration with Australia. Although the coal liquefaction project may be useful for energy development it is seen as too narrow for Mitsubishi Kasei, which was asked to join by Kobe Steel, a major buyer of coke from the company. Mitsubishi would have preferred a project which would have produced pitch from coal rather than fuel, as this would have given have given an intermediate product which could have been further processed into carbon fibre, carbon black and so on.

Researchers from Mitsubishi Kasei have participated in three of the projects organised within the Exploratory Research for Advanced Technology (ERATO), which is discussed in Chapter 7. These include the Kunitake Molecular Architecture Project and the Kuroda Solid Surface Project in each of which two researchers have participated. The ERATO projects are considered to be very useful for Mitsubishi Kasei as they are at the frontline of scientific research, have good scientific leadership and lack the bureaucratic rigidity of many other national projects. Naturally, these views reflect the fact that Mitsubishi Kasei is a company which is increasingly involved in long term exploratory research. Today about one third of the research staff is doing research which relates to material design and control at atomic and molecular levels.

Mitsubishi Kasei has also made an investment in the Protein Engineering Research Institute (PERI) an R&D company sponsored by the Japan Key Technology Centre. When comparing this project with the ERATO projects, the latter offer a more dynamic scientific leadership which corresponds closer to the research activities of the company. An attempt has been made to identify the scientific and technological underpinning of diversification within Mitsubishi Kasei, based on information obtained from the company. Its research policy has three components: to support its business in basic chemicals; to venture strongly into specialty chemicals; and to restructure the company's long term research. The R&D strategy can then be deduced for the various product fields which includes a number of sub-fields in biotechnology and in polymer-related fields. Mitsubishi Kasei has then identified in which technological fields the company should have a strong presence and what this requires in the domain of long term and exploratory (or basic) research. The conclusion is that Mitsubishi Kasei must establish a strong research capability in material design and in control at atomic and molecular level – in order to successfully carry out its diversification. See also Figure 4.3.

The share of researchers with a doctoral degree is presently 9 per cent and the company's management would like to see this level increase to 15 per cent by the year 2000. However, the company expects that it will be difficult to recruit the required researchers with a doctoral degree in Japan. This is one consideration which may prompt the company to establish research laboratories abroad. Today Mitsubishi Kasei only has a technical centre in Palo Alto in California which supports its development of hard disk materials. One way of getting access to foreign expertise is to invite foreign researchers to the company laboratories and at any one time there are presently five to ten foreigners in the laboratories – most of them on a long term basis.

Figure 4.3 R&D policy – strategy activities at Mitsubishi Kasei Corporation

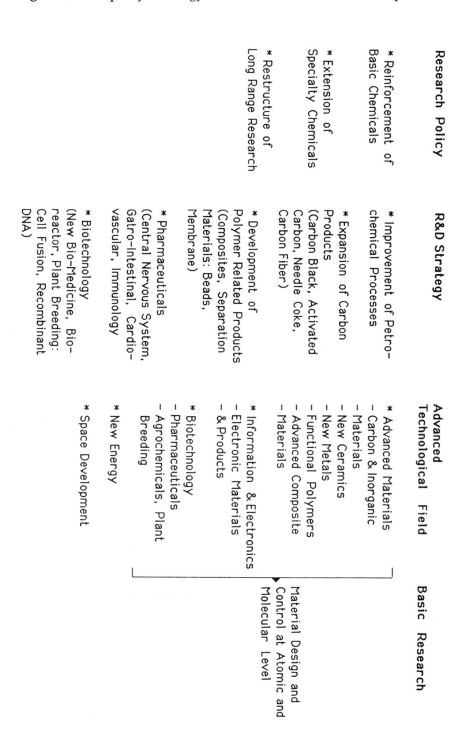

Source: Private communication

Pharmaceutical industry

The Japanese pharmaceutical industry is the second largest in the world, after that of the United States. Most of the production is prescription drugs, and antibiotics account for about 20 per cent. Production of anti-cancer medicines has grown rapidly in recent years.

Research on new drugs is not yet on the same level as that of their major international competitors and the Japanese companies are generally more dependent on licensed-in compounds than are pharmaceutical companies outside Japan. Furthermore, original products developed in Japan are able to capture a substantial share of the domestic market but are as yet much less prominent in overseas markets.

The Japanese pharmaceutical companies have shaped a research system which is decentralised but growing rapidly with a focus on incremental but innovative progress. It appears that the Japanese pharmaceutical industry as a whole is not yet in the position to fully exploit their research results in the overseas markets. However, there is little doubt that Japan will remain an important source of innovative drugs.

R&D expenditure for pharmaceutical companies shows great differences between Japanese and US companies. The latter would normally allocate 15 per cent of sales to research and development, while the Japanese figure is around 6 per cent. However, Japan has over the years generally been approving more new drugs than has the US. There are three possible reasons why Japan is able to turn out a larger number of drugs with considerably lower R&D expenditure. First, the companies in Japan have a large share of licensed drugs which do not require any basic research and only limited development expenditure. Second, the industry may be more geared to second or third generation drugs which are less risky in terms of research. Third, follow-up products are inexpensive to develop – even if they are original entities.

Shortcomings which have to be eliminated include the rather rigid personnel policies which hinder creative research. The industry has in the past been unfamiliar with the regulatory procedures outside Japan which has hindered a rapid diffusion of original products. Furthermore, the weak patent protection has in the past also compelled companies to accentuate process rather than product research. Finally, the abundant availability of licensed-in technology has in the past led to an emphasis on development rather than basic research.

Takeda Chemical Industries

Takeda Chemical Industries is a leading pharmaceutical company with total sales of Y700 billion in 1990. The number of employees was 10,900 in 1990, with an average age of 41 years. Takeda Chemical Industries, which owes its origin to activities started more than 200 years ago, is today the largest pharmaceutical company in Japan. The company also maintains a strong presence in fine chemicals, food products, chemical products, agricultural chemicals, and animal health products. Pharmaceuticals constitute about two thirds of total sales, industrial chemicals another 14 per cent, and 10 per cent each for food products and agriculture-related products.

Takeda Chemical, which in fact started to export Vitamin B_1 to the United States in 1952, has assumed a leading role to internationalise the Japanese pharmaceutical industry. However, its export share is only about 6 per cent, to be compared with Merck & Co and Pfizer in the US which have approximately 40 per cent of their sales abroad. The big Swiss companies like Ciba-Geigy, Roche and Sandoz have a predominant part of their sales outside Switzerland.

The expenditure on research and development was Y48,000 million in 1990 which is close to 7 per cent of sales and an increase of 10 per cent over the preceding year. As all other pharmaceutical companies Takeda Chemical is active in the three stages: search for new compounds; selection and scrutiny of drug candidates; and manufacturing development. The last task is served by three laboratories for chemical development, pharmaceutics and applied microbiology. Most of the resources and facilities for research and development are located centrally in the grounds of the Takeda Chemical manufacturing plants in Osaka.

The search for new compounds is served by four laboratories: chemistry laboratories; applied microbiology laboratories; biotechnology laboratories; and applied plant biology laboratories. The biotechnology laboratories were established in 1981 to pursue basic and applied research which, in operation terms, means an obligation to produce bio-pharmaceuticals using recombinant DNA, cell fusion, and cell culture technologies as well as the technology for purification and structural analysis of protein products. Successes so far include recombinant interferon-alpha and two promising drugs in clinical trials, interleukin 2 and a hepatitis B vaccine created through protein engineering.

Researchers in the applied microbiology laboratories exploit functions of micro-organisms and animal cells. Uses of these functions are also allied in veterinary medicines, feed additives, agricultural chemicals, and flavour enhancers. One of the research groups is involved in developing biologically-active microbial products, including antibiotics, for treating cancer and other intractable diseases. This has required extensive collaboration and prompted Takeda Chemical to enter into joint research with Harvard Medical School on angiogenesis and cancer metastasis.

The applied plant biology laboratories supplement botanical research on herbal medicines with studies on plant breeding and artificial cultivating techniques based on advanced biotechnology. One research group within the company pursues research on pharmacognosy and seeks chemical components of commercial potential.

The drug safety evaluation laboratories are responsible for all aspects of toxicity and for gauging long-term effects of potential drugs on humans. Testing on acute toxicity, sub-acute toxicity, and chronic toxicity is done at the main facility at Takatsuki near Kyoto while other testing is done at laboratories attached to the manufacturing plants.

In January 1988 Takeda Chemical opened its research laboratories for basic research in the Tsukuba Science City. Activities at this centre will focus on the exploration of new fields, new substances and new technologies, which will then provide the company with the scientific and technological basis for drugs which will be internationally competitive. The research at the Tsukuba Research Laboratories is going into three major areas: search for compounds that control cell differentiation, growth and ageing; the investigation of synthetic vaccines; and the biological and chemical modification of enzymes, hormones and and other biological substances.

In 1987 the company took several steps in order to become a thoroughly international pharmaceutical company with a strong basis in research and development. Takeda Chemical expects to be in the position to develop more new drugs for global distribution. Consequently, the company has expanded its joint development activities with Abbott Laboratories in the US and established, in April 1988, its Europe Research and Development Centre in Frankfurt, Germany. The activities at this centre will include the development of new drugs and co-ordination of R&D at European licensees and of the joint ventures in Europe. The centre also collects information bearing on medical technology and pharmaceutical regulations.

Chapter 5

Science and government

The private sector dominates the funding of R&D to an extent for which there is hardly a parallel in other industrialised countries. Many if not most of the large companies have set up central research laboratories which increasingly pursue long term exploratory research. Several of the very large companies maintain separate basic research laboratories which have almost the same freedom as academic institutions. However, the government still plays an important role in shaping the research agenda and shoulders the financial burden not only for big science but also for emerging scientific and technological themes.

The presentation of long-range "visions" constitutes an important means of formulating economic and development plans in Japan and has been an important characteristic of planning in the post-war period of rapid economic growth. The government has considered it important to provide many sorts of relevant information and achieve consensus from different sectors of the society. The purpose of the "visions" has been to identify the role of the state and a desirable course of industrial and social development based on a consensus.

These visions are considered to have been extremely useful in an environment which has been affected by drastic changes both inside and outside Japan. Similar visionary plans have also played an important role for guiding the development of the science and technology sector. The supreme body for formulating and promoting science and technology policies in Japan is the Council for Science and Technology, which was established in 1959 – following the creation of the Science and Technology Agency in 1956.

Council for Science and Technology
(Kagaku gijutsu kaigi)

The Council for Science and Technology is chaired by the Prime Minister and establishes a general framework for the science policy in Japan which is then to be promoted by the individual ministries. However, the various ministries have a great degree of freedom in formulating their own policies and negotiate with the Ministry of Finance for the necessary funds, which undermines the possibility of achieving a close co-ordination.

There are three dominant forces for implementing science policies: the Science and Technology Agency, which is directly under the Prime Minister's Office; the Ministry of International Trade and Industry; and the Ministry of Culture and Education (Monbusho). Other ministries are also important in their respective fields.

There are several other councils involved in policy formulation and recommendations and they will be mentioned in this context in order to avoid future confusion. The Ministry of Culture and Education has its own Science Council which guides the ministry on its own policy matters. MITI has an operational agency, the Agency for Science and Technology Agency (AIST), which has an Industrial Technology Council guiding its operations.

Furthermore there is the Science Council of Japan, sometimes referred to as the "Parliament of Scientists", which consists of eminent scientists. The members of the Science Council of Japan (which was established shortly after the end of the Second World War) are elected by the academic community. This council was originally expected to provide the government with necessary policy recommendations. However, strong differences in opinion between this council and the government, partly reflecting differences in political beliefs, have tarnished their relations and made the council barely effective in influencing government policies. Still, the president of the Council of Japan is a permanent member of the Council for Science and Technology.

The Council for Science and Technology consists of a chairman – the Prime Minister – and ten members. These are the two ministers for Finance and Education, the two ministers of state for Economic Planning, and Science and Technology, the President of the Science Council of Japan, already mentioned, and five prominent members selected by the Prime Minister in consultation with the parliament (Diet). Other ministers can also be requested to participate in council meetings as temporary members. Among the members in early 1990 were one ex-minister for science and technology, one ex-president from the University of Tokyo, one advisor to the president of the Nippon Telegraph and Telephone Corporation, one advisor to the Board of Toshiba Corporation and the president of the Kansai Electric Power Co. See Figure 5.1 for the overall organisation of the Council.

In 1960 the Council for Science and Technology submitted its first recommendation, with the title "Comprehensive and Fundamental Measures for the Development of Science and Technology for the Next Decade". This was the basis for the first comprehensive policy adopted by the government in the sphere of science and technology. The first plan, which among other things, indicated the need to improve the quality and availability of researchers and the introduction of advanced knowledge from abroad, was a starting point for active guidance in science and technology. As a consequence the Ministry of Education decided to increase science and engineering enrolment, which increased rapidly. Furthermore, a funding system for development of new technologies was created by the Japan Development Bank (JDB). Under the new scheme JDB offered long-term, low-interest loans for commercialising new technologies which involved technical and economic risks.

The next major recommendation followed in 1966 and included an emphasis on infrastructure which, among other things, initiated the planning for Tsukuba Science City and selective promotion of research activities in the private sector. The next major report, No. 5, in 1971, may have been less significant, as the Japanese economy was advancing very successfully without any major problems. The following council report, No. 6 in 1977, naturally emphasised the energy-related efforts and also stressed that it was necessary to strengthen the scientific and technological capability to be able to deal with economic crises and drastic changes in industries and markets. The plan also

Figure 5.1 Organisation chart of the Council for Science and Technology – in Science and Technology Agency (STA)

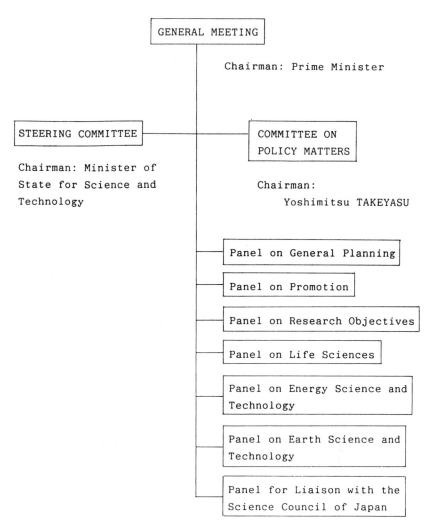

Source: Profile of the Council for Science and Technology, STA, Tokyo, March 1990, p. 5

provided a long-term and global perspective on the need to consider the "humanisation" of society on the one hand and advancement of science and technology on the other. A few months later, in July 1977, the council proposed a "Master Plan for Energy Research and Development" which had a strong effect on many of the energy R&D initiatives which followed.

The next principal recommendation came in November 1984, and advocated more strongly the need for long-term planning in science and technology. Although the plan is comprehensive it may be possible to single out major points. First, scientific creativity had to be strengthened since Japan had completed the phase of technology catch-up and the new situation required more basic research and improved infrastructure for research. Second, science and technology policies have to be formulated in order to alleviate international conflicts. Third, Japan has to strengthen the humanistic side of science and technology.

The major contents of the Recommendation No. 11, referred to above, with the general title "Comprehensive Fundamental Policy for Promotion of Science and Technology to Focus Current Changing Situations from the Long-term View", was combined with "The Administrative Reform Embodiment Policy in the Immediate Future" (September 1985) and formulated as General Guideline of Science and Technology Policy, of March 1986.

This short document, reprinted in Appendix I, is the closest thing to an official science and technology policy in Japan. In understanding implemented policies and changes to come it may be helpful to highlight some of the main features of this document. In its basic principles it says that efforts are needed to create technological seeds for the future and that it is increasingly imperative to be able to combine a wide range of knowledge domains. In developing the science and technology system we learn that universities should improve and upgrade their research activities and possibly exceed the international level. The university system is also expected to make special efforts to improve the quality of undergraduate-level and graduate-level training The national research institutes, to be discussed later on, should strengthen their role in basic and leading research and also change their internal structures.

It is of interest to note that "increased opportunities for industrial-academic-Government co-operation in all stages of R&D" emerge as a consequence of increased basic research activities in the private sector. As a corollary the government should "promote industrial-academic-Government research exchanges by improving pertinent systems, operating them more flexibly, encouraging practical applications of research fundings ... The Government should also improve co-operative research projects, comprehensive research projects, flexible research systems and other systems". In identifying new areas in which progress is expected, the following seven have been singled out:
– Matter and materials sciences.
– Information and electronics sciences.
– Life sciences.
– Soft sciences.
– Space sciences.
– Ocean sciences.
– Earth sciences.

Since its major recommendation in 1984, the Council has prepared more specialised recommendations, one of which deals with reorganisation of national research institutes (August 1987), to be discussed further on. Another discusses the development of matter and material sciences, and the March 1989 recommendation suggests basic plans for research and development in the information technologies and electronics.

Throughout its reports the Council for Science and Technology has reiterated the need to increase expenditure on research and development, and in mid-1985 suggested that efforts should be made to attain the level of 3.5 per cent of GNP in the early 1990s.

The secretariat services for the Council for Science and Technology are

Figure 5.2 Committees of the Council for Science and Technology – in Science and Technology Agency (STA)

Organization

```
┌─────────────────────────────────┐
│ Committee on Policy Matters      │
└─────────────────────────────────┘
  ├──┌──────────────────────────────────┐
  │  │ Subcommittee on Research Projects │
  │  └──────────────────────────────────┘
  │
  │     Study on important research projects in the Special
  │     Coordination Funds for Promoting Science and Technology
  │
  ├──┌────────────────────────────────────┐
  │  │ Subcommittee on Research Evaluation │
  │  └────────────────────────────────────┘
  │
  │     1 Study on research evaluation
  │     2 Review concerning research projects in the Special
  │        Coordination Funds for Promoting Science and Technology
  │
  ├──┌──────────────────────────────────┐
  │  │ Subcommittee on Policy Studies    │
  │  └──────────────────────────────────┘
  │
  │     1 Study on science and technology policy formulation
  │     2 Study on policy research in the Special Coordination
  │        Funds for Promoting Science and Technology
  │
  └──┌──────────────────────────────────────────────────────────────┐
     │ Subcommittee on Information System for Science and Technology  │
     └──────────────────────────────────────────────────────────────┘

        Study on promoting science and technology information
```

```
┌──────────────────────────────────────────┐
│ Ad-hoc Committee on International Affairs  │
└──────────────────────────────────────────┘

     Study on international affairs in Science and Technology
```

```
┌──────────────────────────────────────────────────────────────┐
│ Ad-hoc Committee on Cooperative Affairs between Industries,    │
│ National Institute and Academia                                │
└──────────────────────────────────────────────────────────────┘

     Study on cooperative affairs between industries , national
     institute and academia
```

Source: Profile of the Council for Science and Technology Agency, STA, Tokyo, March 1990, p. 25

provided by the Science and Technology Agency and the Ministry of Education. More important is the structure of the council which, aside from a number of panels, has the important committee on policy matters which generally meets twice a month. See Figure 5.2. With sparse meetings of the Council it was considered necessary in 1983 to establish the Committee on Policy Matters, a standing organ which considers various important issues and can take timely decisions.

The members include six people from the Council itself, the chairman presently being an ex-minister for science and technology. The other eight people in early 1990 included two representatives from the universities, two chairmen from major industries, one person from the banking sector, the vice president of the Japan Society for the Promotion of Machine Industry with another two members representing research and information institutions. Naturally all are figures also renowned for their understanding of science and technology policy issues, such as Professor Hiroshi Inose, who is also very well known outside Japan.

The Committee on Policy Matters has a number of subcommittees (See Figure 5.2), of which one will be singled out for attention. However, it is of special interest to note that there exists, since February 1988, a specific ad-hoc committee on co-operative affairs between industries, national institutes and academia. The committee on research projects supervises the Special Co-Ordination Fund for Promoting Science and Technology, which adds another dimension to the co-ordinating role of the Council. See Figure 5.3. The Fund, under the supervision of the Council, was established in 1981 and replaced similar funds for the various ministries. The system aims to promote leading research on basic technologies in co-operation with private industry, government research institutes and universities, and the purpose was to attain a shift from application to more basic/generic research of relevance to leading technologies.

Many observers of the Japanese science and technology scene notice the intense competition among different ministries and agencies and may draw the wrong conclusion that policy implementation based on a common framework is almost impossible. Such hasty conclusions obscure the fact that the policy recommendations from the Council for Science and Technology are based on the involvement of a large number of researchers in all sectors of society. Many of them have participated as members in formal committees, in ad-hoc committees or in special study groups or have been consulted on specific issues. Thus it may not be an exaggeration to say that the whole scientific community in Japan has directly or indirectly been involved every time a major policy report reaches the public.

The direction is then set and various rival ministries attempt quickly to implement the new policies by using available funds or trying to persuade the Ministry of Finance that they have a worthy cause. So it is quite natural to find that similar programmes are started at approximately the same time. Parallel with the Special Co-Ordination Fund for Promoting Science and Technology above, two similar programmes were initiated in the same year. One is the Next Generation Industry Basic Technology Research and Development Programme established by MITI in 1981. The objective was to develop new technologies in the three fields of new materials, biotechnology and new functional devices. The other was the Exploratory Research for Advanced Technology (ERATO) Programme, administered by the Japan Research Development Corporation which belongs to the Science and Technology Agency. Although of different character, all three programmes flow from a basic assumption that the time had come for Japan to embark on more advanced research in more innovative forms involving researchers from different sectors. The three programmes are discussed in some detail in Chapter 7.

Figure 5.3 STA Special Co-ordination Funds for Promoting Science and Technology (SCF) – administrative structure

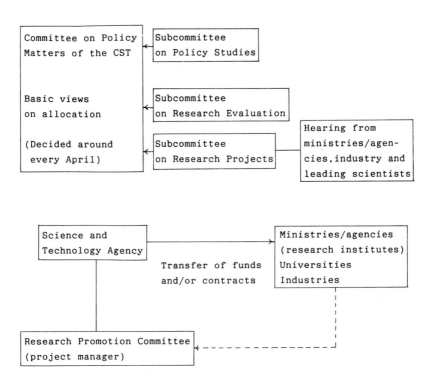

Source: *Profile of the Council for Science and Technology*, STA, Tokyo, March 1990, p. 23

Science and Technology Agency (STA)

The Science and Technology Agency was established in May 1956 though expansion and transfer of budgets originally controlled by other ministries and agencies. In fact STA was mainly based on the Atomic Energy Bureau of the Economic Planning Agency, the secretariat of of the Council for Resources Study, an earlier Science and Technology Advisory Committee and the Aircraft Research Laboratory. This origin of STA partly explains the present heavy orientation towards support for development in the nuclear and space/aircraft fields.

In historical reviews it is generally commented that STA came into being against the opposition of the scientists in the Science Council of Japan and against the interests of MITI. However, a major triggering effect was the political decision to embark on a major atomic power development programme which was strongly supported by the business circles represented, among other bodies, by Keidanren. It should be observed that, while STA is funding and operating major activities to develop atomic energy and space technologies there are two commissions which have special responsibility for co-ordinating national efforts. These are the Atomic Energy Commission and Space Activities Commission respectively.

Major administrative changes and gradually changing focus for science and technology since the mid-1980s have affected the structure and orientation of STA. The Provisional Council for the Promotion of Administrative Reform started its deliberations in June 1983 following on the heels of the Second Provisional Commission for Administrative Reform. In both fora it was clearly stated that the continued nation-building must be based on science and technology. This would require the following conditions:

1. improved conditions and more resources for creative and basic research;

2. expanded and more efficient interchange among research institutions in the private, government and university sectors; and

3. reorganisation and re-orientation of the national research institutes.

As a consequence STA was reorganised with more weight given to the science and technology policy. However, the basic principles of many of the suggested reforms were modified or diluted because of opposing opinions from various ministries who questioned both the justification and the timing of many of the changes.

STA operates six national research institutes, of which the National Aerospace Laboratory and the National Research Institute for Metals are the most important. A number of research activities for which STA has been given responsibility are organised as public corporations. This is the case for the Japan Atomic Energy Research Institute (JAERI), National Space Development Agency (NASDA) and the Institute of Physical and Chemical Research, usually known as Riken, which is one of the advanced research centres in Japan. In 1988 the earlier research institute for natural resources was transferred into a National Institute for Science and Technology Policy (NISTEP).

The Japan Research Development Corporation (JRDC) was founded in 1961 with the explicit purpose of promoting the industrial exploitation of basic research carried out in Japan, and is loosely controlled by STA. The original emphasis on technologies for the improvement of production processes and development of large-scale production equipment has shifted to environ-mental and energy-conserving technologies, and increasingly to high technologies. To this end, in 1981 JRDC launched the Exploratory Research for Advanced Technology (ERATO) Programme to extend creative science and technology through basic research. See Chapter 7 for details of this highly innovative programme.

One of the main functions of JRDC is the facilitating of licensing between researcher, mainly in the government sector, with the commercializer in the private sector – both domestically and internationally. Another function, closely related to licensing, is the development of selected topics for industrial utilisation in close co-operation between inventor and industrial companies. JRDC selects projects for development which are difficult to commercialise but which are of importance to the national economy. Development work is entrusted to companies but money is loaned for necessary equipment, facilities and running expenses. However, there can be no doubt that the ERATO Programme is today the major activity of JRDC.

The annual White Paper on Science and Technology prepared by the STA surveys and analyses general science and technology trends and government measures and is an important source for comparison with other countries.

Agency of Industrial Science and Technology (AIST)

The research organ of MITI is the Agency of Industrial Science and Technology, although the ministry also has a public corporation – New Energy and Industrial Technology Development Organisation (NEDO) – which organises major research activities mainly within the energy field, except atomic energy, and with an increasing responsibility for promoting advanced industrial technologies. The activities of AIST are manifold and may possibly be best comprehended by dividing them into the following five categories. First, AIST operates sixteen laboratories of which five are designed to serve five of the country's eight specific regions. The national institutes include mechanical engineering, chemical engineering and electronics for which the Electro-technical Laboratory (ETL) serves as the lynchpin in a number of activities.

Second, AIST has been promoting since 1966 what is generally called Large Scale Projects which have in the past been aimed at costly and major development projects, of which many have been within the electronics sector. Government funds are given by contract to participating private enterprises which usually work closely with national laboratories and academic organisations. See Chapter 7 for a description of the this programme and ongoing projects.

Third, the agency operates the research and development project on basic technologies for future industries, which is aimed at the development of innovative basic technologies for the establishment of new industries. This programme, which is now receiving less attention, is also discussed in Chapter 7. Both programmemes were incorporated in 1988 into the reorganised NEDO.

Fourth, AIST is also conducting and sponsoring researches on energy conservation technology (the Moonlight Project) and on new energy technology (the Sunshine Project), which are organised within NEDO. In the reorganisation of NEDO which was completed in October 1988 the new order requires the following responsibilities: undertaking research and development projects, carrying out research facility development projects, and engaging in international joint research grant projects.

Fifth, MITI is, together with Ministry of Posts and Telecommunications, responsible for the Japan Key Technology Centre, a highly innovative structure for research promotion, which among other things provides investment for development companies. Although the seed money for this important programme came from the privatisation of NTT which was under the control of MPT, MITI took an early lead in promoting the concept of the Key Technology Centre. Although MITI was also very active in the early promotion of the Human Frontier Science Programme the ministry is now only marginally involved. See also Chapter 19.

Serving AIST, or rather MITI, there is the Industrial Technology Council which was established in 1973 as an affiliated institution of the ministry. The council carries out investigation and considers important policy matters relating to scientific technology in response to inquiries from MITI. It is of importance to note that the background documents for many of the programmes started within the three major programmes mentioned above are prepared by researchers or staff in the AIST laboratories.

Ministry of Health and Welfare

The ministry supports a considerable amount of research at ten attached institutes of which the largest is the National Institute of Health. Its principal activities are to conduct and co-ordinate research projects of national importance in public health with regard to the causes of infectious diseases and other specific diseases such as cancer and their prophylaxis, therapy and diagnosis. Other significant institutes are the National Institute for Neuroscience, established in 1978 and the National Cancer Centre Research Institute, established in 1962. The Ministry supports large-scale research programmes in several of its research institutes.

In addition, there is also the Japanese Foundation for Cancer Research, which is a non-profit organisation for research, treatment and control of cancer with close associations with the Cancer Institute.

Ministry of Agriculture, Forestry and Fisheries (MAFF)

The ministry has a large budget for research and development – the third largest after the Science and Technology Agency and the Ministry of International Trade and Industry. In total the ministry controls 30 research institutions, including seven experimental stations in agriculture and another seven for fishery.

These centres focus on the problems specific to the regions mentioned in Chapter 2. The ministry maintains separate agencies for forestry and fishery which supervise their respective research institutions.

One of the key institutes is the National Agriculture Research Centre, established in 1981 which carry out research related to agricultural production systems in various specialised fields of agriculture. It undertakes specialised research in farm mechanisation and improvement of varieties and also research particularly related to the Kanto and Tokai areas.

The ministry has added two more institutes during the 1980s. One is the National Institute of Agrobiological Resources, established in 1983, with a mandate to incorporate into agriculture up-to-date biotechnologies made possible through the rapid advances through the application of molecular biology. More recently a Genetics Research Centre was established, in 1986. Another addition is the National Institute of Agro-Environmental Sciences, established in 1983, with the expressed purpose of developing fundamental techniques for combining highly productive agriculture in harmony with the natural ecosystem.

Aside from seven regional laboratories for fisheries research the ministry has two national institutes for the fishery sector, both of which were established in 1979. One is the National Research Institute of Fisheries Engineering which researches aquaculture, port engineering and fishing boats, among other things. The other, the National Research Institute of Aquaculture, conducts basic studies on various aspects of aquaculture. It has divisions for fish genetics, reproduction, nutrition, environmental management and fish pathology. Finally it should be observed that the Ministry also supervises a important new organisation, the Bio-Oriented Technology Research Advancement Institution (BRAIN), which is run jointly with the Ministry of Finance which is also responsible for the Research Institute of Brewing attached to the National Tax Administrative Agency.

Ministry of Transportation

This ministry is responsible for shipping, road transportation, railways and civil aviation. There are two separate agencies, the Maritime Safety Agency and the Meteorological Agency, which have their own research centres among which the Meteorological Research Institute is the major one. There are four research institutes directly under the ministry, three of which are directly related to shipping. Two of these, the Ship Research Institute and the Port and Harbour Research Institute, were established at the time of the ship-building boom in Japan in the early 1960s. A more recent addition is the Electronic Navigation Research Institute, which engages in research for the safety of air and marine transport. The fourth institute is the Traffic Safety and Nuisance Research Institute which studies the prevention of public nuisance, and energy saving, mainly with regard to motor vehicles and railway transportation facilities.

Although not under the direct supervision of the ministry the new Railway Technical Research Institute (RTRI), established in 1986, has been given a significant role and a very substantial budget – annually around Y12 billion. The Institute is a research foundation which came into existence on the occasion of the restructuring and privatisation of Japanese National Railways (JNR). The RTRI has taken over research and development which was previously performed by JNR and has incorporated the following research organisations of JNR: Railway Technical Research Institute; Railway Labour Science Institute; and the Miyazaki Maglev Test Centre. The new institute also includes the earlier JNR offices for Structure Design and Rolling Stock Design.

Ministry of Posts and Telecommunications

The ministry requires scientific services for one of its bureau, Radio Regulatory Bureau, and maintains a radio research laboratory, the Communications Research Laboratory. The institute has been changed extensively both in organisation and focus since it was first established in 1952. Its main orientation is now towards communications including various issues related to satellites and maintains facilities at the Kashima Space Research Centre. Related to this is the Telecommunications Satellite Corporation of Japan which is supervised by the same ministry.

The ministry has, until the privatisation of telephone services, indirectly been responsible for the very major research activities of NTT in the domestic arena and KDD for international services. In contrast to the reforms of the railway system, NTT and Kokusai Denshin Denwa Company Limited (KDD) have basically remained intact, mainly due to their profitability and subsequent control of financial resources, and have independent control of their research facilities, which are discussed in Chapter 10.

Finally, the ministry oversees the Japan Broadcasting Corporation which has a major research institution – NHK Science and Technical Research Laboratories. The R&D activities include both fundamental and practical studies in three main areas:

1. development of new broadcast media and applications;

2. improvement of current broadcast services and techniques; and

3. fundamental studies for future broadcast engineering.

This included early attention to improving TV picture definition and has resulted in the Japanese proposal for an international standard in High Definition Television (HDTV) which has been highly contested both in the EC and in the USA. It should be mentioned that the laboratory engages in studies on properties of various solid-state materials, such as semiconductors and magnetic materials, and their application to broadcasting techniques.

The Japan Key Technology Centre mentioned under MITI is under the joint supervision of the Ministry of Posts and Telecommunications which has occasionally contributed to friction in the selection of relevant topics or projects to be sponsored.

Other ministries

The Ministry of Construction maintains two large research institutes – the Public Works Research Institute and the Building Research Institute. The Ministry of Labour also has two institutes – the Research Institute of Industrial Safety and the National Institute of Health. Naturally several other ministries and agencies are responsible for various research activities although these are not covered in the context of this presentation.

Defence Agency

Military research has gradually emerged as a major element in the national scene for science and technology in Japan. The total budget in 1990 amounts to Y100 billion which corresponds to 40 per cent of MITI's budget for research and development. The Defence Agency maintains a large Technical Research and Development Institute which is divided into five research centres. Japan's activities in military research are discussed in Chapter 13

All the institutes, agencies and ministries discussed above are shown in Figure 5.4 which gives the administrative structure of science and technology and clearly indicates the lines of supervision. The reader wanting more specific information should consult one of the works listed among the References.

Government budget and pattern of funding

The total government budget for research and development was Y1,920 billion in the fiscal year of 1990. The largest chunk of this, Y894 billion, goes to the Ministry of Education and the second largest share, Y495 billion, is taken by the Science and Technology Agency. The Ministry of International Trade and Industry comes next with total R&D expenditure amounting to Y250 billion. For information on the other agencies refer to Table 5.1 which also provides figures for expenditure for the preceding five years.

Table 5.1 Government expenditure on R&D – by ministry/agency (in million yen)

Agency	1986	1987	1988	1989	1990
Diet	517	525	517	533	533
Science Council of Japan	863	856	903	867	951
National Police Agency	899	925	972	1,020	1,055
Hokkaido Dev. Agency	142	143	143	147	149
Defence Agency	66,133	74,135	82,700	93,068	104,268
Econ. Planning Agency	704	710	716	764	809
Science & Tech. Agency	427,754	432,525	440,193	466,623	494,775
Environment Agency	8,320	7,914	7,752	7,882	9,217
National Land Agency	210	160	105	–	–
M. of Justice	808	806	849	871	939
M. of Foreign Affairs	6,594	6,298	6,417	6,408	7,095
M. of Finance	938	1,009	978	1,087	1,087
M. of Education	745,591	780,174	812,954	854,322	894,301
M. of Health & Welfare	36,121	39,761	44,059	48,371	51,242
M. of Agr., For. & Fisheries	66,477	66,748	66,642	68,037	70,007
M. of Int. Trade & Industry	217,557	221,409	221,226	233,649	249,832
M. of Transportation	13,271	14,516	14,627	16,303	17,410
M. of Posts & Telecom.	24,672	29,046	30,282	30,864	31,199
M. of Labour	2,970	3,635	3,708	4,557	4,190
M. of Construction	5,817	5,506	5,459	5,689	5,979
M. of Home Affairs	527	536	543	555	565
Total	1,606,386	1,662,336	1,715,746	1,815,616	1,919,603

Source: Indicators of Science and Technology (Kagaku Gijutsu Yoran). Compiled by Science and Technology Agency, Tokyo 1990. Printing Bureau, Ministry of Finance, p. 114

In the MITI vision of 1980 an indicative goal was set that the public expenditure for research and development should reach 40 per cent by the end of the decade, and from then only little less than 30 per cent. However, the serious budget constraint and the political incapacity to increase taxes, combined with the aggressive R&D spending of the private sector, has actually reduced public expenditure to less than 20 per cent in the fiscal year of 1990. The absolute levels of R&D spending and shares for various parts of the

Figure 5.4 Administrative structure of science and technology in Japan

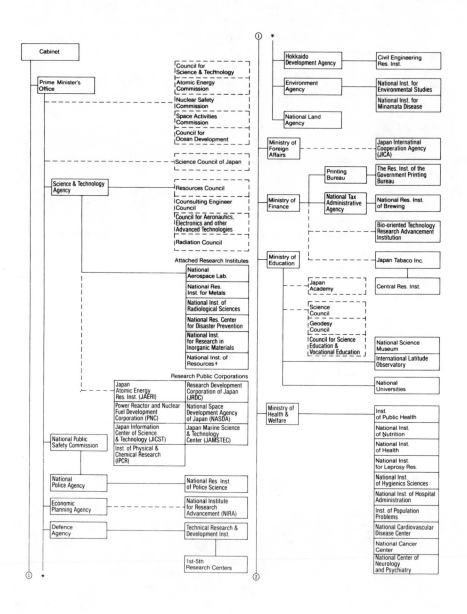

Source: National Laboratories and Research Public Corporations in Japan, Tokyo: Science and Technology Agency, p. 150-51

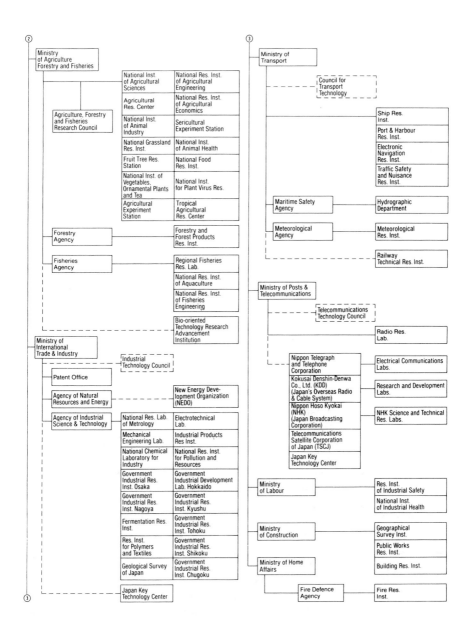

†Name changed to National Institute of Science and Technology Policy

Figure 5.5 R&D expenditure by sector

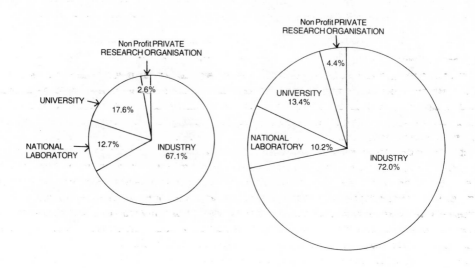

Source: Science and Technology White Paper 1989, (translated in "Changing Roles of National Research Institutes in Japan", Kawasaki Masahiro, National Institute of Science and Technology Policy)

system, for 1980 and 1987, are given in Figure 5.5. This shows that non-profit private research organisation has almost doubled in relative terms while the national research laboratories receive a decreasing share.

Another way of looking at the spending pattern for R&D in Japan is to relate the expenditure to the gross national product. The public share has remained at almost the same level since the mid-1970s, slightly above 0.5 per cent with a slight decline during the period. This contrasts with the private sector, which has increased its share from approximately 1.3 per cent of GNP to nearer 2.5 per cent in the fiscal year 1990. See Figure 5.6.

The flow of R&D funds are finally illustrated in Figure 5.7. This shows that the government funds only a small proportion of industrial research. The research at the government research institutions is basically financed by the government with a minute share coming from the private sector and nothing from private sources. The non-profit private foundations show a more complex funding with resources coming from the government, directly from industry and from special private sector research organisations. The university sector, which is made up of private and public institutions, receives a major share of total funds from the government, which is also a reflection of the fact that most research activities are concentrated in the public part of the university system.

Figure 5.6 Japan's expenditure on R&D as share of GNP, 1970-88

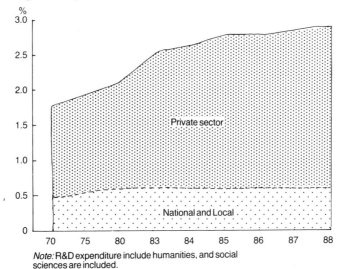

Note: R&D expenditure include humanities, and social sciences are included.

Source: Indicators of Science and Technology (Kagaku Gijutsu Yoran). Compiled by Science and Technology Agency, Tokyo 1990. Printing Bureau, Ministry of Finance, p. 12

Figure 5.7 Main flows of research funds in Japan (1988)

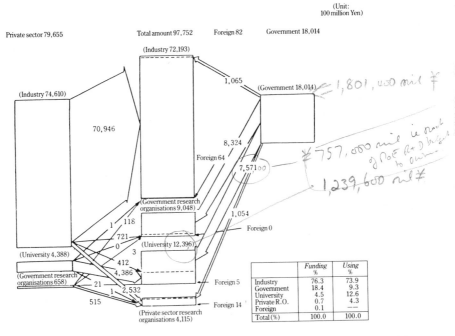

Source: Indicators of Science and Techology (Kagaku Gijutsu Yoran). Compiled by Science and Technology Agency, Tokyo 1990. Printing Bureau, Ministry of Finance, p. 7

National research institutes and structural change

The ministries supervise altogether 94 national research institutes in various fields, as exemplified above. The share of national manpower in R&D of these institutes has decreased from 3.3 per cent in 1970 to 2.3 per cent in 1987. However, parallel with this development there has been a rapid expansion of the Public Research Corporations – Tokusho-Hojin – of which there are now altogether 11 major ones. The Tokusho-Hojin is a legal entity for which most of the capital is provided by the government. Most of these corporations are conducting research in their own laboratories, and/or under contract with industries or universities. Such corporations are responsible for a major part of research in areas such as energy, space and marine technology. Three of the corporations conduct supporting activities through supply of information services and initiation and through providing investment to R&D companies, which is the case for the Japan Key Technology Centre. Today, these corporations disburse 4.6 per cent of national R&D funds and engage 0.7 per cent of all national researchers.

The funding of national research institutes has characteristics which are specific to Japan. The budget of an institute generally consists of five different parts. The first is the Special R&D Fund which is allocated to each institute for specific research projects. The second category is the R&D Running Cost Fund which is allocated in relation to the number of researchers with a fixed amount per capita. This covers heating, lighting and other routine costs. However, a portion of this fund is, in most institutes, allocated to outstanding researchers for promoting original basic research – decided by the institute leader.

A third category is the Special Facility Operation Cost Fund which covers the costs for using specific facilities such as a wind tunnel or a clean-room for semiconductor research. Another category is the Contract Research Fund which appears in the budget only if the institute has been charged with carrying out research for a specific company, although the funds are still channelled through the Ministry of Finance and not directly from the company to the national research institute.

Finally, there is the R&D Facilities Fund which covers construction costs for R&D facilities, including laboratory buildings. Furthermore, additional funds

Table 5.2 R&D budget by funding category in National Research Institutes
(hundred million yen)

	1975	1980	1985	1988
Special R&D Fund	94	170	175	207
R&D Running Cost Fund	103	127	123	121
Special Facility Operation Cost	94	230	217	212
Contract R&D Fund	1	1	2	4
R&D Facilities Fund	95	89	79	79

Source: "Changing Roles of National Research Institutes in Japan", Kawasaki Masahiro, National Institute of Science and Technology Policy

are allocated to important fields of basic research through the "Special Co-Ordination Fund for Promoting Science", which is handled by STA. Table 5.2 shows that running costs have remained almost stagnant since the mid-1970s while the special R&D funds have increased considerably. Contract funds are still minuscule but have in relative terms increased dramatically.

The system of the national research institutes is presently undergoing major changes which in a certain sense is a continuation of earlier reform initiatives. Most institutes were established after World War II, although the Electrotechnical Laboratory (ETL) and the Geological Survey have their roots in the 1880s. Since the early 1950s, the institutes were mainly depended on to conduct research and provide technical services to meet the needs arising from industries engaged in rapid catch-up activities.

After a decade or so the private companies gradually realised the need for internal research and development and quickly took on many of the activities of the national research institutes, which initiated a discussion of the future role of the government institutes. In its first recommendation, in 1960, the Council for Science and Technology indicated that the institutes should be more geared to national and welfare needs and should take large-scale and long-term projects which the private companies would face difficulties in carrying out. The same CST recommendation suggested that Public Research Corporations should be established – for which capital should come both from the government and private companies – which would provide more flexible ways of funding and conducting research than the national institutes.

Already in 1963 CST had recommended important policy changes for the national institutes which should focus basic or scientific research and engage in new frontier research such as space and nuclear energy research. An important element was the separation of technical services which had hitherto been quite significant. The same policy recommendations were reiterated on several occasions until the CST recommendation 13, in 1987, which specifically aimed at major changes in the structure of national research institutes.

The suggestions stressed that the institutes should focus on basic research which must be creative and exploratory. The institutes were also expected to make major contributions in an international context and also co-operate and compete with both universities and industries. The same CST report also highlighted the unfavourable age structure of the national research institutes, compared with laboratories in the private sector. Related to this the report also indicated that the institutes had too limited possibilities for vigorous new research, due to the ceiling on funds and low staff mobility. Another problem, although not spelled out in the recommendations, is the lack in some supervising ministries of the capacity to formulate strategies and affect co-ordination in their institutes.

Chapter 6

Major government science and technology programmes

Japan has, like other big countries, embarked in a major way on the development of big science and the efforts are very evident in three areas: nuclear energy, space, and ocean development. The endeavours in these three areas are discussed in considerable detail in Chapters 11, 12 and 16 respectively. The presentation in this and a following chapter will instead focus primarily on the various structures which have been developed in order to handle the changing situation for research and development in Japan. Several specific research projects are discussed, not only to illustrate the programmes but also to highlight the research content of various undertakings.

The efforts in nuclear energy and space development were both initiated in 1955, while ocean development research received its first major boost in 1971.

Nuclear energy development

Nuclear power already meets a considerable share of the nation's total energy requirements, more than 11 per cent in 1987, providing 26 per cent of the electricity in the same year. With the number of completed reactors approaching 40 Japan is one of the major nuclear energy countries in the world – after the USA, France and the USSR. The Minister of State for Science and Technology stated in 1989 that

> Ten years from now, nuclear power will fill about 40 per cent of Japan's energy needs. Demand for energy will continue to grow, but restraining this demand will mean restraining the industrial and economic development of Japan. As this is not an alternative, it is essential to ensure that the Japanese people benefit from nuclear power while harbouring no anxieties about its safety (*Science & Technology in Japan*, April 1989).

The long-term plans for nuclear energy have been revised on several occasions. In its first revision, in February 1961, the Atomic Energy Commission provided a Long-term Programme for the Development and Utilisation of Nuclear Energy. The Commission indicated the long-term prospects for atomic power generation, atomic powered ships, nuclear fuel, and utilisation of radiation and also outlined the necessary research and development programmes for the coming decade. A number of research reactors were built and atomic power was generated for the first time on 26 October 1963, which has since been celebrated as Atomic Energy Day in Japan.

Again in 1966 the Atomic Energy Commission meditated on a Basic Policy for Developing Power Reactors which strongly suggested the development of an independent nuclear fuel cycle. The Commission also recommended the development of a Fast Breeder Reactor and an Advanced Thermal Reactor (heavy water moderated, boiling water cooled reactor). Following from this the Japan Atomic Fuel Corporation was reorganised into the Power Reactor and Nuclear Fuel Development Corporation. A following report by the Commission in August 1969 provided the Basic Programme for Research and Development of Uranium Enrichment.

The next major revision came in mid-1982 when the Commission released the Long-Term Programme for Development and Utilisation of Nuclear Energy. The new programme integrated research and development on the various reactor types which aimed to provide a source of energy until the middle of the next century.

The programme notes that light water reactors will continue to be built and are expected to provide 30 per cent of generating capacity by the end of the century. The plans also envisaged joint development of overseas uranium deposits, stockpiling of nuclear fuels, domestic uranium enrichment and reprocessing in Japan. Plutonium obtained by reprocessing would be used by the fast breeder reactors which will come into commercial use from about 2010.

While research is proceeding for the commercialization of fast breeders, plutonium will be used as the fuel for thermal neutron reactors (heavy water reactors). For this purpose, research on advanced thermal reactors will be carried out with the aim of incorporating them in power generation systems, and at the same time efforts will be made to use plutonium in light water reactors. Following the fast breeder reactors, later in the next century the fusion reactors will come into existence and, if successful, solve Japan's energy problems permanently.

Following on the Chernobyl accident and factors affecting the energy supply and demand situation the Atomic Energy Commission decided on a new long-term plan by reviewing the past 30 years of nuclear development and utilisation in Japan. The Commission, in a document which was published in the second half of 1987, reiterates that nuclear energy is significant not only to secure a stable supply of energy but also to upgrade a wide range of scientific and technological fields. Thus, Japan will promote the development and utilisation of nuclear energy and position it as the key energy source capable of maintaining Japan's fragile energy supply structure, while at the same time assuring peaceful use and safety. The plan expects Japan to utilise uranium resources more efficiently and to reprocess spent fuel and utilise plutonium and recovered uranium. It should be noted that high energy physics research is mainly carried out at national universities.

It is expected that major technological innovations will be realised by searching for technological seeds and by systematically embarking on R&D in creative and innovative areas. It is realised that a solid technological foundation will require close co-ordination and co-operation among industries, universities and government research institutions. Thus special efforts are required to consolidate the national organisation structure for R&D supporting nuclear industry development.

The Commission estimated that the envisaged plans would require Y7 trillion for the period until the end of the century, of which Y1.5 trillion is for basic research only. Other costs relate to nuclear power generation including the development of new reactors, development of nuclear fuel cycles, etc. It is expected that the private sector, from its own sources, will spend about Y2 trillion on research and another Y14 trillion on the construction of light water reactors and commercial nuclear fuel cycle facilities.

The nuclear energy research is now focused on two approaches – for medium-term fast breeder reactor and long term fusion reactors, aside from ongoing activities in nuclear-powered ships. Based on results from a test reactor, Joyo, a prototype reactor, Monju, is now being constructed and will be ready for initial operation in 1992. The Power Reactor and Nuclear Fuel Development Corporation, which is responsible for the Monju reactor, has contracted the Japan Atomic Power Co to manage the actual construction. The company which consists of a consortium of nine electric utilities, has then contracted the actual work to four major equipment manufacturers – Toshiba, Hitachi, Fuji Electric and Mitsubishi Heavy Industries. Following Monju the plan is to construct a full-scale demonstration reactor, and Japan Atomic Power Co has been requested to determine the basic specifications in 1990, with the objective of starting construction towards the end of the century.

The other major research and development effort, designated as a National Project, is to lay the technological foundation for nuclear fusion to generate electricity. There are presently four major participants and Japan, USA and EC have chosen a similar approach using the tokamak (doughnut-shaped) design of fusion reactor. The Japanese design, JT-60, is run by the Science and Technology Agency, and reached the target area of break-even plasma conditions in September 1987. The reactor has since been used for performance improvement and is bridging the gap awaiting the replacement of the large vacuum vessel. In May 1989 a Nuclear Fusion Research Institute was established by the Ministry of Education, Culture and Science, based on the earlier Nagoya University Plasma Research Institute. The institute will build a novel, helical design of fusion reactor that will be the largest of its kind in the world. A large number of research institutes are involved in the Japanese fusion research efforts. The major ones are JAERI, National Research Institute for Metals, ETL, the Variotron Fusion Research Centre at Osaka University, the Plasma Research Centre at Tsukuba University and the Applied Physics Research Institute of Kyushu University which has a Tokamak.

International collaboration has come to play an increasingly important role. Close research relations have long existed between the US Tokamak Fusion Test Reactor, the EC Joint European Torus and the JT-60 at the Japan Atomic Energy Research Institute. More recently, JAERI is also participating in the conceptual design of the International Thermonuclear Fusion Reactor – ITER – with EC, USA and USSR under the auspices of the International Atomic Energy Agency.

The total research expenditure for nuclear energy was Y450 trillion in 1988, with R&D on power plant technology getting Y173 trillion and another Y133 trillion going to the nuclear fuel cycle and fusion research receiving Y40 trillion. The nuclear energy share of the national R&D efforts amounts to roughly one half of the efforts in all fields of energy R&D with Y320 trillion going to energy conservation.

The Science and Technology Agency is the key disburser of government funds for nuclear energy R&D. Its total budget for this purpose was Y176 trillion in 1988, with approximately the same amount budgeted for 1990. The major part of this, Y154 trillion, goes to JAERI, specific reactor research projects, and fuel processing projects.

Space research and development

The emergence of space development in Japan presents a very different picture from that of nuclear energy development and has actually developed along two parallel paths which are now closely co-ordinated. Space research was started at an early stage at the University of Tokyo, when the ban on rocket research was lifted in 1954. With limited funds from the Ministry of Education, the research initially focused on unguarded rockets of a modular design, the result of which would be useful for later stages. There was considerable progress after Japan decided to participate in the International Geophysical Year 1957-58.

In the early 1960s a number of initiatives and changes gradually provided a new framework for space development in Japan. First, the Council for Space Development was established in 1960, to be followed by the re-organisation of Aircraft Research Laboratory into the National Aerospace Laboratory (NAL) in 1963. The following year saw the formation of a national space development section within the Science and Technology Agency, and in the same year the space research activities at Tokyo University were reorganised into the Institute for Space and Aeronautical Science.

A drastic measure to boost space development was taken in May 1968 when the council, mentioned above, was replaced by the Space Activities Commission (SAC). The purpose of the Commission was to centralise the space activities of the various government agencies and have them executed under a systematic programme. This may occasionally pose difficulties as funds and activities are controlled by several ministries. However, a research co-ordination bureau of STA provides the secretariat for SAC to plan, deliberate and decide important matters on space activities and to review annually the Space Development Programme.

The newly established Commission in October decided on its first space development programme for the next ten years. Among other things the programme set out the goal of developing a basic experimental satellite, an ionosphere sounding satellite, and an experimental communications satellite. The overall aim was to develop satellites, the launching rockets and the necessary equipment and expertise required for launching and tracking within a period of five to six years. The following year, 1969, the National Space Development Agency (NASDA), modelled after NASA in the USA, came into existence based on the Space Development Centre which had been created, by STA, in 1964 to launch rockets at Niijima. In the meantime a new rocket range had been opened at Tanegashima in 1966.

NASDA has two different funds, capital investment and research grants and may also accept investments and grants from non-government organisations. The Agency has four major activities: carrying out research and development on satellites and their launch vehicles; launching satellites including tracking and earth observation; receiving and processing satellite data used for remote sensing; and promotion of experiments in space.

The following years saw a very rapid expansion of the budget for space development, which increased from Y9 trillion in 1969 to Y88 trillion in 1976 – most of the expansion accruing to NASDA during this period. However, the Institute of Space and Aeronautical Science (ISAS), at the University of Tokyo, continued to expand and play an important role and was in April 1981 transformed into a National Research Institute for Joint Use by Universities belonging to the Ministry of Education. It should be noted that this institute still maintains the responsibility for the design and launch of all purely scientific satellites.

Following the completion of the first 10-year plan the Space Activities Commission drafted a new plan for the next ten years, made public in March 1978 – often referred to as the Fundamental Guidelines of Space Policy. The plan essentially committed Japan to a non-military programme aimed at gaining an autonomous launching capability. Immediate goals of high priority were the development of ocean observation and communication satellites; satellites capable of observing resources and geophysical environmental conditions; and techniques for manufacturing materials in outer space.

A first revision of the plan was made in 1984 and a contributing factor was the major problem facing the Commission at the time, was that none of the rockets available in the development programme would be sufficiently large to put the coming generation of communications satellites, in the 1990s, into orbit. So the Commission decided to embark on the domestic development of rockets, the H-II, capable of putting a 2,000 kilogram payload into orbit.

However, new technological possibilities and new demands soon required a second revision of the Fundamental Policy. The Commission started their deliberations at the end of 1987 and announced, in June 1989, new guidelines which have three major characteristics. First, demands inside the country – in particular for various information and telecommunications purposes – must be more precisely met. Second, the basis for future space development must be broadened and Japan must prepare itself and engage much more actively in international endeavours. Third, the involvement of the private sector should be promoted. With space development activities, so far mainly implemented under state leadership, the Commission expected a role-sharing system which would exploit the vitality of the private sector.

Furthermore, the revised Fundamental Policy envisages a wider diversification and mentions manned space activities, utilisation of space for experimentation in the fields of materials and life science. It also assumes participation in the Space Station programme and suggests development of means to exploit space environment. Finally the more futuristic aspects are also included such as next generation platform satellites, the unmanned orbiting shuttle HOPE and the development of space planes.

Aside from the Commission, STA, NAL, NASDA and the Ministry of Education with its joint ISAS, it is also necessary to mention the involvement of a couple of other agencies and ministries. First, the Ministry of Transportation (MOT) supervises the Japan Meteorological Agency (JMA) which is responsible for services using geo-stationary and orbital satellites as well as observations using rockets. Attached to JMA there is a Meteorological Satellite Centre which is responsible for the control and operation of satellites, image acquisition and meteorological data analysis. Supervised by MOT is the Electronic Navigation Research Institute which carries out research on satellite navigation.

The Ministry of Posts and Telecommunications (MPT) is, through its Communication Policy Bureau, responsible for planning and promoting policies on satellite communications and broadcasting systems as well as radio regulation with regard to space. Naturally, MPT has a further indirect involvement in space development through Nippon Telegraph and Telephone

Corporation (NTT) and the Kokusai Denshin Denwa (KDD), which not only sign international agreements but also have relevant research activities in their large laboratories. Finally, it should also be noted that MPT, jointly with STA and MOT, supervises NASDA, and independently the Telecommunications Satellite Corporation of Japan (TSCJ). The latter organisation was established in 1979 to operate and control operational communications and broadcasting satellites. This includes having satellites launched by other agencies, to control the position and behaviour of satellites and provide required equipment on board the satellites.

Aside from the involvement of various other ministries the Federation of Economic Organisations (Keidanren) also plays an important role in influencing space development activities. In Keidanren the major private industrial companies involved in space development are represented in the Space Activities Promotion Council. The representatives from this Promotion Council generally meet with high-ranking officials of the Space Activities Commission, NASDA and STA several times a year.

After the rapid expansion in the early 1970s the total government budget for space development renamed stable at a level slightly above Y100 trillion. Since the mid-1980s the government allocations are again increasing and the budget for 1990 amounts to Y162 trillion. The majority of this, Y119 trillion, comes from STA and is allocated for activities carried out by NASDA. The Ministry of Education has a budget of Y18 trillion which has also increased rapidly during the past few years. The same is true for MITI which spent Y15 trillion on space development in 1990.

Ocean development

In the early 1960s ocean development attracted much interest as a promising future industry and the country witnessed a boom in marine development. Both the University of Tokyo and Tokai University had already in the preceding decade established a marine research institute and marine department respectively. A Council for Ocean Science and Technology was established in 1961. Partly in response to its deliberations and reports in 1963 and 1964 Japan embarked on major ocean surveys and launched its first deep-sea exploratory vessel, *Shinkai*, in 1968. A number of changes followed in response to a report from the council in 1969 – the Development Plan for Ocean Development on Science and Technology. This can be seen as the actual start for more intensive efforts which were to follow after the Council for Ocean Development, replacing the earlier body, was set up in 1971 to serve the Prime Minister's Office as an advisory body.

Beforehand the government had already carried out preparations to promote ocean development which had included a liaison conference for the promotion of marine science and technology. This played an important role in mobilising interest and resources and also served to facilitate co-ordination. An important instrument for the future of ocean development in Japan was the creation of the Japan Marine Science and Technology Centre (JAMSTEC) which came into existence, in 1971, through the joint efforts of industrial circles, the academic society and the government.

The strong interest in ocean development must be understood in the special context of Japan as an island country completely surrounded by the sea. Furthermore, it is a country with limited natural resources, limited land area, and frequent earthquakes. However, the territorial waters around Japan offer potential riches such as minerals and biological resources, as well as being a vast potential source of energy. Thus, it was considered necessary for Japan to develop marine science and technology so that these potential benefits could be exploited.

The early euphoria gradually gave way to more gloomy views, partly triggered by the first oil crisis in 1973. The new energy situation naturally raised expectations for submarine oil explorations. However, the structural change of the Japanese industry, away from heavy and chemical industries, retarded the orientation towards ocean development. In the first report – Basic Concepts and Measures Concerning the Promotion of Ocean Development in Japan, in 1973, – from the then recently established Ocean Development Council the same mood was reflected. The international deliberations for establishing a new international framework for ocean-related matters, under U.N. auspices, started in the same year. Then, the Third U.N. Conference on the Law of the Sea soon made it clear that a 200-mile economic zone would naturally benefit Japan.

It would take until the United Nations "Law of the Sea" Conference held in Caracas at the end of 1982 to establish the economic zone and another few years before the treaty was finally signed. The law is of tremendous benefit to Japan, for its land area is only about 380,000 square kilometres while its sea area, within the 200-mile zone is between four and five million square kilometres, almost twelve times the land area. Furthermore, Japan's total sea area is the sixth largest in the world, following those of the USA, Australia, Indonesia, New Zealand and Canada, and a little ahead of the USSR and Brazil.

The prospect of exclusive access to these large sea resources revived interest in ocean development, and in 1979 and 1980 the Council provided new guidelines for the following decade. The same year also saw the establishment of the Liaison Committee for Ocean Development which has the mandate to direct the development efforts of ministries and agencies in order to improve the efficiency of the national efforts. The Japan Marine and Science and Technology Centre, already mentioned, is organised as a public corporation (tokushuhojin) and has a major responsibility for R&D related to ocean development – covering four areas. The two major ones are actual research and development, and operating and maintaining various facilities such as high pressure facilities. The first function presently includes deep ocean floor survey system and manned undersea work system. The other two functions are training and education, and providing technical information.

The R&D funds for ocean development are considerably smaller than those allocated for space development – about one third or Y49 trillion in 1990 – and have remained at a stable level for the past five years. In contrast to nuclear development and space development the activities are much more diverse and also much more widely distributed among ministries and agencies. The budget resources are almost equally shared among four agencies – STA, Ministry of Agriculture, Forestry and Fishery, MITI and the Ministry of Transportation – with the remainder going to five other ministries or agencies. This situation requires occasional contacts through the Liaison Committee to eliminate problems and facilitate the necessary co-ordination.

Chapter 7

Major government programmes in industrial science and technology

In 1990 the private sector will allocate approximately Y8,000 billion to research and development activities, which is a little more than 80 per cent of all national expenditure on R&D. Only a minute part, or about Y100 billion, is a *direct* contribution to the R&D efforts of the private sector. Limited financial contributions notwithstanding, close R&D links between private companies and government research organisations have been fostered in a number of ways. The network of these links appears not only to have become more finely meshed but also to have taken on a more long-term nature with a focus on more fundamental knowledge. This chapter will focus on the role being played by MITI and its changing character, although other support programmes supervised by other ministries will also be discussed.

The following presentation will start by discussing the oldest formal initiative, the so called Large-Scale Projects, started in 1966, which are usually organised around an engineering research association which is generally also the case for the the Research Programme on Basic Technologies for Future Industries, which came into existence much later. Both programmes have in the late 1980s been incorporated into a new organisation which carries the name of New Energy and Industrial Technology Development Organisation.

The new trend towards more flexible structures geared to the support for more basic and exploratory knowledge is exemplified by the creation of the Japan Key Technology Centre (JKTC) in the mid-1980s soon to be followed by Bio-Oriented Technology Research Advancement Institution (BRAIN). The Adverse Drug Sufferings Relief and Research Promotion Fund, although much less significant, is one more example of the new type of policy instruments.

The Exploratory Research on Advanced Technology Organisation (ERATO), which has a mandate to explore more fundamental issues, not necessarily related to any immediate prospects for industrial applications, is one more example of the innovativeness of the Japanese bureaucrats in the 1980s. Information on projects being sponsored under each programme will be given throughout the presentation, which, due to the large number of projects, will only provide a sample of what is being attempted.

MITI, the Agency of Industrial Science and Technology and the formulation of technology policy

Although industry supplies the bulk of research and development funds the role of government is still very important for setting the agenda and providing structures for future-oriented research. Roughly one half of government R&D

funds goes to the universities and another quarter is allocated to the "big science" projects, discussed in the preceding chapter. Of the remainder approximately 15 per cent or a little more than Y200 billion is being handled by the Ministry of International Trade and Industry, mainly through its Agency of Industrial Science and Technology (AIST).

The agency carries out research at its own sixteen research institutes – employing close to 3,700 staff of which roughly 2,500 have the status as researchers. Furthermore, AIST devises long-term research plans and promotes them, usually in co-operation with private industry. To make relevant plans the agency carries out detailed surveys of technological development in private industry, in energy and trade, and closely monitors science and technology developments abroad which may have an effect on industrial structures, environment and so on. The aim is to produce broad, long-term policies that are at the same time sufficiently specific to provide guidance for needed projects and programmes.

Before going into the details of programmes, projects and the changes in the systems for promoting industrial science and technology it is helpful to look briefly into the earlier stages of planning which have often had the character of "visions" – similar to those already described for the Science and Technology Agency. An early visionary report was prepared in 1963 by the then Industrial Structure Investigation Council, which was later to become the important Industrial Structure Council.

The report contained MITI's policy vision for an economy which had already passed the post-war rehabilitation stage. The very rapid economic growth, with annual growth rates exceeding 10 per cent in several years, posed the challenge of new structures throughout the economy. MITI had its sights set on support for domestic development which would replace the still prevalent technology transfer imports. This would require a different balance between government and private industry with the latter up-grading and up-scaling their research efforts. MITI also conceived an industrial technology development system which would include large-scale funding and joint research projects. The creation of the Tsukuba Science City was also envisaged at the same time.

A following report, in May 1971, with the title "Basic Course of International Trade and Industrial Policy in the 1970s" was less significant as the overall economic and industrial situation was soon to be changed by the first oil crisis in 1973. This period saw the establishment of the Sunshine Project to develop new energy resources. Until this time MITI's technology policies were handled by an Industrial Technology Committee within the Industrial Structure Council. The committee was reorganised into the Industrial Technology Council which in August 1975 submitted an interim report on the "Future Course of Industrial Technology Promotion Policy". The report indicated a number of technologies worthy of support, which included nuclear fusion and computers, and again emphasised the need for environmental preservation, a concern which had already been voiced in the preceding report. The Moonlight Project to develop energy conservation technologies was created a couple of years later.

The philosophy of technology-oriented national development was a cornerstone in the "Vision of International Trade and Industrial Policy for the 1980s" which MITI's Industrial Structure Council presented in March 1980. This was at the time of increasing trade friction and rapidly increasing energy prices. The vision expected that special national efforts would be taken to overcome energy restrictions and to promote technological development for knowledge-intensive and creative industries which, it was expected, would cause less trade friction. Then followed in November 1984 a report with the title "Desirable Course of Industrial Technology Development Policy", which emphasised the need to exploit nationally the research vitality of the private sector and reinforce the links of industrial-government-academic co-operation.

There is obviously a close link between this report and the deliberations which two years later led to the establishment of the Japan Key Technology Centre. Since the late 1970s there had been a growing concern about the insularity of the R&D system in Japan and the urgency of international requests for closer co-operation in science and technology. This theme was also covered in the May 1986 report, "Basic Concept of Industrial Society in the 21st Century", which was prepared by a Planning Sub-committee of the Industrial Structure Council. This and other propositions set in motion the project which has become known as the Human Frontier Science Programme.

A few years later, in September 1988, MITI presented a white paper on industrial technology which has a main title of "Trends and Future Tasks in Industrial Technology" and the more indicative subtitle of "Developing Innovate Technologies to Support the 21st Century and Contributing to the International Community". The lengthy and detailed report notes that, while Japan has scored exceeding well in developing and applying industrial technologies, it has done less well in generating a real scientific research capability, and the international dimension had also partly been neglected. Based on this report and careful and lengthy deliberations, the two advisory bodies, the Industrial Science and Technology Council and the Industrial Structure Council, in July 1990 presented the MITI vision for science and technology in the 1990s.

The vision rests upon four pillars. First, Japan will enhance the international character of its research and development policy through international research like the Human Science Frontier Programme, international environmental research, international research co-operation and technology transfer to developing countries. Next comes the strengthening of basic and creative research which will include centres of excellence open to foreigners, support for new research areas and stimulation of the private sector to do more basic research. Third, Japan should promote science and technology which is sympathetic to man and nature and will allocate research resources for an ageing nation, with more concern for the human dimension in technology development and societal improvement rather than solely economic and industrial growth. Finally the vision stresses the role of industrial technology in regional vitalisation, which envisages that regional needs will be considered when locating new research activities or forming consortia, while also strengthening regional capability for new developments.

For comparison it may be useful to examine briefly the results of the MITI Vision from 1980 and its subsequent implementation of technology policies. It was expected at the time that the expenditure on research and development should have reached 3 per cent by 1990 – which has in fact basically been achieved. However, it was also expected at the time that the government share of funding should increase to 40 per cent in 1990. In contrast it has gradually declined in relative terms and is below 20 per cent, which is 0.6 per cent of the GNP.

Oil dependency has not been reduced, as expected, and alternative and new energy sources have hardly been developed. It was envisaged that means should be found to encourage technological creativity and encourage private industry to take risks and engage in the development of more creative technologies. Looking at score cards for technological levels of Japanese companies – in almost any field – with the competitors in the USA and western Europe clearly indicates a more than partial success. However, another aspect of the vision was the promotion of international co-operation in technological development among industrialised nations and technology transfer to developing countries. Available evidence indicates that Japan still has a long way to go to achieve this goal, although the full burden can hardly be expected to be taken by Japan alone.

Even before the Vision of 1990 was made public the bureaucrats at MITI were busy promoting their special designs to implement the new policy. One of the blueprints suggested a Foundation for Basic Research which will be jointly managed with private industry and in close co-operation with the universities and national laboratories.

Large Scale Projects and Engineering Research Associations

Under the National Research and Development Programme, generally known as Large Scale Projects, the Agency of Industrial Science and Technology carries out projects on technologies which are both important and urgently needed. This programme started in 1966 and altogether 26 projects have been started of which sixteen have already been completed. Generally there are at any one time eight ongoing Large Scale Projects (LSPs). Those in operation in Summer 1990, as well as the completed ones, are listed in Appendix IV.

Almost all projects have large budgets, in the region of Y15 to Y20 billion, and run over a period between five and ten years, although some earlier projects have been much smaller. Two of the earliest projects focused on a super high performance computer and a de-sulphurization process, which exemplifies the concern for technological development at the time. Still in the early 1980s the staff at AIST and other concerned bodies considered it necessary to organise a LSP for a high speed computing system and for an automated sewing system. More recent LSPs include research for clearly emerging fields like marine systems, which is also true for the manganese module mining system started in 1981, hypersonic transport propulsion system and underground space development technology.

There are two other AIST programmes which have a close resemblance to the LSPs. These are the R&D on New Energy Technology Programme, launched in 1974 and usually referred to as the Sunshine Project, and the R&D on Energy Conservation Technology, launched in 1978 and usually referred to as the Moonlight Project. The scope and duration of the projects show great similarities with the LSP programme and actually emerged out of this when the energy crisis hit Japan. The Sunshine and Moonlight programmes are discussed in Chapter 11.

Government funds were in the past given directly to the participating companies and the necessary funds were also provided to the national laboratories and other participating organisations. In order to handle the programmes AIST is organised in divisions which correspond to the ongoing R&D programmes. So there is an Office for LSPs which has eight executive research managers – one for each ongoing project. There is a team for each LSP, set up when the project starts, with an executive research manager and three to four supporting staff on secondment from the national laboratories under AIST supervision. Naturally the same rules of rotation applies to these teams as elsewhere within the administration which means that a team member may stay for two to three years whilst a project may last eight to ten years or longer. However, since the beginning of the 1970s almost every single LSP is organised around an Engineering Research Association (ERA) which provides continuity.

The ERAs are non-profit organisations which are established according to certain rules contained in a law which was promulgated in 1961, when a first ERA – for high polymers – was established. In 1990 almost 100 ERAs had been established, most of which have already completed their tasks, and which involved almost all of the major Japanese companies in various development projects. In the mid-1960s the ERAs had almost completely ceased to be used as a policy instrument. However, this instrument was revitalised in the early 1970s and a major contributing factor was the need to find a new organisation form for the LSPs.

It appears that the role of the ERAs is now coming to an end and there are two major criticisms, which also reflect on internal project management at AIST. First, it is argued that the system does not function well when there is a need to modify or even abolish a research project. Second, it has also been pointed out by several observers that the system does not provide independent and critical evaluation of projects. Considering the increasing complexity of technologies and scientific disciplines involved and often dramatic changes in the technological and economic environment the time had come to modify the system, which was done in 1988.

Before passing on to the new system and the other research projects affected a few glimpses will be provided of the ongoing LSPs.

Manganese Nodule Mining System

The oldest current Large Scale Project is the Manganese Nodule Mining System, which started in 1981. The objective is to develop the necessary technologies for a system which can mine nodules containing nickel, copper, cobalt and manganese existing at water depths around 5000 metres. The mining system being developed is a hydraulic one in which nodules are collected by a towed vehicle on the ocean floor and raised by a hydraulic lift system. There are five major subsystems: collector, material lift, machinery handling, data assembly and control and the system integration. At the approaching final stage a pilot mining test is planned, to be carried out in one of the nodule-rich areas in the Pacific Ocean.

Inter-Operable Database System

The main feature of this project, started in 1986 and to be completed in 1991, is the development of a protocol for interconnections among computers. It is conducted as a development project for the Open Systems Interconnection – OSI – in compliance with the International Organisation for Standardisation. The development of interoperability, which enables the interconnection of different systems, is considered as the key ingredient for an information-oriented society, which Japan is already. The project aims at developing technology for constructing a convenient database system and will also develop technologies to process characters, graphics and images.

Super/Hypersonic Transport System

This project, which is in its early formation stage, aims at combining two propulsion techniques – ramjet and high performance turbo-jet. It is expected that the project will clarify the basic characteristics of a combined-cycle engine which could provide high reliability at both the sub-sonic and hypersonic level. The project will carry out research and development for a system which can not only measure the relevant parameters but also control the entire engine. Another major task is research on the system concept to identify the optimal combination of the two jet functions. Finally, it is foreseen that a prototype system will be manufactured, within the project, which will permit testing and analysis of data. It is expected that such an engine could provide safe flights at Mach 5, making it possible to fly between Tokyo and London in three hours and between Tokyo and New York in five hours.

Underground Space Development Technology

This project, which is in its formation stage, draws its major justification from the extremely high land prices in the major urban concentrations which make it difficult to construct new facilities in these densely populated areas. The project will explore underground conditions at 50 metres or below and will cover four approaches. First, it is expected that the project will develop computer tomography techniques for evaluating underground structures. Sealed machines, which can work underwater, will be developed for automatic excavation and lining, among other things. Third, techniques for air conditioning and preventing hazards will be developed. Finally, during the second half of the project a pilot dome will be constructed so that the engineering feasibility of the developed technologies can be demonstrated. AIST says in its 1989 brochure of Large-Scale Projects that "(I)t is hoped that the developed technologies will be used to construct energy storage and supply system as well as cultural and commercial facilities" – although not living quarters.

Research and Development Programme on Basic Technologies for Future Industries

This programme, which was started in 1981, aims at the development of technologies considered significant to the growth of future industries. The fields covered include new materials, biotechnology, new electronic devices and more recently superconductivity. When the programme started there were altogether twelve projects, some of which have been transferred or dropped while others have been added. At present there are fourteen projects with recent additions in high performance plastics, one newcomer each in biotechnology and new electron devices, apart from the superconductivity project which was started in 1988. See Appendix IV for a complete listing of ongoing projects.

The organisation of these projects is somewhat different from the Large Scale Projects. All of them have formal organisations outside AIST. The Fine Ceramics Project is organised as an Engineering Research Association, which is also the case for synthetic membranes, Synthetic Metals Project and High Performance Plastics Project, which are in fact organised in the same association, Research Association for Basic Polymer Technology (RABT). The Large-Scale Cell Cultivation is organised in the Research Association for Bio-Technology (RAB), as is the Technology for Application of Functional Protein Complexes and Recombinant DNA Utilisation Technology.

The three projects in new electronic devices are organised in the Research and Development Association for Future Electronic Devices (FED). The superconductivity project is split between this association and the newly created International Superconductivity Technology Centre (ISTEC). The High Performance Materials for Severe Conditions is linked to what is called the Research and Development Institute of Metals and Composites for Future Industries, while there is a Japan High-Polymer Centre of the Non-Linear Photonics Material Project. Brief descriptions are given for a few projects to illustrate the character of research of this programme.

Fine ceramics

This project belongs to the first batch of projects which were started in 1981 and will be completed in 1992. It was started partly as a Japanese response to the widely publicised reports on German and US efforts to develop a ceramic engine. The project has a major focus on powder and sintering technology to develop structural ceramics which have high corrosion resistance and can withstand abrasion at high temperatures. One of the ultimate purposes is to be able to use ceramics as structural components for coal gasification ceramic turbine engines. An integral part of the project is research on evaluation and application of new technologies which can properly evaluate the mechanical properties of various ceramics.

Bio-electronic devices

This project, which started in 1986 and is to be completed in 1995, has the goal of producing a prototype model of a device for evaluation and thereby, possibly, establishing the basic technology for bio-electronics. There is a general belief that by studying and identifying the sophisticated information processing functions of organisms it may be possible to develop a new bioelectronic device – as a first step towards a bio-computer. In this project, research and development are being conducted to identify the algorithms of logic and memory that operate in the neural system of organisms. The ultimate aim is to identify the technology with which it will be possible to build a device composed of molecular organisms which have the plasticity of living matter, the capability of identifying molecules, and a self-organizing ability.

Technology for application of functional protein complexes

This project, which started in 1989, has the objective of establishing the technology which will enable material production and conversion based on a complex of organic functions. The starting point is that all advanced functions which an organism may have, such as its energy conversion, material recognition, transmission and protein composition, arise as a result of composite multistage reactions which take place in an advanced molecular complex such as that represented by the membrane of an organism. The project will conduct research and development to identify technologies which can structure functional protein complexes through handling of advanced molecular complexes at molecular level. The project will also analyse and evaluate technology related to the detailed structure of functional protein complexes.

Research and development programme on medical and welfare equipment technology

This is a motley collection of research projects which have been supported by AIST since the mid-1970s when the Agency established an interest to support the medical equipment industries, based on perceived societal need. Throughout the period the promoted projects have been organised within the Engineering Research Association of Medical and Welfare Equipment, which is jointly administered by MITI and the Ministry of Health and Welfare. The projects are generally of shorter duration and less costly than those within the two programmes described above. An example is given below.

Three-dimensional display for the blind

This project started in 1989 and will be completed by 1992. The aim is to develop a high-density pin display and copy system which enable three-dimensional displays to be easily recognised by the blind in a very short period of time. This will be carried out through appropriate descriptions of visibly recognisable two-dimensional and three-dimensional graphic images on a computer.

New Energy and Industrial Technology Development Organisation – a new research offshoot for MITI research promotion

All three research programmes discussed above were incorporated on 1 October 1988 into a new organisation – the New Energy and Industrial Technology Development Organisation (NEDO) – which is formally a Public Corporation similar to NASDA for space research, JAERI in nuclear research,

JAMSTEC in ocean development and the RIKEN research institute to be introduced towards the end of this chapter.

NEDO used to belong to the Agency of Natural Resources and Energy, which is one of the agencies belonging to MITI. In the conversion, which was prompted by a desire not to create new organisations, NEDO has maintained old responsibilities which include the following three tasks: to promote the co-ordinated development and commercialization of alternative energy resources to reduce the dependency on imported oil; to promote rationalisation and consolidation of the coal mining industry; and to produce industrial alcohol.

However, there can be doubt that the main mission of NEDO lies in a fourth objective.

To carry out basic and advanced research and development on industrial technology; construction and operation of large-scale research and development facilities; international joint research and to co-ordinate these activities for the purpose of improving Japanese industrial technology and making a contribution to the international community through technological development and co-operation.

It is also obvious that the creation of NEDO has created considerably more flexibility than the earlier system although it is not yet clear to what extent the various projects can be easily modified or even scrapped if and when the need arises. It should be noted that NEDO does not maintain its own laboratories or research staff. Its role is to administer and co-ordinate research which is carried out by national laboratories and industry. Furthermore, the members of the NEDO council include high-ranking experts from the private sector and the organisations' capital is partly composed of investment from the private sector.

A new and significant activity is the research facility development programme. Through this NEDO will establish basic research facilities which are required for the promotion of international research and development on advanced industrial technology which cannot be established or owned by individual companies due to the extremely high costs involved. Such state-of-the-art facilities are established through joint investments made by NEDO, local governments and private industry. These facilities are then made available to domestic and foreign researchers at moderate costs. NEDO also indicated that it will undertake to develop the needed equipment and support systems in cases where it is particularly difficult to establish basic research facilities.

There will be special research corporations for establishing and maintaining the special research facilities: three have already been established and two more will follow, all of which are briefly introduced below.

Finally, NEDO also have two international programmes of which one provides international joint research grants for basic research on materials to elucidate material functions, the other, international research co-ordination, includes researcher exchange, joint research and researcher training.

Ion Engineering Centre (IEC)

The Ion Engineering Centre will be an integrated ion research facility which will be equipped with low speed to high speed ion beam radiation equipment to be used for technology development for semiconductor materials and advanced materials to be used in aeronautic and marine applications. The Centre is located in Hirakata City, near Osaka, and is scheduled to start operation in 1990. The Ion Engineering Research Institute Corporation, attached to the Centre, will conduct research and development and will be active in promoting international exchange.

Research Centre for the Industrial Utilisation of Marine Organisms

This research centre will have equipment and facilities for biotechnology research, including production technology for high performance chemical products using marine organisms and physiological function utilisation technology to refine metal through the use of marine organisms. The Centre will have laboratories, one in Shimizu City in Shizuoka prefecture (warm current) and another one in Kamaishi City in Iwate prefecture (cold current), and both laboratories are expected to begin operation in 1990. Similarly the Marine Bio-Technology Institute Corporation Ltd (MBI) is established separately from the Centre itself. The Corporation is a joint venture by 24 private corporations active in marine technology and actively works to promote international research exchange.

Japan Microgravity Centre (JAMIC)

The Japan Microgravity Centre is designed to create a microgravity environment for ten seconds under conditions of $1 \times 10\text{-}4$ G in an abandoned mining shaft. This facility will allow scientists to carry out various experiments which can be applied to the manufacturing of special alloys, perfect crystal, and ultra-fine particles that cannot be produced under normal near-gravity conditions. The development of advanced drop capsule started in 1989. The laboratory is located in Suanagawa City, Hokkaido, and is scheduled to begin its operation in 1991.

Japan Ultra-High-Temperature Materials Research Centre

The Centre will have equipment and facilities to develop advanced technology for ultra-high-temperature-resistant materials, including composite materials and metal alloys. Such materials are expected to be used under temperature conditions of about 2,000 degrees C. The Centre is planned to have two laboratories with one in Ube City in Yamaguchi prefecture and the other one in Taimi City in Gifu prefecture. The final title of the Centre is yet to be established.

Applied Laser Engineering Centre

The Centre will be equipped with various laser devices such as CO_2 laser, YAG laser and CO laser. These devices will be used for the technology development to modify the surface of materials, new approaches to medical treatment and new concentration methods for uranium. The Centre is planned to be located in Nagaoka City, Niigata prefecture.

Japan Key Technology Centre (JKTC)

The Japan Key Technology Centre is a quasi-governmental special corporation which was established in October 1985 for the specific purpose of promoting R&D on advanced basic technologies in the private sector. "Japan Key-TEC was founded to provide broad-ranging services for the promotion and administration of joint governmental/industrial/academic R&D of key technologies in a manner most conducive to private-sector vitality."

The idea of establishing the Centre is contained in a proposal from the Industrial Structure Council of MITI and was formally discussed in a Parliament session in 1984. The proposal was directly tied to the privatisation of NTT, the Japanese telephone company, on 1 April 1985, which would release substantial funds. A small part of those funds, it occurred to MITI officials, could be conveniently and efficiently used for financing a new and badly needed, policy instrument.

There are two factors which may have been significant in establishing Japan Key Technology Centre as a new policy instrument. First, Japan has in recent years suffered from a very tough budget squeeze which has made it extremely difficult to persuade the Ministry of Finance to allocate more money for government R&D. This partly explains the constant lowering of the government's share of Japan's total R&D expenditure – now down to 20 per cent or less.

Second, the engineering research associations were often perceived as too inflexible organisations to handle research topics, where the target was moving, and patents and other intellectual property were becoming an increasingly thorny subject. The ERAs may been more efficient and more relevant for clearly defined development tasks, although they have in recent years increasingly been used for basic research of a long-term nature. Many of the projects within the "Basic Technology for Future Industries" programme are organised as ERAs. Almost all the projects are of a long-term nature and are much closer to basic research than is the case for many of the earlier ERAs.

These factors prompted the MITI officials to grasp the opportunity of the privatisation of NTT to create a new policy instrument for a more flexible long-term support for basic technologies. Japan Key-TEC has the mandate to engage in the following activities:

1. Capital investment in development companies.

2. Loan services to reduce the risks and capital burden of research and development.

3. Mediation in arranging joint research – among private companies and national research institutes.

4. Execution of consigned research – involving national research institutions.

5. Japan Trust International Research Co-Operation Service – to be used for inviting foreign researchers in key technologies.

6. Research Information Service.

7. Survey services.

8. Other services.

The first five categories all aim at creating new groups and more efficient linkages within the research community. The JKTC investment in R&D companies is one of the more important functions. The requirements are that two or more companies jointly establish an R&D company for a fundamental research project or comprehensive development research projects. The Japan Key-TEC will then provide up to 70 per cent of the capital requirements. The biggest projects have an expected life span of ten years with project costs in the region of Y10-Y17 billion. The investment share coming from the Centre for a single project would then be of the order of 50-100 million US dollars – at the present exchange rate.

There are ten development companies which also include the participation of national laboratories. So far there are none which include the direct participation of university departments. Similarly there are not yet any development companies which have been formed with foreign company participation (foreign company being defined as having more than 50 per cent foreign equity). However, the Protein Engineering Research Institute, which was established in 1985, located in Senri, Suita near Osaka, has two "foreign members", TOA Nenryo (Fuel) Company and Japan LaRoche while Japan Digital Equipment Corporation and IBM Japan participate in another R&D company.

In 1990 the total number of R&D companies was 47. See Appendix IV for a complete listing. Some 20 are of short term nature – three to five years – and their basic objective is limited to information processing and communication among members. The remainder have been established specifically for carrying out research and development of a basic nature. Almost all of them will have joint facilities although usually without any major laboratory equipment. The following four development companies will have central joint laboratories including major pieces of equipment:

– Protein Engineering Research Institute
– Sortec Corporation (synchrotron orbital radiation facilities)
– BCC Technology
– Advanced Telecommunications Research Institute (ATR)
– Opto-Electronics Development Corporation

It is of interest to note that the VLSI Project 1976-79 was the first joint research project to have joint laboratories as an integral part. This was later followed by the establishment of the Joint Opto-Electronics Laboratories patterned on the earlier precedent. Some of the development companies sponsored by JKTC can trace their origin to earlier engineering research associations. This is the case for Sortec, where the idea of synchrotron orbital radiation technology was voiced already in the early phase of the VLSI Project organised as an engineering research association.

The Opto-Electronics Development Corporation can be seen as a direct continuation of support for the development of certain technologies where development was initiated in the Opto-Electronics ERA started in 1981. The Japan Electronic Dictionary Research Institute is a spin-off from ICOT of the Fifth Generation Computer Project. Similarly, it is possible to trace the origin of other companies to earlier projects supported by the government, which in fact shows the relay character of technology support in Japan.

The Japan Key Technology Centre was born out of a proposal originating in MITI and seed money coming out of the privatisation of NTT controlled by the Ministry of Posts and Telecommunications. Knowing the rivalry which exists between ministries in Japan there are obvious questions. How did the two rivals form a consensus? How is it possible for the two ministries to jointly supervise the growth of their common baby? I will not discuss the birth process but only refer briefly to the composition of staff and management. The total staff number 54, equally divided among MITI, Ministry of Posts and Telecommunications (MPT) and the banks. The MITI staff come from specialised agencies such as the Agency for Industrial Science and Technology (AIST), the Patent Office and the Machinery and Information Industry Bureau. The MPT staff come from various regional offices. The bank staff come from several banks which include Bank of Tokyo and Japan Development Bank. The projects are discussed in committees and one would assume that MITI staff would generally be better versed in identifying and advocating the needs of industrial technology projects.

The director of the Centre comes from MITI while the vice director comes from MPT. Other senior staff come from the Ministry of Finance with three of JKTC directors from MITI, MPT and Japan Development Bank.

All the R&D companies of the Japan Key Technology Centre suffer from a structural dilemma. They are organised as profitmaking entities which are – in principle – expected to pay dividends on the invested capital. In most cases this will never be possible and the R&D companies will have to be liquidated.

A few R&D companies such as ATR and PERI are discussed in other chapters while Sortec is discussed below.

Sortec Corporation

The Sortec Corporation was established in June 1986 and will wind down after a period of ten years. The corporation is scheduled to use Y14 billion for the ten-year period. Synchrotron facilities have been constructed in the company's laboratories in Tsukuba and were basically completed in 1988. Research and development of applications started in 1990.

Many manfacturers have recently made outstanding marches towards getting the particle accelerators down to sizes for commercial uses such as making the printing on IC wafers and medical diagnostics. One of the leaders is Sumiotomo Heavy Industries, which in 1989 announced the world's smallest SOR unit – only a metre in diameter due to the use of superconductive magnets. IshikawaJima-Harima Heavy Industries Company is also completing its accelerator project. There is no doubt that the competition will be heating up as the market is considerable once the IC makers start shifting to SOR X-ray technology. Small particle accelerators, such as the spiral-shape cyclotron, have another important application for producing radioactive isotopes. When injected into the body the isotopes can be traced with a proton camera to determine the condition of an organ – today the most advanced means of diagnosing cancer and cerebral thrombosis. Nearly two-thirds of the roughly 30 compact cyclotrons now in use worldwide to produce radioactive isotopes are installed in Japanese hospitals.

In early 1990 Matsushita Electric, a member of Sortec Corporation, announced that in co-operation with Sortec it had jointly developed a mask aligner for the etching of circuit pattern on silicon wafers using synchrotron radiation. Utlizing the mask aligner in combination with SOR, IC firms expect to fabricate next generation chips, such as 64 and 256 megabit dynamic random access memories with linewidths of the order of 0.25 microns.

Bio-oriented Technology Research Advancement Institution (BRAIN)

BRAIN was formally launched on 1 October, 1986 as a corporation authorised under a law specifically passed for its establishment. BRAIN is a specially approved corporate body (*Tokubetsu Ninka Hojin*) and does not have the legal status of a "special corporation" with the consequence that funding does not necessarily come only from the government. Both BRAIN and JKTC, while still "special" in nature, have been approved as only organisations under special laws but are in fact more "special" than the special organisations (*Tokubetsu Hojin*). Thus the founding capital, in both cases, comes from both the government and private sector with the overall purpose that these organisations should be making the most of the resources and capabilities in the private sector. For both organisations any research activities to be supported must be proposed from the private sector and actual projects at least partially financed by the proposing party. RIKEN, to be mentioned later on, provides a very different situation with all its expenditure coming from state allocations.

BRAIN is mainly disbursing its funds for capital investment in R&D consortia and special loans for R&D activities. The major activities are:

1. Capital investment.

2. Loan services.

3. Mediation in arranging joint research.

4. Mediation in obtaining genetic resources.

5. Providing technical services.

6. Contract research and survey studies.

Its structure and functions are very similar to those of the Japan Key Technology Centre, although funding is on a much more modest level. BRAIN has a yearly budget in the region of Y4 billion while JKTC has approximately Y25 billion.

Surprisingly enough BRAIN also operates a research institute, the Institute of Agricultural Machinery, originally founded in 1962 as a semi-governmental co-operative – with joint finance from the government and private sector – under the Agricultural Mechanisation Promotion Law. Its incorporation into BRAIN is explained by the need for its continued functions while also following the strict administrative reform guidelines of not expanding the bureaucratic apparatus.

BRAIN is basically responsible for furthering experiments and research on technologies closely related to biotic functions and characteristics which may be applicable in the following specific areas: agriculture, forestry and fisheries (both production and and distribution); food and beverage production and distribution; tobacco production and distribution; wood production; and yarn-making.

Thus it can be seen that BRAIN is active in areas of direct concern to the Ministry of Agriculture, Forestry and Fisheries, while JKTC is concerned primarily with industrial, mining and telecommunications technologies, the areas for which MITI and MPT are responsible. BRAIN projects are listed in Appendix IV.

Exploratory Research for Advanced Technology Organisation (ERATO)

The ERATO programme was initiated in 1981 as a new and innovative research for the purpose of fostering the creation of advanced technologies through exploratory research. The system is centred around key individuals who serve as project directors. Each project is made up of young researchers from academic, government and private sectors. The projects are funded at fairly generous levels for periods of up to five years.

The procedure for the selection of the project leader is an important part of ERATO. The project leader is required not only to be a well-known scientist with deep insights into the problems he and his team members are to deal with, but also to have the ability to attract young and promising researchers into new scientific endeavours. The director has the overall responsibility for the execution and management of his project.

The project would normally consist of less than 30 members who are grouped in three to five sub-project teams which may be allocated at institutions in various parts of Japan, or even abroad. In fact, many if not most of the projects have foreign team members. The members are employed on yearly contracts which are renewable for a period of up to five years. A project would normally have a total budget in the region of a little less than Y2 billion. The ERATO programme is administered by the Japan Development Corporation which is a public corporation supervised by the Science and Technology Agency.

JRDC has no research facilities of its own, and research under the ERATO system is carried out in laboratories which are judged to be the most suitable for the execution of a particular research project.

ERATO funds projects in two broad areas – physical sciences and bioscience, with roughly half in each area – and has so far provided support for 25 projects. See Appendix IV for a complete listing.

A basic assumption of the ERATO programme is that the scientific contacts among researchers of different backgrounds would produce a creative atmosphere. Consequently, the ERATO programme is carried out not only by scientists from Japan but also by scientists recruited from abroad. It is in fact the first research programme of this kind in Japan in which foreigners have been invited to participate and the rate of foreign participation is around 10 per cent. The innovative character of the programme has attracted much interest abroad and a summary evaluation was carried out by a team from the USA in 1988 (Japanese Exploratory Research for Advanced Technology (ERATO) Programme, JTECH Panel Report on, NSF/DARPA/Department of Commerce, Washington, D.C. 1988).

The evaluation panel notes that ERATO has attractive features from both industrial and university viewpoints. It offers young industrial scientists the freedom to perform in the area of basic research before they become fully occupied with development work. For the university scientists it offers the freedom of time and funding which is rarely available in Japanese universities. Thus, it was a very early and in all likelihood a successful policy instrument to bridge the gap in Japan between basic research in the universities and applied research in industry.

The panel also notes that some projects are very specific and oriented towards applications while others are open-ended and exploratory in nature. The selection of projects indicated that JDRC has in the past tended to choose high-risk and daring areas that are not generally in the mainstream of research in Japan, although becoming highly noticed, if successful. A brief introduction is given below to some of the ongoing projects.

Kimura Metamelt Project, 1990-95

The scientific tools for studying melt structures are just being established – including methods using X-rays and neutron beams. The project will focus on the changes which occur in melts over time and will explore new ways to grow crystal. Melts of semiconductors and oxide materials will be used. Quick and precise methods will be developed to determine the causes of change. These will include measurements of viscosity, surface tension, density and heat conduction, as well as research on the measurements themselves. The expected increased understanding of the micro-structure and ordering of melts is expected to lead to new materials and new processing technology.

Nagayama Protein Array Project, 1990-95

Very sophisticated chemical conversion systems have arisen in living organisms – through spatial arrangements of minute reaction systems, which assemble themselves. The project will take proteins as the element in which selective interactions between molecules could be built. It will investigate how protein assemblies are made. The inter-protein interactions and surface structures necessary for assembly will be designed and the proteins actually made through protein engineering. The project will also explore methods for reading and writing information, from the outside, for activities inside the assemblies. Such research will provide a first step for reproducing biological objects. The results are expected to become a basis for future materials whose functions are beyond those of constituent molecules.

Frontier Research Programme at RIKEN

The Frontier Research Programme was launched as a new research programme at the Institute of Physical and Chemical Research (RIKEN) in October 1986. The objective was to provide a flexible research system which would bring scientists together in an internationally open system. The motive was to conduct fundamental research of a pioneering nature which would also serve as a basis for technological innovations in the coming century. The programme has the following characteristics:

1. Researchers in a variety of fields are invited from a wide range of backgrounds, including industry, universities and government circles.

2. About one third of the researchers, including team leaders, are invited from overseas.

3. Researchers have their own periods of service but research in a specific team will be set for a period which may extend up to fifteen years.

4. Meetings are organised for participating researchers from different fields in order to encourage an open flow of ideas.

There are currently three main research directions: Bio-Homeostasis Research, Frontier Materials Research, and Research on Brain Mechanism of Mind and Behaviour. The first two started in 1986 while the latter was initiated in 1988. Each area is divided in research groups or laboratories of which there are altogether ten. See Chapter 15 for additional information.

Concluding remarks

The inventory of various government programmes to support research and development, as illustrated above, not only indicates the dynamic character of the science and technology scene in Japan but also provides examples of highly innovative policies. Furthermore the government support system has during the 1980s shifted in three fundamental ways. First, the system is much more attuned to support long-term and exploratory research which is approaching basic or fundamental research, although the possible technological and industrial applications are lurking around the corner in almost all programmes. Second, the involvement of the private industrial sector has taken on a new dimension as the large and many small companies not only need basic research but are also increasingly able to join forces with scientists in government laboratories and universities in Japan and also with renowned foreign scientists coming to Japan. Third, Japanese science and technology is gradually opening up to the international scientific community.

Chapter 8

The universities and academic research

There are four types of higher educational institutions in Japan:

1. *Daigaku* (university);

2. *Tanki-daigaku* (junior college);

3. *Koto-senmon-gakko* (college of technology); and

4. *senshu-gakko* (special training schools).

A university has one or more undergraduate faculties, which offer courses lasting four years. However, medicine, dentistry and veterinary science require six years. The university may have a graduate school.

Junior colleges offer two-year, or three-year college level programmes. Those who have finished the upper secondary school are qualified to apply for admission into universities and junior colleges.

Colleges of technology offer five years of integrated education to those who have completed the first stage of secondary education. Graduates of junior colleges and colleges of technology may be admitted into universities as second or third year students.

The *senshu-gakko* is a new type of educational institution which was created in 1976. Such schools offer secondary courses for those who have finished lower secondary education, or college courses to those who have finished upper secondary education. In the latter case the school is called *senmon-gakko*.

Although this chapter will discuss the Japanese universities and their research it is important to have a historical perspective of education and the emergence of the educational system. Japan today has the most highly educated population in the world. Almost 90 per cent remain at school until they are eighteen, and more than 30 per cent of these go on to a university or college of higher education. Illiteracy, at well below 1 per cent, is the lowest in the world. There are almost nine hundred colleges and universities in Japan, a number greater in total than any other country except the USA.

The high level of education of the population in general is by no means a new phenomenon. Even though Japan did not establish a formal education system until after the Meiji Restoration, historical studies show that the general level of education was the highest in the world even one hundred years ago or more. Many local *daimyo* – the clan leaders – set up schools for samurai, while rural communities operated schools for the wealthier members of the merchant and farming classes. In urban areas a kind of private school, the *terakoya*, attached to a temple, was found where reading, writing and arithmetic were taught to children of the common people. Schools attendance in 1866 is estimated at 56 per cent for males and 15 per cent for females, with an illiteracy rate of below 30 per cent, which would put Japan well ahead of the rest of the world at that time.

Despite a great emphasis on education and a large number of colleges and universities, facilities for research in the universities, in the main, still remain poor and the general standard of research is lower than in other major industrialised countries. University teaching is characterised by large classes and little personal tuition. Examinations standards are not high, even though the entrance into the national universities and the best private universities is often extremely difficult.

Rather than providing a complete specialist education the universities should be seen as suppliers of a large number of generally educated people, particularly engineers, demanded by industry. It is not in universities but in industry, in the applied research institutes belonging to various ministries, and in special research corporations that really good research facilities are found. This reflects the attention given to applied-product-oriented research rather than basic research. In recent years the private sector has increasingly been investing in research facilities which would normally be used for basic research in a university setting, which will increasingly challenge the role of universities for carrying out basic research.

Various initiatives have been promoted during the 1990s as the Japanese government has become aware that the country has already caught up with, or overtaken the large industrialised countries in almost all areas of applied technology other than in aviation, life sciences and defence technology. This realisation is now forcing Japan to stimulate basic research and originality in order to retain a strong internationally competitive position in high technology. Thus, greater efforts are now being made to concentrate research projects within the universities and to set up new kinds of university institutes with facilities as good as those in other countries.

Educational system

At the beginning of the Meiji era a modern educational system was created by the Fundamental Code of Education, proclaimed by the government in 1872. This called for the establishment of 53,760 primary schools to give compulsory education to all children from the ages of six to fourteen, and the creation of middle schools and eight universities. The plan turned out to be far too ambitious and six years after its inception school attendance had reached only 41 per cent.

A few years later, in 1886, the educational system was again reorganised and split into two parallel structures that reflected the political thinking of that time. Three or more years of education were made compulsory – extended to six years in 1908 – but for the masses top priority was given to "moral education" to "foster" Japanese subjects who would acquire the ethics of the family and pledge allegiance to the state. In contrast, imperial universities were set up to train an elite group which monopolised science, adopted western civilisation, and was brought up to understand modern technology and management. A route for this elite to reach university was established through highly selective middle schools while the majority progressed through very regimented schooling in "normal schools".

The decades following the Meiji Restoration in 1868 saw the establishment of the modern universities in Japan. The national government first founded the University of Tokyo in 1877, which was followed by universities in Kyoto in 1897, in Tohoku in 1907 and in Kyushu in 1910. These were, together with two more additions, the imperial universities which were reserved for a privileged elite.

In the early part of the Meiji period the training of those who should serve the industrialisation and other modernisation efforts was very critical and three institutions, aside from the University of Tokyo, played an important role. First, there was the College of Engineering (*Kobudaigaku*) established by Kobusho, the forerunner of MITI. Second, there was the College of Jurisprudence (*Hogakko*) established by the Ministry of Justice (*Shihosho*). Third, there was the College of Agriculture (*Nogakko*) established by the Ministry of Agriculture (*Noshomusho*).

During the first twenty years of the Meiji Restoration these colleges were more important than the University of Tokyo because they provided critically needed practical training. A number of the engineering students served in the government to direct the modernisation efforts, and it was only later that law students became a dominant force within the administration. The College of Engineering was incorporated into Tokyo University in 1886, one year after the College of Jurisprudence, and formed the basis for respective faculties. The College of Agriculture was transferred in 1890 after the university had become Tokyo Imperial University.

When Japan established a modern educational system the universities in the USA and Europe were seen as models. The University of Tokyo was founded with four departments – law, literature, science and medicine – with faculty initially composed of Europeans and Americans who taught in their own languages. One of the main purposes was to provide national leaders with a good understanding of the situation outside Japan in order to carry out the modernisation. Naturally, a long introductory period, mainly in foreign languages, was required in order to gain entrance.

The fledgling university system received a formal structure through the Imperial University Order of 1886. Under the new order the government created five higher middle schools in various parts of the country to serve as preparatory schools for the university. Two new departments – in engineering and agriculture – were added at the same time. Gradually the foreign instructors were replaced by Japanese faculty. Aside from the imperial university system, which was gradually expanded, the government also established institutions of higher learning which were called *senmon gakko* (professional schools). These schools received official authorisation in 1903 and their number increased rapidly.

Until the end of the Second World War higher education in Japan consisted of two types of institutions – universities and *senmon gakko*. The rising quality of the *senmon gakko* was officially recognised when the Ministry of Education promulgated the University Order of 1918 which acknowledged the establishment of public and private universities in addition to the imperial universities. The more important private *senmon gakko* became universities while some of the government *senmon gakko* became colleges. The enrolment in higher education remained low until after the Second World War. It was 3 per cent in 1935 while enrolment in secondary education had already reached 40 per cent. A very high level of enrolment in elementary education had been reached already at the turn of the century – with 95.6 per cent in 1905. See Table 8.1.

Table 8.1 Enrolment in the Japanese educational system – 1875-1988

	1875	1895	1905	1915	1925	1935	1947	1955	1965	1970	1975	1980	1985	1988
	%	%	%	%	%	%	%	%	%	%	%	%	%	%
Elementary education	35.2	61.2	95.6	98.5	99.4	99.6	99.8	99.8	99.8	99.8	99.9	99.9	99.9	99.9
Secondary education	0.7	1.1	4.3	19.9	32.3	39.7	61.7	78.0	82.7	89.0	95.3	96.5	96.3	96.2
Higher education	0.4	0.3	0.9	1.0	2.5	3.0	5.8	8.8	14.6	18.7	30.3	33.5	32.1	32.4

Source: Education in Japan: a graphic presentation. Tokyo, 1988, Ministry of Education, p. 18

The number of universities gradually increased and various reforms were suggested. There were also growing demands for autonomy from government meddling in teaching and research, demands which came to be completely rejected in the early 1930s – until the end of the war. Although various attempts at reforms had been made it was not until after 1945 that the whole system was recast. Acting on the advice of a mission of 27 educational experts brought from the USA by the Allied Occupation, the Fundamental Law of Education was promulgated in March 1947. The earlier multi-track system was replaced with a single track 6-3-3 system modelled on that of the USA and equal opportunity was guaranteed for all people. The new educational system established that six years of primary school education are to be followed by three years of compulsory secondary education at junior high school.

Those graduating from junior high school can continue to senior high school for a further three years and are then qualified to try the entry examinations for university or other higher educational institutes. See the organisation of the present school system in Figure 8.1 for further details. Junior colleges offer two- or three-year courses while university courses generally last for four years, the first two of which are devoted to general education in a college of general education or college of liberal arts within the university. University education in medicine and dentistry requires six years followed by professional training.

Colleges of technology were introduced in 1962 and are aimed at the training of technicians. Special education schools are those for the blind, the deaf and otherwise handicapped children.

The educational reform had a great impact on the national institutions of higher learning. The earlier six imperial universities became national universities while every prefecture acquired its national university by combining various national institutions of higher learning existing in each prefecture. The already existing private universities continued to operate while most private *senmon gakko* were given university status. Some of the professional schools were lacking staff and facilities and were given temporary

Figure 8.1 Organisation of the Japanese school system – 1875-1988

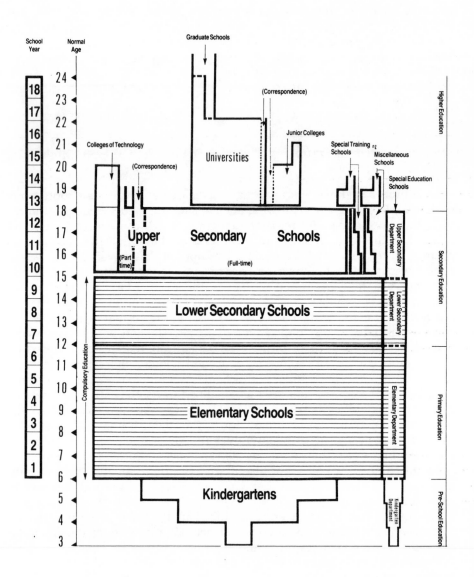

Source: Education in Japan: a graphic presentation. Tokyo, 1988, Ministry of Education, p. 14

accreditation until 1964 when they were fully recognised as junior colleges. The *senmon gakko* in the public sector and almost all the public universities were reorganised as four-year universities. After the completion of the reforms in 1949 there were 68 national universities, 13 public and 92 private universities.

University enrolment increased very rapidly after the reform from a level of slightly above 300,000 to more than one million in 1965. Since the mid-1960s the expansion has continued and has now reached 2.5 million (1989). The private universities grew rapidly in number in the 1960s as the demand for educated manpower grew alongside the new industries. Between 1960 and 1970 an average of thirteen new universities a year were opened.

The best private universities have a reputation as high as those of the best national universities but their science faculties – with few exceptions outside the medical faculties – are much weaker and support very little research. The number of municipal and prefectural universities remains the same today as it was in 1955 at 34. The low fees, similar to those at national universities, make these institutions attractive but facilities are rarely as good as in national universities.

Apart from the establishment of the University of Tokyo, many private schools concerned with legal and political curricula were also established in the early Meiji years. Tokyo Hogakusha, the forerunner of Hosei University, was established in 1879 and Senshu Gakko, the forerunner of Senshu University, in 1880. In the following year the school which was to become Meiji University – Meiji Horitsu Gakko – was founded. In 1882 the school which was to become Waseda University – Tokyo Senmon Gakko - started its teaching. The forerunner of Chuo University, Igirisu Horitsu Gakko, commenced instruction in 1885.

Many of the private universities constitute a more or less integrated education system which also includes private secondary schools although admission into the university is not automatically granted.

The number of high-school graduates – and consequently the number of students going on to university education – has risen rapidly during the 1980s and will peak in 1992, and then decrease rapidly. It appears that the government contrived to hold enrolment increases at the national and local-public universities to a minimum, due to budget squeeze and subsequent financial constraints and to approve temporary admission increases for the private universities – in order to admit most of the new students.

These intentions are most clearly expressed in the June 1984 recommendations with the title "Systematic Improvements in Higher Education from 1986" which was prepared by the Sub-Committee on University Planning of the University Chartering Council. Thus, the brunt of the expansion during the 1980s has been taken by the private universities which have strained their resources, although tuition fees have increased accordingly, while the national universities have been given only modest budget increases.

The temporary increases in admission will be followed by a reduction from 1992 onwards which will challenge the university planners to cope with the increases in staff and equipment made possible through the expansion. There is little doubt that some of the smaller and less consolidated private universities will close down or merge while some may go bankrupt. However, another possibility is that many of the private universities will increasingly expand their research activities and postgraduate teaching for which there will be a growing demand during the coming decades – particularly in engineering.

Almost all the private universities have a weak financial basis as they depend mainly on tuition fees and entrance fees for their income. Very few of the private institutions of higher learning have the large endowments that provide financial strength for many of the private universities in the United States. The government started to provide financial support to the private universities, with a formal law for subsidy in 1970. Initially it was at the level of 7.2 per cent and gradually increased both in absolute and in relative terms and peaked at 29.5 per cent in 1980. Since then the absolute level of government support stagnated and its share went down to 17 per cent in 1987 as the private university sector continued its expansion (Figure 8.2).

Figure 8.2 Expenditure (100 million yen) and government support levels for private universities

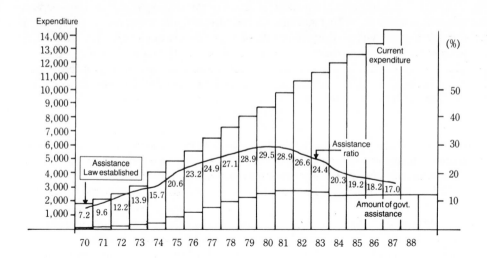

Source: Education White Paper 1989, p. 304

Education is provided free up to the age of fifteen although some minor expenses, amounting to 13 per cent of the total, have to be met by parents: roughly Y40,000 a year for a child at elementary school and Y66,000 a year at junior high school. At higher levels fees must be paid and total costs rise to Y130,000 per year at public senior high schools. The average annual fee is Y300,000 per year in national universities and approximately double that amount at private institutions. There are great differences for different types of education. For example, the medical schools of a number of private universities charge more than ten times the standard tuition fes and also require a large entrance fee. As a rule, most educational expenses are covered by the parents while contributions from scholarships and employers' contribution are minimal.

University entrance, and engineering and graduate training

There are great differences among universities, which are reflected in the difficulty of entrance examinations, the quality of students and the opportunities for employment after graduation. These factors together translate into a generally recognised ranking of the various universities which is much publicised in newspapers and journals.

Entrants to universities are selected on the basis of an entrance examination conducted by the university – according to nation-wide rules – and by credentials supplied by the upper secondary schools. Applicants are required to have completed twelve years of formal education. Under the present system there is keen competition to enter certain universities, among which the University of Tokyo is among the top ones. Some 80 per cent of the government's yearly intake are graduates from this university. A great majority of the intake to the large industrial companies and, recently, financial institutions will come from the University of Tokyo, Kyoto University, a handful of the other old imperial universities and a few top private universities like Keio University and Waseda University.

Employment in a prestigious company or in one of the ministries will generally mean steady promotion and employment for life. Thus the most critical stage in many people's career is the university entrance examination as success provides almost automatic entrance to a prosperous career. Naturally this has led to intense competition in entrance examinations among those who want to enter the higher-ranking universities, a situation which is generally referred to as examination hell (*shiken jigoku*). A consequence is that a large share of students aspiring to university education enrol in crammer schools (*yobiko*) parallel to their final years in secondary school so as to be better prepared for the entrance examination. Similar schools (*juko*) exist to provide additional training at the level of junior high school.

Another phenomenon is that a number of those who have failed to enter a certain university may spend a year or more trying to enter the prestigious university of their own or their parents' choice. Such students are called *ronin* students – accounting for one third of all students entering the universities – and spend one year or more after leaving school preparing for university entrance exams at a prestigious university rather than go to a lesser university.

There are intermittent calls to do away with the "examination hell" and to let career judgements be made later in life, but so far only minor modifications have been achieved. Attempts have been made to introduce a standard entrance examination for all universities. This makes the preparation for the university entrance examination less strenuous although it hardly changes the employers' preferences for graduates from Tokyo University and other high-ranking universities. Some of the private universities participate in the national university entrance examination and are usually more flexible than the national universities in weighting the test scores in different subjects. However, there is no expectation that the system will change in a major way unless there are changes in the job market and in the attitudes of employers.

The "joint achievement test" is a standard first-stage achievement test administered by all national universities and the National Centre for

University Entrance Examination. The test, first introduced in 1979 and compulsory for all applicants for admission to national and public universities, is designed to assess basic scholastic achievement in upper secondary school. In addition to the first-stage test, each national and local public university separately conducts its own second-stage examination which comprises scholastic examination, interview and so on. Private universities have yet all to agree to employ the joint achievement test, and public universities differ in the weighting they give the joint achievement test relative to their own entrance examinations.

The school year starts in April and the year is usually divided into two semesters. Universities are made up of schools which are sub-divided into departments. The students, when entering the university, generally enrol in a particular school and department. They will spend the whole university period at the same university in the same school, as transfer to another department or school, or to another university, is allowed only in very exceptional cases.

Following the credit system the students are awarded a bachelor's degree after fulfilling the credit demands. The vast majority of students are employed as soon as they graduate and have often been courted by the employers for a considerable part of their final year at the university and many are given firm job commitments before they graduate. At present (1989) less than 7 per cent continue their studies at graduate school – 7.9 per cent for male and 3.5 per cent for female students.

The role of universities in graduate programmes is only slowly increasing and has grown only a couple of percentage points since the mid-1960s. However, graduate schools already exist at 60 per cent of the universities with a four-year curriculum although only 43 per cent have full graduate programmes leading to a doctoral degree. See Table 8.2. Almost all the national universities have graduate programmes with 61 per cent of them being able to offer doctoral programmes. The private universities are less advanced: only half have graduate and fewer still are able to offer doctoral programmes – 39 per cent.

Table 8.2 Graduate programmes in the Japanese university system (May 1989)

	Total	National	Public	Private
All universities	497	96	37	364
Universities with graduate school	302 (61%)	94 (98%)	22 (59%)	186 (51%)
a. Master programme only	87 (18%)	35 (36%)	6 (16%)	46 (13%)
b. Doctoral programme	215 (43%)	59 (61%)	16 (43%)	140 (39%)

Source: Education White Paper 1989, p. 280

New structures for graduate training are emerging. The national research institutes for joint use by universities, which include the Okazaki Research Institute, the National Laboratory for High-Energy Physics (KEK) and others, jointly set up Japan's first graduate university in 1988. It was initially based in the campus of Tokyo Institute of Technology in Yokohama. The first graduate students enrolled in April 1989. The need and interest in graduate teaching are also fostering linkages across ministerial borders, exemplified by Saitama

University (see description at the end of the chapter). The collaboration between advanced research institutes and middle ranking universities may become increasingly common in order to expand graduate training.

The slow emergence of graduate training and still low level of enrolment in the graduate programmes signifies a low proportion of people with master or doctoral degrees. When comparing the enrolment of graduate students with the total population the Japanese ratio is 0.6 per 1,000 persons while the corresponding figure is 2.9 for France and an astonishing 6.9 per cent for the USA. See Table 8.3.

Table 8.3 International comparisons of graduate training

Country	No. of university students (A)	No. of graduate students (B)	Ratio of graduate students (B/A) %	Total population x 1000 (C)	No. of graduate students per 1000 people (B/C)
USA (1985)	9,414,074	1,650,381	17.5	239,283	6.9
UK (1985)	265,512	86,907	32.7	56,424	1.5
France (1985)	711,885	158,015	22.2	55,062	2.9
Japan (1987)	1,806,024	78,914	4.4	122,264	0.6

Source: Education White Paper 1989, p. 280

In the universities great emphasis is placed on the study of engineering, at the expense of the study of pure science – a situation which contrasts with the situation in several of the large industrialised countries. Japan has considerably more engineering graduates than in the USA and the difference is even more striking when making a comparison with the UK. In the pure sciences the trends are reversed.

The university enrolment in engineering constituted 19.8 per cent of all university enrolment in the four-year system. See Figure 8.3. Engineering makes up only a small share of the students in the two-year courses while almost all students in the higher technical schools which are in fact integrated with the technical education. Engineering is also a considerable part - 27.3 per cent – of the specialised two-year training schools. It is of interest to note that engineering education constitutes almost one half of the enrolment in the master programmes while only 14 per cent in the doctoral programmes.

Role of the Ministry of Education, Science and Culture

Organisation and support for research

The total budget for science and technology of the Japanese government in 1988 amounts to Y1,700 billion, excluding humanities and social sciences. The share controlled by the the Ministry of Education, Science and Culture (MESC) accounts for 48 per cent or Y813 billion. When identifying research activities

Figure 8.3 System of engineering education in Japan

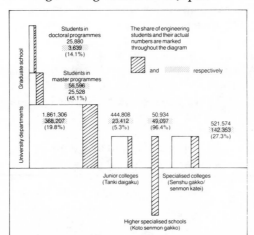

Source: Engineering Education Reform (Henkakuki no Kogaku Kyoiku).
Ministry of Education, Science and Culture, Tokyo, December 1989

and the level of expenditure Japan is faced with difficulties which are similar in all other countries – how is time to be divided between teaching and research for university staff? There is, among many analysts, an assumption that the official figures may exaggerate the role of university research in Japan. Indeed, a recent estimate by John Irvine and co-workers at the Science Policy Research Institute of the University of Sussex, UK, puts the university budget at only Y535,000 million (Investing in the future: an international comparison of government funding of academic and related research). In the following, for the sake of argument, the official figures will be used. However, there can be doubt that they give an incorrect presentation of the relative weight of the university's role in Japan's science and technology system and also misrepresent the relative importance of the various parts of the university system. These questions will be discussed at the end of this chapter.

The universities employ a large proportion of the researchers in Japan – altogether 190,000 out of a total of 440,000 if one accepts the official figures from MESC. This corresponds to a share which is 43 per cent of the national total, which should be seen in relation to the ministry budget which is less than 10 per cent of the national total for research and development. These figures indicate that the university researchers are generally poorly equipped, and given limited research funds beyond their salaries, or that the number of university researchers is grossly exaggerated. The explanation appears to be a combination of both factors. The apparently limited funds for university research denote a situation in which a a limited number of universities are engaged in front-line research while most others linger on or are wholly engaged in teaching aside from laboratory tests required by the curriculum.

The ministry provides support for research in the national universities with four different types of funds of which the first two are the most significant in terms of allocations. First, general research funds are allocated to each chair or professor – koza, to be discussed in the following – or to each division of a department of a university faculty. Funds are decided by a standard formula

Figure 8.4 Organisation of research activities under the Ministry of Education, Science and Culture

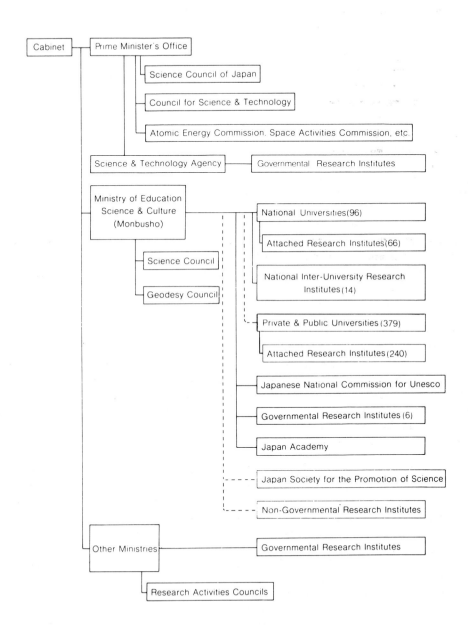

Source: The University Research System in Japan (1988). Tokyo, Ministry of Education, p. 3

based essentially on the number of researchers, the nature of research – experimental, non-experimental or clinical – and whether or not the koza is in charge of graduate courses.

Second, special research funds are allocated to national universities for the provision, construction and maintenance of facilities and equipment necessary for specific research programmes. Requests for such funds are incorporated into the ministry's own budget requests to the Ministry of Finance. These institutions include both attached institutes for the joint use of all national universities and separate national inter-university research institutes, which are both discussed further on in this chapter. In addition many universities have their own specialised research institutes for their own exclusive use.

Third, the ministry also acts as a research council by providing various types of grants to researchers or groups of researchers whose applications are approved by the Science Council of the Ministry. The organisational chart for the ministry provides a useful tool for understanding the various activities of the ministry. See Figure 8.4. The ministry influences the research activities in three major ways – according to the diagram. First, MESC controls all the 96 universities with their 66 attached research institutes, of which twelve are for joint use. In addition there are some 341 research centres/facilities attached to the national universities, some of which are for inter-departmental joint use or even open to all researchers. Second, the ministry also directs the research activities of the national inter-university research institutes which number twelve including the well-known National Laboratory for High Energy Physics – also known under its acronym, KEK.

Fourth, the ministry also maintains six research institutes under its direct control, which include the National Institute for Educational Research and the National Research Institute of Cultural Properties. Finally, the ministry also exercises an indirect control over the 379 private universities which have a total of 240 attached research institutes. Figure 8.4 also lists some other activities, some of which, like the Japan Society for the Promotion of Science, which is also important for international contacts.

For its research grants, but also for its overall guidance, the ministry maintains a Science Council. See Figure 8.5. The Council consists of 30 eminent scholars and scientists appointed by MESC. It provides basic advice and recommendations on policy concerning scientific research, administration of the research grant programmes for scientific research, measures to be taken to promote research in specific fields of science, science information and other related matters. The Science Council has six subcommittees, of which the Committee on Scientific Research Grants may be the most important as it controls a sizeable budget and can direct or redirect research. This committee has a large number of advisory committees dealing with requests for grants from the various fields of science. More than 800 people, largely university professors and some emeritus professors, all appointed by MESC, serve on these committees and award ten different categories of research grants which totalled close to Y50 billion in 1988. However, the Special Committee on Scientific Research System is considered to be the most important one as it establishes policy.

The Committee on the Promotion of Research in Specific Fields has five sub-committees at its disposal and it should be noted that two of these are concerned with space and nuclear fusion, which indicates the role of the

Figure 8.5 Organisation of the Science Council of the Ministry of Education, Science and Culture

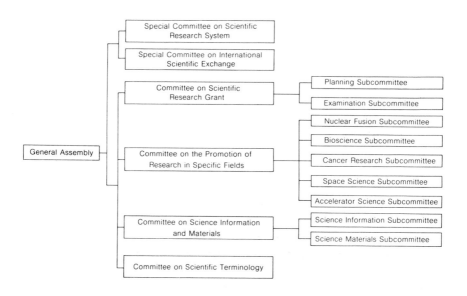

Source: The University Research System in Japan (1988). Tokyo, Ministry of Education, p. 4

university in supporting big science, already discussed earlier. The Special Committee on Scientific Research System has a primary responsibility for analysing different policy options and offering guidance to the general assembly to take decisions on major issues. However, a comparison of its role with the science council of some other ministries indicates that the council has seldom been able to exercise a strong influence on the research agenda for the ministry which has generally been case for the functional equivalent at MITI.

Administration of national universities

All national universities, with the exception of the recently established Tsukuba University, are administered in much the same way. So the description of one of them, Kyoto University, will serve as an example.

The president holds the highest executive position in the university and convenes and chairs the University Council (or Senate) and the General Board of the Graduate Schools. The president is elected by a general ballot of all academic personnel for a term of four years, extendable by a further two years on re-election.

Affairs concerning the whole university, for example, the enactment, revision, or abolition of university regulations, the university budget and student enrolment numbers, are considered by the University Council. It is composed of the president, the deans of the faculties, the dean of the College of Liberal Arts, two professors elected from each faculty and the College of Liberal Arts, the directors of research institutes with more than five full-time professors and the director of the university library. The conclusion of the University Council becomes the university's decision.

The College of Liberal Arts, at the University of Tokyo, where the equivalent organisation is referred to as the College of General Education is responsible for the general education of students for their first two years at university. The equivalent organisation at the University of Tokyo is called the College of Liberal Arts.

Matters concerning the graduate schools with regard to organisation, regulations, instructions, degrees and so on are dealt with by the General Board of the Graduate Schools. Its members are the deans of the graduate schools, the deans of faculties, the dean of the College of Liberal Arts, the directors of research institutes and one professor elected at each graduate school from among the members of the Board of Graduate Schools. The president of the university convenes the meetings and presides over them.

The faculty operates, in most respects, as the actual unit of the university administration. Each faculty, or research institute, is headed by a dean, or director, who is elected among the professors by all the full professors and senior academic staff who represent the faculty, or the institute concerned. The faculty meetings also deliberate on subjects and curricula, admission and graduation of students, degrees, personnel, and regulations. Similar matters pertinent to the graduate schools are decided by Boards of the Graduate Schools composed of the director and the professors of the graduate school concerned.

The administrative structure of municipal universities is modelled on that of national universities while that of private universities is more variable.

Organisation of research within national universities

Research is, within most faculties of science and engineering at the national universities, organised on the *koza* – chair – system. A *koza* consists of a professor and an associate professor together with two assistants and a technical staff of two, all of whom are employed by the ministry and consequently have status as civil servants. Each individual *koza* is responsible for both research and education in a particular topic and each *koza* receives separate funding.

The system has the advantage of ensuring the freedom of each *koza* but also the corresponding disadvantage that co-operation between different *koza* is difficult to secure. Naturally, this is a difficult problem when expensive equipment is required. Research funds within the university system have generally been constrained and there has in the past been no real mechanism to co-ordinate the interests of different *koza* for the joint purchase of equipment.

Until recently the problem was compounded by the rather equal distribution of funds to all *koza* within a faculty. There was in the past no possibility to provide extra funds for large-scale funds when a *koza* was initially set up and direct grants-in-aid were very limited. The various research grant programmes to be detailed in the following have at least partly improved the situation although the funds are very limited considering the needs and the earlier starvation of university research. Another problem which has not been addressed is the low level of technical support for university research.

Research grant programmes

The ministry administers research grants in ten different categories which totalled Y49 billion in 1988. This funding system resembles the activities of the National Science Foundation in the USA, although on a more modest scale and without the full, open process of peer review used there. The largest grant category is general scientific research, referred to above, which received Y15.7 billion in 1988.

All grants in the ten categories are given directly to researchers or groups of researchers working at universities and research institutes within the university system. The grants are given after applications have been evaluated by committees belonging to the Research Grant Committee within the Science Council. See Figure 8.5 above.

General Scientific Research: Y15.7 billion (1988)
This programme has become very popular with university researchers. The grants are given to an individual researcher or to a group of researchers belonging to the same institute. There are basically three types of grants according to the amount of funds needed. Category A provides Y10-50 million, category B Y3-10 million and category C less than Y3 million.

Priority area research and special projects: Y10.7 billion (1988)
These grants provide funds for research in targeted areas for a limited period of time, usually three to six years. Such researches, which are characterised by strong scientific and social needs, include materials science, information electronics, life sciences, space sciences, energy sciences, humanities and social sciences. Each targeted area is given Y50-600 million for the designated period. This is a rather unusual category of grant for it is essentially awarded to a whole field rather than to individuals. Applications are received for very general projects involving workers in many different sub-divisions of one field scattered at universities throughout the country. As many as 100 researchers can be involved in one field and the grant enables the level of research to be raised throughout a particular research field.

Special promoted research: Y2.3 billion (1988)
These grants are given to individuals or small groups to support, on a generous scale, internationally recognised research which is likely to produce outstanding results. This grant category, which was started in the 1980s, breaks away from the tradition of funding all researchers rather equally and allows a few groups to attain the highest international levels.

Special long term research: Y2.9 billion (1988)
These grants are awarded in areas where there are especially strong scientific and social needs. The grants are divided into four categories – cancer, natural disasters and environmental sciences, and energy (including fusion research).

Co-operative research: Y2.7 billion (1988)
These grants are given to projects which are carried out by researchers from different institutions and usually have a duration of three years.

Developmental scientific research: Y4.1 billion (1988)
Grants are given for research which is likely to find some application in the near future and projects usually last three years. The ministry encourages applications which involve joint research between university scientists and researchers in the private sector.

Encouragement of young scientists: Y4.7 billion (1988)
Grants are given to researchers who are not older than 37 years. Eligible to apply are not only researchers in universities but also school teachers and researchers in various other government offices.

Overseas scientific research: Y2.3 billion (1988)
Grants are given to carry out surveys or research abroad and are usually given to individuals who spend a year at foreign university or research institute.

Scientific research promotion: Y2.3 billion (1988)
These grants are used to support urgent and important research.

Publication of scientific research results: Y1.2 billion (1988)
These grants are given for publishing and various supporting organisations which diffuse research results and information materials of high scientific value.

University research institutes

Given the individualistic nature of the koza system and its limited resource base it is natural that research institutes have become an important part of the Japanese university system. This development started in the early decades of this century and provided a foundation for centres of excellence in the fields concerned. The system of university research institutes has undergone two major modifications, in 1953 and 1971. The first modification meant that a new type of university institute was established, the first of which were the Institute for Cosmic Ray Research at the University of Tokyo and the Research Institute for Fundamental Physics at Kyoto University. These and another eleven institutes established in the following years are open to all university researchers in Japan. See Table 8.4.

However, it was later realised that it would be more advantageous if research facilities for joint use were not affiliated with a particular university but established as an independent institute. Thus, the ministry in 1971 created an institute system which has become known as "National Inter-University Research Institutes" of which there are altogether twelve since the institutes for life sciences have been integrated into the Okazaki National Research Institutes. See Table 8.5. Recent additions are NACSIS for information systems and Japan Studies Centre.

With the new system coming into existence there has been no addition to the attached institutes for joint use. The national inter-university research institutes are not attached to any particular universities and are open for the joint use of all university researchers. As national centres of research activity, they have been established in fields of science where there are clear needs either for the use of large-scale research facilities and equipment of the systematic collection of data, or for team research with the participation of a large number of researchers.

The inter-university research institutes have a somewhat peculiar place because they are neither university nor national research institutes. Legally they have the same status and independence as national research institutes but are more directly attached to the ministry. They are governed by a board of trustees with a nation-wide representation.

The unique position of the inter-university research institutes provides a number of important advantages. The direct sponsorship of the ministry makes it possible efficiently and directly to promote important research programmes in basic science, to negotiate budgets directly with the government and to develop new ideas for promoting national and international co-operation. At the same time, because the institutes have the same legal status as national universities, scientists within the institutes hold ranks as

Table 8.4 University-attached institutes for joint use

University	Research institutes	Research objectives	Established
Tohoku	Institute for Materials Research	Study of material sciences	1987*
Tokyo	Institute for Cosmic Ray Research	Research into cosmic ray	1953
	Institute for Nuclear Study	Research into atomic nuclei and elementary particles	1955
	Institute for Solid State Physics	Study on physical properties of matter	1957
	Ocean Research Institute	Research of ocean sciences	1962
Tokyo Foreign Studies	Institute for the Study of Languages and Cultures of Asia and Africa	Comprehensive study of the languages and cultures of Asia and Africa	1964
Nagoya	Institute of Plasma Physics	Study of plasma	1961
Kyoto	Research Institute for Fundamental Physics	Study of fundamental physics such as theory of elementary particles	1953
	Research Institute for Mathematical Sciences	Comprehensive study of mathematical analysis	1963
	Research Reactor Institute	Experiment and related research using the nuclear reactor	1963
	Primate Research Institute	Research into the Primates	1967
Osaka	Institute for Protein Research	Study of protein	1958
	Welding Research Institute	Research of welding engineering	1972

*Originally set up in 1949 as an ordinary institute attached to Tohoku University
Source: *The University Research System in Japan* (1988). Tokyo, Ministry of Education, p. 10

professors, associate professors, and so on. Thus, exchange between the institutes and universities, both national and private, is easily made. The professors at these institutes, though, need not carry out any teaching, but they may devote themselves fully to research. The creation of the general research graduate university has in fact been very beneficial.

However, it is certain that the facilities provided by the inter-university research institutes are far superior to those found in universities and they are in the position to make a very strong contribution to advanced scientific research. Brief information is given below for a sample of the inter-university research institutes.

Table 8.5 National inter-university research institutes

Institutes	Research objectives	Established
National Laboratory for High Energy Physics (KEK)	Research into elementary particles using high energy particle-accelerators, research by synchrotron radiation facilities and other related researches	1971
National Insitiute of Japanese Literature	Investigation, collection, classification and safekeeping of books and other reference materials on Japanese Literature	1972
National Institute of Polar Research	Comprehensive scientific research of the polar regions and observation activities thereon	1973
Institute of Space and Astronautical Science (ISAS)	Research of space science and engineering and their application	1981
National Institute of Genetics	Comprehensive research of genetics	1984
Institute of Statistical Mathematics	Research into mathematical principles of statistics and their application	1985
International Research Centre for Japanese Studies	International and interdisciplinary research into Japanese culture and research cooperation with Japanologists abroad	1987
National Observatory	Research of astronomy and its related fields, observations of astronomical phenomenon, compilation of almanacs, "Japan Standard Time Casting", etc	1988
Okazaki National Research Institutes		1981 (integrated)
Institute for Molecular Science	Research into structures and functions of molecules	1975
National Institute for Basic Biology	Comprehensive study on basic biology	1977
National Institue for Physiological Sciences	Comprehensive study on physiology	1977
National Centre for Science Information System (NACSIS)	Collection, classification and provision of scientific information, and research and development of scientific information system	1986
National Museum of Ethnology	Collection and sakefeeping of materials on various races in the world as well as their exhibition before the public and research of ethnology	1974
National Museum of Japanese History	Collection and safekeeping of materials on Japanese history as well as their exhibition before the public and the research of history, archaeology and folklore	1981

Source: The University Research System in Japan (1988). Tokyo, Ministry of Education, p. 9

Okazaki National Research Institutes

These institutes, located near Nagoya, which became integrated in 1981, now consists of three parts which are focused on molecular biology, basic biology and basic physiology. The origin was the Institute for Molecular Science, established in 1975 to meet the needs of molecular scientists for an expanded and integrated research environment. The new institute permitted experimental and theoretical studies of structures and functions of molecules. This was an important institutional bridge for molecular science research lying between chemistry and physics, and almost immediately proved a great success in attracting scientists from all over Japan and simultaneously building up close collaboration with foreign researchers. Due to the excellent research facilities and high quality of researchers the Okazaki complex has become a major research centre in life sciences.   ·

The institute section for basic biology has departments for cell biology, development biology and biological regulation. The section for physiological sciences has departments for molecular physiology, cell physiology, information physiology and biological control systems.

National Laboratory for High-Energy Physics (Ko-Enerugi Butsurigako Kenkyusho – KEK)

The laboratory, located in Tsukuba, was created in 1971 and is the first of the inter-university research institutes, although it has an earlier origin.

The Allied Occupation in Japan decided that cyclotron and all related facilities should be destroyed. This meant that high-energy physics started late in Japan and it was not until 1953 that the Science Council of Japan recommended that an Institute for Nuclear Study should be set up at the University of Tokyo, which was initiated two years later. A small synchrotron was constructed but Japan continued to lag far behind the West. Various proposals were made by the Science Council of Japan while other government agencies fuelled a dispute on how to proceed, and it was not until 1970 that the establishment of KEK was authorised.

KEK completed the construction of a 12 GeV synchrotron in 1976 which is the only proton accelerator for high-energy physics in Japan. More recently, in 1986, KEK has completed the TRISTAN project which is an accelerator of electron and positron colliding type. The TRISTAN – Transposable Ring Intersecting Storage Ring – has a three-kilometre-circumference ring and provides the world's third highest energy, 30 billion electron volts after SLAC at Stanford University and LEP at Geneva. Electron-proton collisions will be studied with the aid of intersecting storage rings installed in the same tunnel.

An earlier major experimental project is the Photon Factory, completed in 1982, which is one of the most powerful sources of synchrotron radiation in the world. Among uses of synchrotron radiation are X-ray lithography for semiconductor integrated circuits, probes for the electronic structure of materials, the properties of materials and the micro-structure of living organisms. Research on superconductivity, cavity systems and ultrahigh vacuum systems are other research fields in which KEK is active. KEK also has a co-operative research programme under the sponsorship of MESC and the US Department of Energy. A number of physicists are collaborating at US high-energy physics laboratories with funds provided by the ministry.

National Institute of Polar Research

The National Institute of Polar Research was established in Tokyo in 1973 with two major aims: to promote comprehensive research on important scientific problems in the polar regions and to operate the Japanese Antarctic research expeditions, except for transportation, and the two field observatories Syowa and Mizuho in Antarctica. Many of the Japanese scientists involved in polar research come from outside the Polar Research Institute but the institute acts as the sole central co-ordinating agency.

Research is being carried out in five areas: upper atmospheric physics, meteorology and glaciology, earth sciences, biological science and polar engineering.

National Centre for Science Information System   NACSIS

The centre was established in 1986 as a national inter-university research institute. It is the nucleus of a new information system which is to be connected to computer centres, information processing centres, university libraries and other inter-university research institutes by a data communication network. The system can also be linked to the private sector and information networks abroad in order to enhance its usefulness.

The main functions of the system are as follows:

1. to plan and co-ordinate science information systems;

2. to conduct comprehensive research and development of science information and systems for the utilisation of science information;

3. to provide early information about publications and materials held at universities;

4. to provide retrieval services for thesis abstracts, experimental data, graphic information etc.;

5. to promote the design and development of databases;

6. to provide electronic mail services; and

7. to organise seminars and seminars for training and education.

University-industry co-operation

State-industry partnerships have been a common feature for industrial technological research and development in Japan and have been most prominently promoted by MITI and its Agency for Industrial Science and Technology, and by the Ministry of Posts and Telecommunications through the now privatized Nippon Telegraph and Telephone Company. Various forms of state-industry partnerships have also been incorporated in the research programmes of other ministries and the Ministry of Education, Science and Culture is no exception. The ministry presently has four different programmes or approaches to encourage closer scientific co-operation with the private sector.

Joint research with industry

A system of joint research involving researchers at the national universities and researchers in private companies was created in 1983. The number of joint research projects was 390 in 1988, involving 555 researchers from industry and with the total project budget of Y2.6 billion. Such joint research is particularly carried out in materials development, electronics and biotechnology.

Contract research and contract researchers

The system of contract research enables a national university to carry out research which is commissioned by private industrial company, government institutions or other external bodies. The income from such contracts amounted to Y5.8 billion in 1988. The contract researcher system makes it possible to employ researchers and engineers from industry to carry out research, inside a national university, at graduate level. There are currently more than 1,000 contract researchers implementing various research projects which provided the national universities with an income of Y0.3 billion in 1988.

Centres for co-operative research

In 1987 the ministry created a new system of centres for co-operative research to promote closer and longer-lasting co-operation between national universities and private industry. Such relations at first included only Kobe University, Toyama University and Kumamato University. Centres were established in 1988 at five more universities – including Muoran Institute of Technology in Gunma Prefecture, Tokyo University of Agriculture and Technology, Gifu University and Nagoya University. Later on more universities have been included.

Donations

National universities have been authorised since 1976 to receive donations from outside organisations, such as private companies, for the purpose of encouraging scientific research within the university. These donations can be used flexibly for research or educational activities – in line with the objectives of the donors – and can also, since 1987, be used for creating new chairs. The donations have steadily increased and the national universities in 1988 received a total of Y24.billion.

In addition it may also be noted that the Science Council encourages applications for one of the grant categories mentioned earlier – Developmental Scientific Research – to cover joint research with the private industrial sector. Finally, the Japan Society for Promotion of Science (JSPS), belonging to the ministry, has set up an "Advisory Committee on University Industry Research Activities" with the purpose of promoting closer links. More specifically attempts have been made to study how such links should be developed in protein technology and for biological functions and electronics. JSPS has a presently a large number of committees to identify specific themes where closer relations between the universities and private companies would be beneficial.

The preceding sections have shown the great diversity which exists within the university sector and also indicated that major new approaches for organising research, although implemented only gradually, are under way within the national universities. Before moving on to brief descriptions of some of the major universities figures will be provided which indicate the broad differences between research in the national and the private universities. See

Figure 8.6 Composition of research staff in the Japanese University system

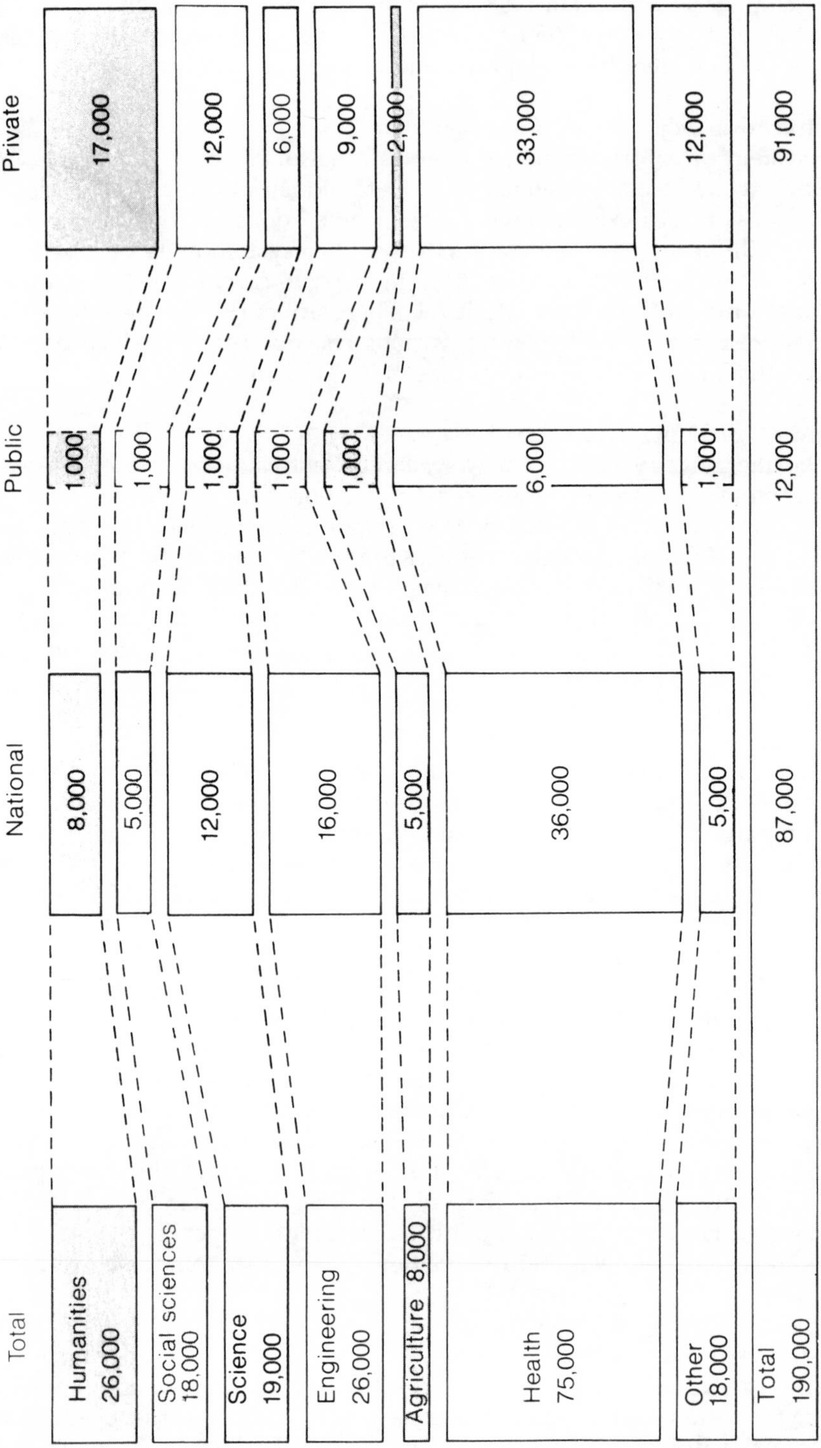

Source: The University System in Japan (1988). Tokyo, Ministry of Education, p. 9

Figure 8.7 The support system for technology development in Japan

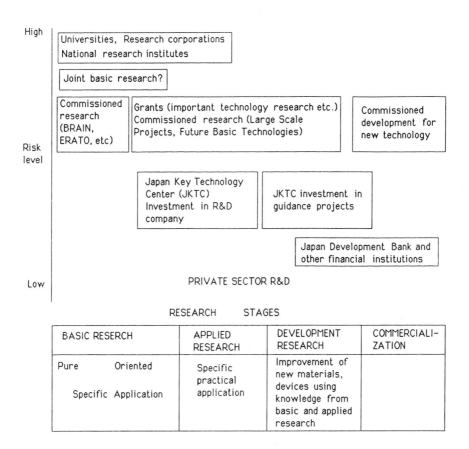

Source: Based on conceptualization prepared by Professor Ryo Hirazawa, Tokyo University

Figure 8.6. The total number of university researchers amounts to 190,000 which includes doctor course students and medical staff. For reasons mentioned earlier this may be an overstatement. The private and national universities are almost equal in research manpower with an additional 12,000 in the public universities. The latter are particularly strong in medicine. When comparing the figures in Figure 8.6 it is obvious that the private universities are much stronger in humanities and social sciences while the national universities are much stronger in science, engineering and agriculture.

Support system for technology development in Japan

After having reviewed the various components of the national system for science and technology, including the role of the universities, an attempt will be made to summarise the main features. First, a symbiotic or synergetic relationship still exists between the government agencies and the private sector, in spite of the growing importance of the latter. Second, the government sector has, during the 1980s, introduced a number of new measures and approaches focusing on exploratory and long-term research which has its parallel in the private sector. Third, following partly from the earlier two features, the private sector is being drawn towards R&D which is more risky and more basic than has previously been the case.

Consequently, financial institutions like Japan Development Bank are becoming less important in promoting the technological vitality of Japan. See Figure 8.7. The national research institutes and research corporations are taking on a more important role in shaping the future science and technology scene in Japan. Programmes like ERATO and BRAIN should be seen in the context of such changes.

The future role of the universities in supporting such developments still remains uncertain, although the national inter-university research institutes are becoming increasingly important. Furthermore it should be noted that close links are being developed between universities and other national research institutes – initially for graduate studies. It still remains to be seen if the private industry sector in Japan will shoulder an increasingly important role for long term and exploratory research – to the detriment of the traditional universities.

Examples of national, public and private universities

To illustrate the historical backgrounds, organisation of research activities and budgets of the three kinds of universities brief descriptions will be given below. These include four national universities, Tokyo, Kyoto, Tokyo Institute of Technology and Saitama, one municipal university, Yokohama and two private universities, Waseda and Keio. A complete list of national universities and public local universities is provided in Appendix III. The appendix also contains highly selective listings of some of the major private universities.

University of Tokyo (Tokyo Daigaku)

The origins of the University of Tokyo go back to some of the oldest educational establishments in Japan: the Shohei Gakko, Kaisei Gakko and Igakko, which specialised in Chinese classics, Western studies and Occidental medicine, respectively. These three institutions in turn originated from three even older institutions: the Shoheiko for Chinese classical studies founded in 1789, the Yogakushu or Institute for Occidental Studies founded in 1855 and the Shutoshu, or Institute of "Vaccination" founded in 1860. The three institutions which were founded during the Tokugawa Shogunate merged in the early years of the Meiji era to form an institution with three colleges. One of these colleges in 1871 became Monbusho while the remaining two through changes of names and metamorphosis emerged as Tokyo Daigaku in 1877 – to become Teikoku Daigaku (Imperial University) in 1886. When a second imperial college was established in Kyoto in 1987 it was renamed Tokyo Imperial University.

The university consisted of four colleges in 1877: Law, Science, Literature and Medicine. Since then the university has added new academic fields such as engineering, agriculture and economics and by 1919, when the colleges became faculties, the shape of the University of Tokyo had essentially been constituted with the exceptions of various research institutes and centres. In 1942 the Second Faculty of Engineering was established to meet urgent wartime demand for skilled engineers, and disbanded in 1951.

In May 1989 the university had a total of 14,967 undergraduate regular students of whom 7,615 were undergoing general education in the College of Liberal Arts – covering the first two years. The large faculties are Law and Engineering with 1,728 and 1,951 regular students respectively. In addition the university also has a small number of research students at the undergraduate level, sprinkled throughout the faculties. The university has a very sizeable postgraduate enrolment with 2,689 regular students in the master's programme and 2,622 in the doctoral programme. The enrolment in the master's programme is dominated by engineering with 1,067 students and science with 546 students. The share of female students is very low both at the undergraduate and postgraduate levels – around 10 per cent.

Also that year there were 887 full professors, 814 associate professors and 196 full-time lecturers, and a total staff of 7,792, including the administrative staff and others who numbered 4,153. The total budget was Y121 billion in the fiscal year 1988 of which 47 per cent went to the university proper, 21 per cent to the university hospital, 18 per cent to the research institutes and the remainder to sundry other activities. In the same fiscal year the university was given projects in the total amount of Y7.1 billion for 1,689 projects which may correspond to some 15 per cent of total grants flowing to the university system from Monbusho. The university has altogether twelve research institutes which are listed in Table 8.6. The two largest are the institutes for medical science and industrial science.

In addition the university has a number of shared research facilities which are open to scholars inside the university. These include the Cryogenic Centre, the Radio-Isotope Centre and the Research Centre for Nuclear Science and Technology and the Research Centre for Advanced Science and Technology (RCAST). The latter was inaugurated in May 1987 with the objective of playing a key role in the research activities of the University of Tokyo, based on co-operation of all the faculties and research institutes of the university. RCAST features four basic mottoes which are the promotion of interdisciplinary studies, international co-operation, mobility of researchers and openness to the public and outside organisations. The institute has four endowed chairs which are open to specialists from abroad: Advanced Materials (Nippon Steel Corporation); Computer and Communication (NEC); Telecommunications (NTT); and Information Science (CSK).

There are sixteen regular chairs in the four departments of Advanced Materials, Advanced Devices, Advanced Systems and Socio-Technological Research, and another four guest chairs each related to one of the departments.

Table 8.6 Research institutes at the University of Tokyo

Name	Number of departments
Institute of Medical Science	25
Earthquake Research Institute	18
Institute of Oriental Culture	4
Institute of Social Science	4
Institute of Journalism and Communication Studies	8
Institute of Industrial Science	44
Historographical Institute	5
Institute of Applied Microbiology	12
Institute of Cosmic Ray Research	7
Institute for Nuclear Study	15
Institute for Solid State Physics	7
Ocean Research Institute	15

Kyoto University

Japan's second university, Kyoto Imperial University was founded in 1897 by imperial ordinance and was renamed Kyoto University in 1947. Two years later the Kyoto Third High School was added to the university to provide instruction in liberal arts. Following the enactment of the School Education Law of 1947 the Kyoto University was reorganised as a four-year instead of three-year university. In addition to the seven faculties which then existed, a Faculty of Education was also established.

Kyoto University had considerable strength in science from very early on. Within ten years of its foundation it had Colleges of Sciences and Engineering and Medicine and by 1919 the university was reorganised into five faculties, three of them being scientific – Medicine, Engineering and Science. A Faculty of Agriculture was added in 1923 and eight graduate schools in 1953 which included those of Science, Pharmaceutical Sciences, Engineering, and Science. Today the university has nine faculties - Letters, Education, Law, Economics, Science, Medicine, Pharmaceutical Science, Engineering, and Agriculture – and eight graduate schools. It may be of interest to note that almost all the Japanese Nobel Prize winners in the field of the sciences have come from Kyoto University.

In May 1988 the total number of regular undergraduate students was 12,219 with an additional 515 students enrolled in the College of Medical Technology. There were 2,250 postgraduate students in the master's programme and and another 1,653 students in the doctor's programme. The large faculties are Law and Engineering with 1,906 and 4,268 postgraduate students respectively. The engineering students completely dominate in the master's programme with altogether 1,222 students. The female enrolment is slightly above 10 per cent at the post-graduate level and in the doctor's programme, but lower in the master's programme. There is a striking difference for the Junior College of Medical Technology, which was established in 1975, with an almost complete dominance of female students which is explained by the fact that it provides university training for nurses.

The university has a total staff of 5,449 (May 1988), excluding the Junior College of Medical Technology (3-year programme). There are 682 full professors, 651 associate professors and 142 full-time lecturers. The total costs for operating the university amounted to Y82 billion yen in the fiscal year of 1987 – with the amount almost equally divided between personnel costs and other expenditure. The allocation of research fund to Kyoto University amounted to Y4 billion in the same year.

Kyoto has a large number of research institutes and research centres which are listed below, of which a couple will be briefly described.

1. Institute for Chemical Research

2. Research Institute for Humanistic Studies

3. Chest Disease Research Institute

4. Institute of Atomic Energy

5. Wood Research Institute

6. Research Institute for Food Science

7. Disaster Prevention Research

8. Research Institute for Fundamental Physics

9. Institute for Virus Research

10. Institute of Economic Research

11. Research Institute for Mathematical Sciences

12. Research Reactor Institute

13. Primate Research Institute

14. Centre for South-East Asian Studies

15. Radiation Biology Centre

16. Radio Atmospheric Science Centre

17. Plasma Physics Laboratory

18. Radio-Isotope Research Centre

19. Environment Preservation Centre

20. Educational Centre for Information Processing

21. Research Centre for Medical Polymers and Biomaterials

22. Centre for African Area Studies

23. Centre for Molecular Biology and Genetics

24. Centre for Archaeological Operations

25. Centre for American Studies

The Research Institute for Fundamental Physics (RIFP) – originally called Yukawa Hall – was established in 1953 in honour of the Nobel Prize awarded to Hideo Yukawa in 1949. Although the institute formally belongs to Kyoto University, its facilities are open to all researchers in related fields from all over Japan. These researchers also participate in the general policy-making and administration of the institute. Its facilities and activities are also open to all foreign researchers in the field.

The Disaster Prevention Research Institute was established in 1951 in order to carry out scientific and engineering studies of the prevention of disasters caused by natural forces. The institute maintains a number of field stations: for volcano studies in Kagoshima prefecture, for micro-earthquake research in Tottori City and in Fukui prefecture, for crustal movement studies in several locations, a sedimentation observatory in North Japan Alps, a landslide observation in Tokushima prefecture and a couple of observatories to study air-sea boundary phenomena. At present the institute has altogether fifteen attached facilities, while more than 100 staff members are working in the laboratories and observatories.

The Plasma Physics Laboratory was established in 1966 for research into the generation and confinement of high temperature plasmas for controlled thermonuclear fusion. The research programme is based upon the heliotron magnetic field concept which originated at Kyoto University.

The Research Reactor Institute was established as an university-attached institute, for common use, in 1963. The main installation is the Kyoto University Reactor, a light water moderated, tank type reactor. In 1975 a Reactor Utilisation Centre was opened to utilise the reactor and the related facilities for tests and research. All experimental facilities are available for co-operative research projects by scientists of other universities and public research organisations. About 2,000 scientists visit the institute in a year.

The Centre for Molecular Biology and Genetics was established in April 1988 in order to provide experimental facilities for recombinant DNA research and animal facilities for transgenic mice to all researchers in Kyoto University. The centre is also responsible for safety control of experiments and for the education of graduates and undergraduate students in recombinant DNA technology.

Tokyo Institute of Technology (Tokyo Kogyo Daigaku)

Tokyo Institute of Technology was established by the government in 1881 and has since then been the leading institution of higher education in the field of engineering and science in Japan. The aim of the original institute, called Tokyo Vocational School (Tokyo Shokko Gakko) was to produce engineers who would fulfil the urgent needs of Japan at the turn of the century. The school was renamed Tokyo Technical School in 1890 and subsequently developed into Tokyo Higher Technical School in 1901. It was promoted to university status in 1929 and renamed Tokyo Institute of Technology.

The university in 1953 added a Graduate School of Science and Engineering which offers a two-year master's programme as well as as a doctoral degree programme. When a new campus, in Nagatsuta, was opened in 1975 the university added a new graduate school which consists of ten interdisciplinary departments. The same campus also houses three research laboratories – Research Laboratory of Resources Utilisation, Research Laboratory of Precision Machinery and Electronics, and Research Laboratory of Engineering Materials.

The university currently has faculties in engineering and science. The number of students is 4,326 in the undergraduate programmes (1988) and another 1,609 students in the master's programmes and 534 students in doctor's programme. The faculty numbers 450, which is equally divided into full professors and associate professors. The total staff numbers 1,583 (1988).

University of Tsukuba (Tsukuba Daigaku)

University of Tsukuba, founded in 1973, is quite different from Japan's other national universities. Indeed it was set up with the special aim of providing a model for university reform by giving new emphasis to the cultivation of creativity and interdisciplinary research, to increased links between university and society and to an increased level of international co-operation. The university was set up by moving the Tokyo University of Education, a national university set up nearly 100 years ago, to Tsukuba, but along with the move and the change in name the university was totally reorganised so that nothing of the structure of the earlier university remains.

The history of the University of Tsukuba goes far back to the Normal School founded in 1872, which was at the time the only school of higher education in Japan. Following the successive changes in the national educational system the school was reorganised on several occasions. It became the Tokyo Normal School in 1883, then Tokyo Higher Normal School in 1903, after that Tokyo University of Literature and Science in 1929 and finally Tokyo University of Education in 1949 by combining the Tokyo College of Agricultural Education and Tokyo College of Physical Education.

In national universities, it is usual that both staff and students belong to specific faculties or departments where both research and education are carried out. This has, in practice, led to the isolation of the departments, prevented co-operation among the different academic fields and caused students to receive their education in only a narrow range of subjects.

At Tsukuba, research and education are structurally separated but functionally interdependent activities. All faculty members are grouped into various research institutes in accordance with their specialities and are expected to engage in their own special studies within their institutes or to engage in co-operative research with members of other institutes. In addition, they have teaching duties which are discharged not in the research institutes but in the colleges and graduate schools of the university, which are free to recruit their teaching staff from any of the research institutes.

In this system, the education of students takes place in the clusters of Colleges, Schools, and Graduate Schools, and the research organisations consist of Institutes and Special Research Projects. The colleges are grouped into units of three or four which are called clusters, each covering such a broad areas of disciplines that it could almost be a university in itself. A student in any of the colleges can take any of the courses offered in the cluster to which his college belongs and thus study a wide range of subjects.

In addition to the clusters of colleges, the Schools of Medicine, Physical Education, and Art and Design are separately organised to provide the specialised education required in these fields, although students are still expected to undertake some more general studies as well.

The number of undergraduate students was 7,458 in 1987 with another 2,312 students in master's and doctor's programme which indicates a comparatively high ratio between graduates and undergraduate students. There are altogether 26 different graduate schools. The university has 443 professors (1987), 414 associate professors and 400 full-time lecturers. Internationalisation is another important feature of the University of Tsukuba. The university currently (1987) has posts for 32 foreign faculty members and is trying to adopt many other features to promote internationalisation – although almost all teaching is still in Japanese.

The University has a number of research institutes and centres most of which are listed below.

1. Agricultural and Forestry Research Centre

2. Chemical Analysis Centre

3. Environmental Research Centre

4. Gene Experiment Centre

5. Particle Radiation Medical Science Centre

6. Plasma Research Centre

7. Shimoda Marine Research Centre

8. Sugadaira Montane Research Centre

9. Tandem Accelerator Centre

Saitama University (Saitama Daigaku)

Saitama University was established in 1949 in order to provide Saitama prefecture with a national university. It was built on the foundation provided by two existing institutions: Urawa Koto Gakko, a senior high school with a strong science faculty, and Saitama Shihan Gakko, which was training teachers. However, the good foundation was partly eroded by a ministry decision to transfer some of the science faculty to Tokyo University – Komaba campus.

The university originally had only two faculties – Liberal Arts (*bunrigaku*), and Education (*kyoiku gakubu*). The university has grown rapidly over the last three decades and undergraduate education is given in five faculties – Liberal Arts, Education, Economics, Science, and Engineering – in addition to the College of Liberal Arts which provides students with general education for the first two years.

Saitama University offers four graduate programmes leading to a master's degree – Cultural Science, Science, Engineering, and Policy Science. In 1988 it started to offer a doctor's programme in science and engineering in co-operation with the Institute of Physical and Chemical Research – RIKEN – located nearby in Saitama prefecture. See also Chapter 15.

The development of the programme for doctoral studies at Saitama University illustrates both the need to expand doctoral studies and the ability to organise such studies in new ways. A proposal was prepared in the early 1980s to establish a doctoral programme in life sciences – although with little effect.

The real starting point for the present arrangement was informal discussions in the Bureau for Science and Technology Policy at the Science and Technology

Agency in 1985. It was then suggested that an educational partnership should be formed between the Institute of Physical and Chemical Research (RIKEN) and the faculties of science and engineering at Saitama University. It is a rather unusual arrangement because RIKEN and Saitama University are controlled by different ministries. The unusual arrangement was welcomed by the two faculties which would have otherwise had to wait for many years to see their doctoral programme materialise. The arrangement was also supported by the president of Saitama University and the top leadership within the Ministry of Education while others were less enthusiastic.

The doctoral programme generally assumes studies during a period of three years although it is possible to shorten the period considerably – for brilliant and well prepared students. The programme which started in April 1988 admits 32 students – in three branches – every year, which will give a total enrolment of 96. However, the enrolment has after two years already reached 84, which is partly explained by the fact that some of the doctoral students maintain their jobs, in company research laboratories, while pursuing their studies.

RIKEN has in the past unofficially accepted doctoral students. The new programme provides an expansion of this activity for the institute while at the same time giving some of the necessary means for Saitama University to upgrade its teaching functions – through access to advanced research facilities. The assumption is that such links should be established between a national institution of higher learning and advanced research institutes located within the same prefecture. Such plans are currently being discussed for Kagoshima University on Kyushu.

Several of the major national research laboratories are likely to enter into similar arrangements. One such agreement which is likely to materialise is between NTT laboratories and the University of Electro-communications (Denki Tsushin Daigaku) in western Tokyo. A similar arrangement is also negotiated for the MITI Electrotechnical Laboratory in Tsukuba.

Another interesting characteristic is that the university in its Graduate School for Policy Science offers a special M.A. programme in policy analysis in which all courses are taught in English. The programme, which started in 1984, was one of the first attempts of the Japanese university system to respond to international demands to make education in Japan more accessible.

Yokohama City University (Yokohama Shiritsu Daigaku)

The Yokohama City University was established as a school of commercial law in 1885 and was given its present status as a university in 1949 – with a faculty of Economics and Business Administration – following the reform of the educational system after the Second World War. The following years saw gradual expansion and consolidation of the university. In 1952 the university established its school of medicine by incorporating the Yokohama University School of Medicine, and the Faculty of Liberal Arts and Science was also established. In 1955 a Premed school was integrated into the university, thus completing the major parts of the university. The yearly freshman enrolment in the three faculties at present amounts to more than 700, of which only 60 enter into medicine. The total number of students in 1987 was 2,960 undergraduate and another 72 graduate students. The university has 103 professors, 86 associate professors and 42 lecturers (1987). The total enrolment is in the region of 3,000 students.

Two graduate schools have been established; the first in 1961 to create a doctor's programme in medicine (enrolling 29 students), followed in 1970 with a master's programme in Economics and Business Administration (enrolling ten students each for first year enrolment). The university has an attached Economic Research Institute, established in 1949, and the Kihara Biology Research Institute, established in 1984.

Yokohama City is the owner of the university and appoints the director of the university administration, as well as confirming the election of the university president who is chosen by fifteen voters (all full-time staff) from each of the three schools. An important characteristic is the very low tuition and entrance fees and also the very low laboratory charges for science and medical students.

Waseda University (Waseda Daigaku)

Waseda University, vying with Keio University for the position of Japan's top private university, was set up as Tokyo College (senmon gakko) in 1882, at a time when Japan was in political turmoil, and was given university status in 1902 when the name was also changed to Waseda University. Its founder, Marquis Shigenobu Okuma, was a member of a political group in opposition to the main government party and was convinced of the need to establish a higher educational institute that was independent of the government's Imperial University but which would train people capable of taking part in government.

The college was set up despite opposition from the government and has been offering courses in law and political science, as well as Japan's first correspondence courses. A junior college and a graduate school were added in 1902 and a school of science and engineering was established in 1908. At present Waseda University has eight undergraduate schools, including two evening divisions, offering courses leading to a bachelor degree, and six graduate schools with courses leading to master's and doctor's degrees. The university also has three affiliated schools and several research centres.

Waseda University retains a particular strength in its Schools of Logical Science and Economics and Law each with an undergraduate enrolment of around 6,000 (1989). Total enrolment at the undergraduate level is 43,799 (1989). However, the School of Science and Engineering has become the single biggest school with 7,550 undergraduate students in 1989. This trend is even more apparent in in the Graduate School of Science and Engineering which enrolled 1,726 out of a total of 3,224 students – the overwhelming majority in the master's programme. The ratio of female enrolment is 22 per cent at the undergraduate level. The university has total staff of 3,171, of which 1,095 are faculty. There are 799 professors, 126 associate professors and 61 lecturers.

The total budget for Waseda University is about half that of Kyoto University despite the fact that the university has three or four times as many students. The difference is mainly a reflection of the massive difference in running a predominantly science-based university as opposed to a teaching university like Waseda. More than one half of the budget for Waseda

University comes from tuition and fees. A student in Humanities and Social Sciences paid Y485,000 for the academic year 1989, with an additional Y375,000 in the year of enrolment to cover admission fee, campus development, laboratory fees etc. These amounts are considerably higher for students in Science and Engineering – Y755,000 and Y1,300,000 respectively. The costs are slightly lower for graduate students.

The university has three important scientific research institutes - Science and Engineering Research Laboratory, Laboratory for Materials Science and Technology and the Systems Science Institute. The first institute was set up in 1940 to engage in research in various fields of science and engineering, in co-operation with the School of Science and Engineering and its Graduate School. Research is being carried out in the fields of theoretical nuclear physics, experimental nuclear physics, development of radiation detectors and their use in particle physics experiments, earthquake-proof structural engineering and system control engineering. More than 200 projects were in progress in 1989, formulated in response to requests from private industry and public organisations. The institute has nine faculty members and more than 230 research associates who are faculty members in science and engineering.

The Laboratory for Materials Science Technology was established in 1938 under the name of the Castings Research Laboratory. Today the main activities cover almost all fields of modern materials science and engineering which include plastic deformation, surface technology, powder metallurgy, composite materials, semiconductor materials and study of the fundamental problems encountered in these various areas. The Systems Science Institute was founded in 1956 with the objective of contributing with research on the general theory of systems – social, management, production, and other systems – and its application. A distinguishing feature lies in its approach to current social issues and problems and the analysis is based on interdisciplinary and international approaches.

Keio University

Keio University, which is also a private university, is the oldest institution of higher learning in Japan. It was founded in 1858 by Yukichi Fukuzawa, a highly recognised intellectual leader who argued that a primary aim in education is to instil in each individual student the spirit of freedom and independence which he conceived as the essence of modern civilisation. The Keio University is unique in being one component in an educational corporation named Keio Gijuku. The integrated system, which has existed since 1898, consists of an Elementary School, two Junior High Schools, three Senior High Schools and the University. Another significant feature is the international orientation. Keio University has, from the earlier days of its history, promoted exchange with academic institutions abroad and in 1881 the university became the first modern institution of higher learning in Japan to admit foreign students.

The university has six faculties including medicine and science and technology, as well as a University Correspondence School. The university has special strength in economics and law and and almost one half of the undergraduate enrolment accrues to these two faculties. There are eight graduate schools which, in addition to the corresponding faculties, also include graduate schools of Business Administration and Human Relations. The total enrolment at the undergraduate level was 23,415 (May 1988) of which 20 per cent were female students. The enrolment in the graduate programme was at the same time 1,915 students with 596 attending the doctor's programme. An overwhelming majority of the master students are enrolled in the Graduate School of Science and Technology.

Keio University was the first to provide correspondence courses at college level. The system was established in 1948 and 6,500 students have so far graduated. Correspondence courses are offered in the Faculties of Letters, Economics, and Law and are managed by the members of the school board elected from each faculty. Presently there are 15,143 students enrolled in the Correspondence School.

Keio University is primarily dependent on tuition and fees to cover its expenditure. A student in economics pays Y753,000 for the year of his admission and then annually Y420,000 according to the charges in 1988. However, it is much more costly for a student in medicine. There the student pays Y2.36 million in the first year and then Y1.7 million for each of the following years. The costs at the graduate level are considerably lower.

The University has a number of research institutes and centres. One is the Keio Economic Observatory, established in 1959 for the purpose of conducting theoretical and empirical researches on economic and industrial studies in the context of the existing economic conditions of Japan, which has extended to include research on economic problems in general. It has three sections: Economics, Law, and Social Psychology. The main feature of the institute lies in its attempt to understand general equilibrium theory in the light of the factual situation of the Japanese economy and to build new theories based on empirical research.

Chapter 9

The information technologies

The electronics industry in Japan has become one of the largest and most advanced in the world and forms one of the central pillars of the country's economy. The sixteen biggest spenders on research and development in Japan in 1990 allocated approximately Y3,600 billion to R&D. Four of these companies are automobile companies while one is Mitsubishi Heavy Industries.

All other eleven companies have their main activities in the electronics sector. There are three general electric companies, Hitachi, Toshiba and Mitsubishi Electric, which now have a dominant presence in electronics. The group includes two companies with strong presence in telecommunications equipment and computers, NEC and Fujitsu, and NTT as a provider of telecommunication services.

Then there are the companies with a strong presence in consumer electronics, with Matsushita Electric as the leader in a group which also includes Sony, Sharp and Sanyo with Canon as an unusual entrant. However, none of the companies is narrowly specialised and almost all of them aggressively pursue development and manufacture in consumer electronics, computers, telecommunication and integrated circuits – with the exception of NTT which is basically a service provider. The R&D expenditure of the eleven electronics companies constitutes about one third of private industry expenditure on research and development.

The electronics sector, which in its broader context is often referred to as information technologies, consists of four major sub-sectors: consumer electronics, telecommunications, computers and semiconductor devices. The information industry, which consists of products and systems as well as services, will by the end of the century, according to the MITI Vision of the Year 2000, produce 21 per cent of the country's GNP, which would amount to Y140,000 billion. Although the value of semiconductors would constitute less than 10 per cent of the sales they will remain critical and strategic inputs for practically every aspect of the information industry.

Japan has in the past singled out the computer industry as requiring special government assistance, that has also resulted in a spillover effect for the semiconductor industry. Japan is, partly as a consequence of government initiatives, the only country which has been able to challenge IBM in its home market. The telecommunication industry, which in the past, was mainly supported to provide technology and equipment for the telecom services has developed into a mature industry.

However, there can be no doubt that the strength and excellence in consumer electronics – with very meagre national programmes in space or defence – has provided an important foundation for the all-round development of the Japanese electronics industry. During the 1980s the

Japanese electronics companies have been in the position to challenge the position of US companies for almost all electronic products, including supercomputers – although not yet in software.

Historical background

From the beginning of the Meiji period the latest devices for telephones, wireless communication and vacuum technology were quickly transferred and applied for use in Japan. Radio broadcasting expanded quickly after its start in 1925. Many companies, usually associated with the *zaibatsu*, entered into electronics but were often closely tied to overseas companies which provided both technology and capital. The war forced the companies to change their orientation, e.g. from development of television to research on radar, which turned out to be beneficial when the war was over. The technological isolation experienced during the war continued through restrictions imposed by the Allied Occupation until the Korean War in 1950. The electronics industry recovered quickly and many of the companies entered into collaborative agreements with foreign manufacturers.

Research on electronics was taken up in university departments and government laboratories. The industry also benefited from the deregulation of broadcasting in 1951, and the launching of television broadcasting in 1953. The potential of the transistor, invented in 1948, was quickly realised in Japan where Sony produced the first portable transistor radio in 1955. In the same year the government (MITI) announced its first promotion law for the information industry – Law Concerning Special Measures for the Machinery Industry – which has since been followed by a succession of laws to facilitate the promotion of the electronics industry – in a broad sense. See Figure 9.1.

Figure 9.1 Information industry promotion laws

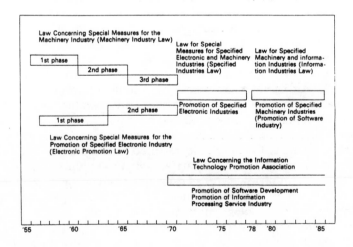

Source: Computer White Paper, 1980 edition. *A Summary of Highlights* compiled from the Japanese original, Japan Information Processing Development Centre, p. 33

The emergence of the transistor at a time when Japan lagged in vacuum tube technology was eagerly exploited by the electronics companies in Japan. During the period of economic growth the electronics sector experienced an annual growth rate of 20 per cent which was sustained by investment and a booming market for consumer electronics. The government restricted direct investment of foreign capital and provided tax incentives in order to stimulate investment in research and development while directing the Japan Development Bank to provide capital for the electronics sector. MITI also encouraged the formation of industry promotion associations, among which the influential Japan Electronic Industry Development Association (JEIDA) was established in 1958. This organisation has continuously served as a forum for contacts among makers and as a platform for urging the government to make initiatives of benefit to the electronics industry.

By the mid-1960s the sector had almost reached the level of the advanced industrialised countries and by the mid-1970s many of the makers had changed their emphasis from consumer products to industrial equipment, or more sophisticated consumer products like video tape recorders. See Figure 9.2.

Figure 9.2 Main consumer electronics products, 1960-2000

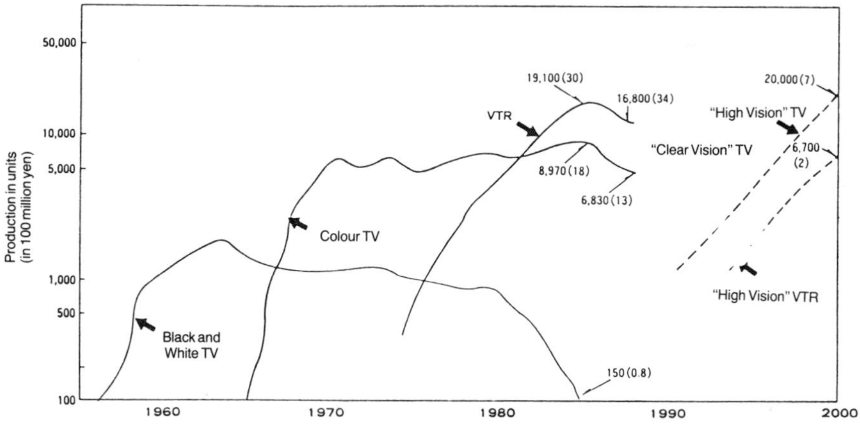

Source: Nikkei Electronics (Nikkei Erukutoronikusu), May 28, 1990, p. 134

Computers

There are no specialised computer manufacturers in Japan, with the exception of Fujitsu for which computer sales constitute almost 70 per cent. NEC and Oki are telecommunications companies while Mitsubishi Electric, Toshiba and Hitachi are general electronic companies which diversified into computers in the early 1960s. The government has played an important role in fostering the computer industry in Japan. Initiatives have generally been taken by the bureaucrats basing themselves on the information industry promotion laws mentioned above. Controls over foreign imports and investment played an important role until 1975 when mainframe computers were withdrawn from quantitative import restrictions.

Included in government assistance was the establishment in 1961 of the Japan Electronic Computer Company (JECC) which is a government-sponsored computer-leasing company. This company has been very important as it was, at times, purchasing more than 50 per cent of the total computer production from the main computer makers and then leasing the machines to users. Other initiatives during the 1960s followed from the Electronics Industry Deliberation Council Report of 1966 in which MITI stressed the importance of national technological excellence and larger market shares for the domestic makers. This document set the orientation for government support for computer R&D and provided direction for Japan Development Bank.

At the time MITI was eager to establish one single computer consortium which would be in a strong position to challenge IBM's position in mainframe computers. The plan failed and during the 1970s the major makers entered into three specialised groups to develop computers good enough to compete with the IBM 370 series. This was followed by another two groups which started another computer project in 1980. Throughout the 1970s the same group of companies had been involved in the "pattern-recognition" computer project which aimed at developing a system which would be capable of inputting, recognising, and processing pattern information such as Japanese characters, drawings, shapes of objects, and also voice recognition.

In the meantime this same group of companies had also been involved in the Very Large Scale Integration (VLSI) project to develop integrated circuits which would be used in future generations of computers. In 1981 MITI organised another computer project with the aim of developing computer technology for high-speeed scientific calculations. To this end, research and development are being carried out on high-speed logic and memory device alternatives to convential silicon devices, a parallel processing system which opeates a number of basic processors simultaneously, and an integrated system to use high speed devices and parallel processing.

One of the earlier computer projects was the FONTAC (acronym derived from the initials of the three participating companies: Fujitsu, Oki and NEC), undertaken during 1962-64 to reduce the technological gap vis-a-vis the US. This was the first project to develop and manufacture a general purpose large-scale computer in Japan. This was immediately followed by another project to develop a high performance computer, in 1966-72, which was subsequently expanded to out-perform the IBM 360 series.

In the late 1970s the government (MITI) and computer scientists started to consider another project which came to have the ambition to do more than catching up – to become known as the Fifth Generation Computer Systems Project with its integral Institute for New Computer Technology (ICOT). The ten-year project, which was initiated in 1982, takes the stand that computer architecture has to develop in order to exploit fully the possibilities offered by memory capacity and VLSI technology and the keyword is parallel inference.

The scientists in the project state that a fifth-generation computer should be oriented to knowledge information processing. In overcoming the technical limits of conventional computers it should provide possibilities for intelligent conversation and knowledge base deduction. Four different functions are desired: problem solving and inference functions; knowledge base management functions; intelligent interface functions; and intelligent programming functions.

The project was initiated as part of the information policies of MITI and has been organised as a national project in cooperation with manufacturers, national research institutes and universities. The project has been divided into three stages – three years for the first term, four years for the middle and final terms which end in 1992. The first stage included the development of a Personal Sequential Inference Machine (PSI) which was designed to serve as a tool and workstation for software development in the middle and final stages. In addition, the Sequential Inference Machine Programming and Operating System (SIMPOS) was being developed as the operating system for PSI. This was the first large-scale software to be developed using a logic language.

The development of parallel control structures was being started in the second phase. The problem of adding parallel control to a logic language has been a major theme of logic programming research worldwide during the 1980s. Furthermore, natural language will be essential in future man-machine communications, and it has been a major concern of ICOT. One of the results of the second phase has been the Multi-PSI, an upgraded version of the earlier PSI with 64 PSIs forming one Multi-PSI system. The purpose was to provide an environment for research on parallel software and a prototype of the PIMOS (parallel inference machine operating system) is being developed on the Multi-PSI.

The third stage will provide the opportunity for in-depth research on parallel inference software which in the past could only be done through simulation. The scientists in the group also expect to build a PIM with 1,000 processor elements. The parallelisation of knowledge processing, natural language processing, and application programmes, albeit on a modest scale, will be a major area of research in the final stage.

The Fifth Generation Computer Project is an attempt to initiate an independent development – although it is not yet clear to what extent this first major project is being successful. The Japanese effort has in the past been more focused on hardware development, which is also realised in JEIDA which has basically been a association for hardware makers. A couple of significant projects also exist in the software domain.

However, much of the energy and innovation in software development goes into meeting individual customers' needs and supplying them with customised software. The situation is illustrated by information released from the Japan Information Processing Development Centre (JIPDEC) which shows that the sales ratio for custom-made software versus packaged software is only 40 per cent in the US while it is 90 per cent in Japan. The low development of packaged software is one important factor which contributes to the expected shortfall of almost 1 million software engineers by the year 2000. In 1985, in order to remedy the situation, MITI launched the Software Industrialised Generator and Maintenance Aids (SIGMA) Project. SIGMA aims to industrialise the production of software and is expected to dramatically enhance software productivity and reliability. A database is being constructed, as part of SIGMA, to provide software development tools and modules for SIGMA users. Once the system is completed the services will be offered nationwide via a user network.

Another project is The Real-Time Operating Nucleus (TRON) Project which, since it was conceived in 1984, has focused on developing a genuinely Japanese open-architecture computer operating system. A major aim is to provide an operating system that is not limited to English but can easily accommodate Japanese and other national languages. The TRON Project is creating operating-system specifications for the major fields of computer applications. The ITRON specification provides basic software for intelligent objects. The BTRON specification offers data standards, hardware standards, and basic software for communication machines. The CTRON specification furnishes the basic software for large-scale scientific computing, database management, and communications protocol.

There is also one final operating-system specification – MTRON – which is a system architecture conceived for an age in which the ITRON-specification software will be built in all objects – according to a statement from the TRON Association which today includes almost all major electronics-related companies in Japan. The US government has in its report on structural impediments (June 1990) identified the TRON association as a trade barrier. However, the global acceptance of MS-DOS as the operating system for personal computers and the rapid emergence of UNIX-based systems for larger computers may be the real stumbling block for the TRON Project in Japan – although the TRON system may take a place among competing systems.

Another large national project is the Interoperable Data Base System, started in 1985, which will permit interoperability between a variety of hardware and software systems and allow users to obtain immediate access to different databases to retrieve multimedia information, including text, data, graphics, and images. Other computer-related activities include the Personal Information Environments of the Future (FRIEND 21) which is funded with Y13 billion for the period 1988-93. Machine translation, including work on electronic dictionaries, is supported in various ways.

The Japan Electronic Dictionary Research Institute is an R&D company, established in 1986 through investment from the Japan Key Technology Centre and eight computer companies. The company is actually a spin-off activity from ICOT which has been tackling the problem of natural languages as one of its AI technologies. The research includes work on a master dictionary, a concept dictionary and on a data management system. The institute co-operates closely with the Electrotechnical Laboratory of MITI, ICOT, other research organisations and with universities in Japan and abroad.

Fuzzy logic has received increasing attention in Japan which could more appropriately be called a fuzzy logic fever. The Science and Technology Agency in 1988 organised the Fuzzy Society to scrutinise research and development themes and other trends in fuzzy systems. The following year, in March 1989, 48 Japanese companies established the Laboratory for International Fuzzy Engineering Research (LIFE), organised as an engineering research association under MITI. Its purpose is to conduct research on engineering applications for the fuzzy theory in co-operation with Japanese universities. The institute has three laboratories of which the first is researching fuzzy control systems and the third is engaged in development on a dedicated fuzzy processor and languages for system description and processing. In addition MITI and Monbusho have collaborated in setting up the Fuzzy Logic Systems Institute in Iizuku City near Fukuoka on Kyushu.

Finally, the Japanese computer industry has gradually become a mature industry in Japan and may become increasingly stronger in global markets. The production value amounted to Y5,000 billion in 1988. The export value in the same year was Y2,000 billion while imports amounted only to Y228 billion, which partly reflects the fact that foreign manufacturers are tending to rely more on local production combined with the fact that Japanese manufacturers have made considerable progress in their own technologies.

Telecommunications

The telecommunication market, which in a broad sense includes both equipment and network services, has an approximate value of Y10,000 billion which is roughly 10 per cent of Japan's information technology market. NTT is still the dominant service provider for most telecommunication services although value-added networks (VAN) are slowly diminishing the NTT dominance. Exchange equipment is dominated by NEC, Fujitsu, Hitachi and Oki while only NEC and Fujitsu are active in delivering transmission equipment. Satellite communications equipment is manufactured by NEC, Matsushita and Toshiba while the mobile (car) telephone equipment is produced by NEC, Matsushita, Mitsubishi Electric, Fujitsu, Japan Motorola and Nihon Musen.

NTT notes that connectivity alone is no longer the driving force behind the further development of the network. It is rather the market demand for higher-level services which pushes the network to modify and expand their services, which includes three trends. First, the non-telephone services have grown rapidly, exemplified by facsimile transmission and electronic mail leading to an increasing demand for multimedia transportability. Further, various services, like video and future HDTV, have hastened the evolution of broadband communications services. Second, another trend is the demand for portability for mobile and portable telephones. Third, there is an increasing demand to make the network more user-friendly in providing it with "network intelligence". This can be illustrated by the ability to contact a particular subscriber at any time or in any place simply by dialling the subscriber's unique personal number.

The number of subscribers to cellular phone and car-mounted phone services reached 400,000 in February 1990 and is expected to reach 10 million by the year 2000. Several mobile communications systems using satellites are being developed – in addition to the Multichannel Access (MCA) system which uses a number of frequencies shared by several phones. One of the satellite systems uses the ETS-V communications satellite and aims to gather the basic technological knowhow for constructing an integrated digital communications system with moving objects. This project involves the participation of the Communications Research Laboratory of the Ministry of Posts and Telecommunications, Electronic Navigation Research Institute, NTT, KDD and others.

The changes in transport system will increase the importance of optical transmission. The history of research and development in optical telecommunications can be divided into the following two stages. First, the optical fibre cable was developed as a new transmission line to replace copper conductors. Then followed the development of fibres with extremely low transmission loss, long-wave, broadband optical devices and single-mode transmission which made it possible to convey data at rates which are of the order of gigabits per second.

The second stage of development, which has just begun, requires research efforts which improve the coherent quality of carrier light waves. Other demands require the development of optical amplifier and other optical technologies which will greatly expand the existing technological base of fibre optics – and greatly enhance future network possibilities.

Since the late 1980s High Definition Television (HDTV) or Hi-Vision, as the Japanese system is called, has attracted great attention as the USA, Europe and Japan are each fighting to have their standard accepted worldwide. The research in Japan was started by the Science and Technical Research Institute of the Japan Broadcasting Corporation (NHK) back in 1962. After Japan made the initial foray to have its system internationally accepted, more and more countries and companies have come to realise its industrial importance. The significance of HDTV lies in the large data processing and memory capacities that the system will require. The new television sets will need sophisticated microprocessors, signal processors and memory circuits. The NHK institute has in recent years been colloraborating with some of the major electronics companies in Japan to develop some of the specialised integrated circuits which will be needed for HDTV.

The Ministry of Posts and Telecommunications has been active in various new telecommunications services in real situations. Many of these projects are known as Teletopia and are usually sponsored through investment from the Japan Key Technology Centre.

NTT is an active member in a number of the R&D companies which have been established with capital investment from the Japan Key Technology Centre (JKTC). In fact, JKTC owes its existence to the privatisation of NTT which provided the opportunity to set aside capital for the new organisation coming from the sale of NTT shares. The Advanced Telecommunications Research Institute International (ATR) with its four integral laboratories is highly significant for NTT.

ATR, which was opened in Kansai Science City in 1989, is funded by the industrial community at the level of Y20 billion. It is the umbrella organisation for four laboratories which are described below. ATR with its laboratories has a total staff of 300. It maintains close international contacts and many foreign researchers come for visits as well as for long-term research.

The general assumption for ATR is that telecommunications will constitute one of the basic infrastructures of a sophisticated information society coming into existence in the next century. Research and development in telecommunications, broadcasting, and optical technology will be important keys in the new information systems. Given such a situation the principles of ATR are fourfold. First, research and development should start by using fresh perspectives, in an environment encouraging a free flow of new and ingenious concepts. Second, to achieve further integration and to utilise resources more effectively industrial, academic and governmental organisations must be encouraged to collaborate and actively to exchange research results. Third, telecommunications is a field in which world uniformity is crucial and it is important to stimulate international co-operation in telecommunications research. Fourth, ATR is located in Kansai Science City which is expected to become a new centre for cultural, academic and scientific research in Japan.

The following four laboratories, all being an integral part of the Advanced Telecommunications Research Institute International, are established as incorporated R&D companies with capital coming from JKTC and the participating companies of which NTT is one.

ATR Communications Systems Research Laboratories, established in April 1986, focuses its research activities on a "human-oriented communications system" which will feature ease of use, natural sensation and reliability. Areas of basic technological research include three-dimensional display techniques and the automatic input of three-dimensional data. Other priorities are to increase knowledge of communication and design methodology, to research new methods of expression and to achieve substantial progress in software generation.

ATR Interpreting Telephony Research Laboratory, established in April 1986, has the goal of providing the basis for an automatic translating telephone system. Such a system requires three major components: speech recognition to identify the spoken message in one language, machine translation to translate this message from one language into another, and speech synthesis to automatically generate natural-sounding human speech in the target language. Each of the component technologies require considerable basic research which is carried out in the laboratories.

ATR Auditory and Visual Perception Research Laboratories, established in April 1986, are doing research on man-machine interface to bypass an earlier narrow engineering perspective and develop easy-to-use telecommunications equipment, human cognition and behavioural mechanisms. The research activities include auditory modelling of peripheral signal processing, and neural network approach to phoneme recognition. Acoustic-phonetic invariance and interaction of knowledge sources in speech perception and recognition processes are also studied.

ATR Optical and Radio Communications Research Laboratories, established in April 1986, are, among other things, doing research on optical inter-satellite communications. The assumption is that such technologies will become the most important element in space communication. The laboratories also carry out research on a mobile communications system which will eventually make it possible to reach anyone, anywhere, at any time. Another research area is the study of materials and devices for new communication equipment which will be small, lightweight and capable of a variety of functions.

Semiconductors

Japanese semiconductor companies have gradually emerged to dominate the global markets for memory circuits. Hitachi, NEC and Toshiba are leading companies although Fujitsu, Mitsubishi Electric, Matsushita, Sony, Sharp, Sanyo and others are also active not only for memory ICs but also for many types of application-specific circuits (ASICs) and microprocessors – although US companies like Motorola and Intel still maintain a very strong lead.

Japanese companies have likewise emerged as dominant suppliers for much of the equipment which is used in the increasingly sophisticated and costly process for ICs. This includes equipment such as the critical lithography equipment (aligner, wafer-steppers), photo-resists, high-speed testers etc. The materialisation of the new strength started in the mid-1970s when it became clear to many electronics companies in Japan that large-scale integrated circuits

Figure 9.3 Nation/EC support schemes and new alliances in (inter)national semiconductor industry

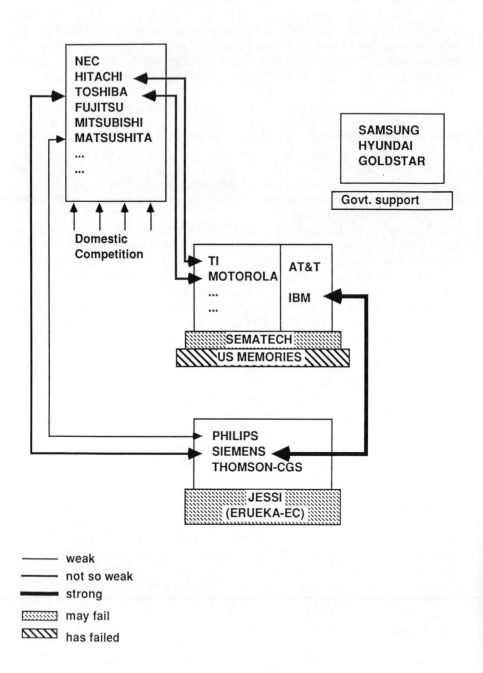

Source: Author, based on reports

would be important not only for computers but increasingly for consumer electronics and all other electronic products. This coincided with the MITI joint project for developing VLSI technology in which five major companies participated – Toshiba, Hitachi, NEC, Mitsubishi Electric and Fujitsu.

The VLSI project has often been seen as a major effort to pool resources for joint development after which ready-to-use results were distributed to the participating companies. This is a grave misunderstanding and an extreme overestimation of the immediate results flowing from the VLSI and other joint research projects. However, the awareness created through the project triggered the companies to commit long-term and substantial resources for VLSI development. Furthermore, the project also triggered the evolution of a comprehensive VLSI industrial structure which closely meshed and where no important component is lacking.

All the main electronics companies have established major VLSI research centres, which together with other laboratories and divisions, continue to generate the technological progress which keeps the companies at the forefront. This has prompted the US government to establish the Sematech consortium to re-establish a US leadership or at least parity in semiconductor production. A similar attempt – the Joint European Sub-Micron Silicon Initiative (JESSI) – will enable the three major European electronics companies to regain their foothold in semiconductor products. However, both projects may fail because of the strength of the Japanese companies which may continue to offer technological partnerships for future development. The emergence of such a situation is illustrated in Figure 9.3.

Given the strength of the companies government support has been reduced to very specific technologies and to future-oriented research. One such project is the Sortec Corporation which was set up by the Japan Key Technology Centre. The purpose is to conduct research and development for constructing synchrotron facilities. It has long been expected that the optical lithography, into ultraviolet and using excimer lasers, will not be feasible beyond 16 Mbit memory circuits. Several companies, not least NIKON and Canon which are leading companies for VLSI lithography, are actively researching the field.

One advanced research project, is the development of the X-ray aligners, and the Canon laboratory at Atsugi has played an important role in developing some of the key components. In order to understand the full significance of Canon's R&D on SOR X-ray lithography it is necessary to look back to the early 1970s. Japan and its semiconductor manufacturers were then dwarfed by the those in the USA. At that time Canon started to make the first aligners for IC chip production – although its competence in mechanical and optical engineering was still overshadowed by NIKON, the other major camera maker in Japan.

Both companies were, in 1976, given specifications and development contracts for wafer steppers to print the fine circuits on IC wafers – out of the VLSI Project which was promoted by MITI. In 1978 Canon introduced its first commercially successful aligners which were good enough for making 16-kilobit dynamic random access memories (DRAM). Since then Canon has continuously upgraded its technology and moved through a succession of machines – contact/proximity aligners, mirror projection aligner and then the wafer stepper.

At present Canon is delivering excimer aligner by which the wafers are illuminated with high-powered excimer lasers. The short wave-length of the deep ultraviolet light of the spectrum makes it necessary to use quartz lenses instead of glass ones. It will eventually be necessary to find another source for printing the wafer patterns – at least when approaching 64 Mbit DRAM. It is generally considered that X-ray lithography is the most encouraging way forward and of the several ways of producing X-ray light, by far the most promising for photolithographic purposes is the synchrotron. This would make it possible to transcribe superfine patterns of less than 0.2 microns.

Leading-edge semiconductor production is presently at the level of 16 and 64 Mbit. To provide the resolution needed for such levels, short-wave light sources like excimer lasers and X-ray lasers are replacing light sources. Canon is combining tracking techniques to position the wafer with precision machine and laser control, and optical technologies for lens design.

Today there are three major manufacturers of wafer steppers: Canon and NIKON in Japan and Perkin Elmer in the USA. Several of the large electronics companies in Japan are also developing future generations of wafer steppers. However, being major producers of semiconductors, they are also major users of lithography machines. It is likely that companies which are both independent of IC manufacturers and able to master or integrate all the required technologies will be the dominant players in an emerging market – and Canon appears to be such a company.

A related project is the Opto-Electronics Technology Research Laboratory (OTL) – also sponsored by JKTC – which is a continuation of the Opto-Electronics Joint Research Laboratory which focused on research for optoelectronic ICs. OTL, which is a ten-year project started in 1986 with laboratory facilities completed in 1987, will study four main subjects:

1. atomic-layer-controlled epitaxy of III-V semiconductors;

2. ultra-fine pattern formation using beam-assisted etching processes;

3. characterisation of surfaces and interfaces on an atomic scale; and

4. study of new quantum effects.

The scientific leader, who also participated in the earlier project, notes that one of the distinctive features of OTL, compared with the former OJL, is that the scientists from different member companies are completely amalgated into each research area according to their personal scientific interests and are largely free to choose a specific subject from the areas mentioned above.

The OEICs (optoelectronic integrated circuits) are seen as the key to the future of optical computing. Such devices will enable every particular function of light and electronics to be combined in one system to give maximum system performance. The scientific leader of the OTL argues that the problem of interconnections facing electronic computers will be overcome by introducing optical signal transferral, and problems of optical computing will be solved by incorporating electronics in optical systems. He also expects that new-generation computers will appear which will utilise new combinations of features. Neuro-Computers which require a large number of interconnections for each cell are well suited to photo-electronic engineering. Three-dimensional integrated circuits, with optical wafer-to-wafer interconnections, will be constructed instead of the wafer-scale integration of ultra large-scale integrated circuits.

Chapter 10

Corporate R&D structure and orientation in information technologies

The Japanese electronics companies have emerged in the 1980s as technological powerhouses. Their excellence is no longer limited to consumer electronics. The large electronics companies, joined by several other Japanese companies today have a dominant position in the manufacture and development of memory circuits. Fujitsu followed by Hitachi has established a strong position for mainframe computers outside Japan and is advancing in supercomputers and workstations. Other companies like Toshiba and NEC have developed a considerable capability in laptop computers. The telecommunications sector has also become strong due to the rapid development of the telecommunications market and the nurturing activity of NTT in the past.

A new combination of integrated circuits, optical fibre technology, and audio-visual technology could become the source for a spate of new developments in the 1990s. The information technologies are changing quickly and the character of change is heightened by the fact that the participants in the development race include some of the country's largest and most dynamic companies. These companies already have extensive experience in such areas as computers, telecommunications, office equipment and consumer electronic products – with a keen understanding of future possibilities.

Research planning and organisation has to change constantly in order to adjust to a shifting environment. In the following text an attempt has been made to describe the shifting R&D structure in Hitachi, Canon and NTT. Hitachi is the largest electrical company in Japan, which is being transformed into an electronics company. The metamorphosis of Canon, which has converted from a camera maker to a maker of electronics equipment and now entering into production of electronics systems may be even more stunning. NTT envisages a similar scenario for the conversion from providing telephone connections to delivering multimedia services based on portability. Thus, the three companies represent a dynamic shift which takes place within the information technologies where Japan is already highly successful.

Research and development in Hitachi

Hitachi is one of the five major electronics companies – together with NEC, Fujitsu, Mitsubishi Electric and Toshiba. The company which was started in 1910 owes its origin to a small workshop repairing electric motors for a mining company (Nippon Mining) in Hitachi City, located on the Pacific Coast in Northern Japan. Since those days the company has grown to become Japan's largest comprehensive electric machinery manufacturer. Total sales in 1990 are

Y6,750 billion of which the traditional fields such as power systems and equipment, cables, and industrial machinery and plant constitute approximately 50 per cent. The remaining half is made up of consumer products (16 per cent) and the rapidly increasing area of information and communication systems and electronic devices (32 per cent). The medium-term aim is to restructure the company so that the share of electronic products reaches 50 per cent. Semiconductors with an estimated production value of Y600 billion make up one quarter of the sales in this sector, roughly 10 per cent of the company's total sales.

The *Hitachi Technology Review Special Issue* of 1989 mentions that the company employs some 264,000 people and manufactures over 20,000 kinds of product, ranging from VLSI and supercomputers to nuclear power stations. Its world-wide sales are in this context given as US$46 billion. The company currently has 40 production sites. Hitachi has 15,000 researchers, according to the Review, which engage in activities ranging from advanced research to product development in 32 laboratories. Total R&D expenditure were Y380 billion in 1990, an increase of 10 per cent over the preceding year (*Nihon Keizai Shimbun*, July 2, 1990), although other sources give the lower figure of Y345 billion (*Japan Company Handbook*, Spring 1990). However, there is no doubt that Hitachi is sharing the top position of the highest R&D spender together with Toyota Motor and Matsushita Elecric.

When discussing Hitachi research and development activities a distinction must be made between Hitachi Ltd and the Hitachi Group. The latter consists of a large number of companies – more than 70 – which are engaged in manufacturing as well as in sales and services, several of them located overseas. Hitachi Maxell, the tape manufacturer, with sales of Y182 billion (1990) and 2,400 employees is one illustration of a company which belongs to the Hitachi Group. In the following the R&D activities and organisation will be discussed only in relation to Hitachi Ltd and not to the group as a whole.

Hitachi Ltd, which employs 80,600 people, had sales of Y3,233 billion in 1989 and allocated Y296 billion to research and development (*Japan Company Handbook*, Spring 1990) which corresponds to 9.2 per cent of sales. A comparison of total R&D and total sales within the Hitachi Group would yield a ratio of approximately 6 per cent which indicates that Hitachi Ltd plays an important role as a technological and scientific power-house for the group as a whole. This role is further highlighted when comparing R&D expenditure with the value-added of Hitachi Ltd which is estimated to be 30 per cent of sales. Thus, the R&D activities of Hitachi Ltd constitute approximately one third of value-added generated within the company. With increasing allocation of funds to R&D and with an expected decline of value-added as certain manu-facturing activities are phased-out or located out, Hitachi Ltd is increasingly becoming a R&D company. Consequently the organisation and focus of its research activities should be understood in the light of the comments above.

The funding pattern in Hitachi appears to be different in one major aspect compared with similar companies in the USA and Europe in that the central research laboratories play a more important role. The total number of R&D staff is 12,100 of which 8,300 are engaged in product development in the various works or divisions. The remaining 3,800 work in the central research laboratories and in the nine corporate research laboratories. One half of the activities in the central research laboratories and 30 per cent in the corporate laboratories is considered to be independent research which means that it is risky and challenging.

A rough estimate would indicate that Hitachi Ltd allocates approximately 10 per cent of its total manpower to long-term and exploratory research. This share may possibly decrease slightly in the future, the reason being that product development is becoming increasingly research-intensive. Company policy is to maintain a 50/50 balance between commissioned and independent research in the central research laboratory.

At present 60 per cent or more of all researchers work on topics related to consumer products and electronics and another 15 per cent on emerging fields and basic technologies. Such allocations, based on strategic decisions, would indicate that the character of the company will increasingly shift towards an R&D company with its main focus in electronics and information technologies.

R&D organisation

The nine corporate laboratories are organised directly under the corporate Research and Technology Development Co-Ordination Department, located in the Headquarters, which operates a R&D Planning Centre. The Business Groups which commission research in the corporate laboratories have a special Consumer Products Research Centre apart from the development activities within the divisions. See Figure 10.1. The different manufacturing plants generally have both development and design departments, and a manufacturing engineering department. The arrangement for the semiconductor division is special as it has a Device Development Centre and a Semiconductor Design and Development Centre.

One feature of the research system at Hitachi is the Tokken System (*TOKubetsu KENkyu* or Special Research) which has three different and important functions:

1. to organise large scale projects for urgent and important R&D at the corporate level;

2. to enable management to utilise directly corporate research resources to gain insights on top priority topics; and

3. to engage R&D resources from different parts of the company.

There are basically two types of Tokken. The first involves both laboratories and the manufacturing plants and is usually established for short-term projects and requirements which need to be met immediately.

The other type which involves only corporate laboratories is used for organising long-term research and for research which is deemed essential for future technologies. The system, which was instituted within Hitachi some fifteen years ago, presently takes roughly 15 per cent of the total R&D budget and 20 per cent of research personnel. At any time there are about 45 on-going Tokken projects with 40-50 researchers/engineers in each group. The average length of a Tokken is 1.5 years. Examples of Tokken projects in the late 1980s include multi-lingual machine translation, high-definition displays and naturally sub-micron technology for future generation semiconductor devices.

Figure 10.1 Hitachi R&D organisation

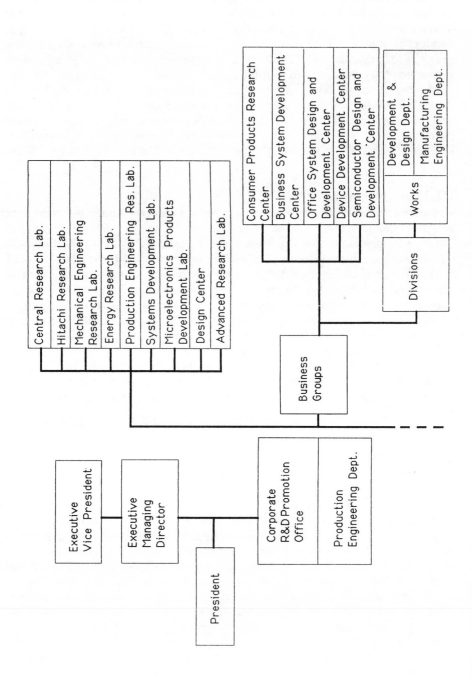

Source: Hitachi brochures and private communication

Corporate research laboratories

Hitachi presently maintains nine corporate research laboratories, which employ a total of 4,910 people, of whom 3,800 are researchers. The oldest is the Hitachi Research Laboratory in Hitachi City, established in 1934. The second oldest, the Central Research Laboratory, was established in 1942, partly in response to the war efforts in science and technology. Two laboratories, the Mechanical Engineering Research Laboratory and the Energy Research Laboratory, are both spin-offs from the Central Research Laboratory. The same is also true for the recently created Advanced Research Laboratory which was created in 1985 – to celebrate the company's 75th birthday – but more importantly perhaps, to provide the fundamental underpinning for the Hitachi Group's development toward the 21st century. See Table 10.1.

The Central Research Laboratory, which has 970 researchers, is active in three major areas: micro-electronics, information technology and fundamental studies in support of information technology and micro-electronics. The laboratory is organised into ten departments and an Opto-Electronics Laboratory, apart from the normal administrative support. The first department carries out research on compound semiconductors, thin films, polymer materials and solid state physics. The second is the Superconducting Electronics Research Centre. Three of the departments are organised into the ULSI Research Centre which includes Process Integration Centre, ULSI Circuits and Systems, and Design Automation. See Figure 10.2.

The laboratory carries out research on sub-micron and nano-meter fabrication technology and also on three-dimensional analysis of the behaviour of electrons and holes within transistors and semiconductor lasers, for the development of new material devices such as ULSI, optical devices and superlattice devices. The laboratory is also engaged in research on high-speed devices for supercomputers. Further development of the superconducting transistor, as a possibility for a new electron wave function device, is also being undertaken.

Various technologies of relevance for High Definition Television (HDTV) and other new media is also being researched. Development is also proceeding on supercomputers and inference machines, as well as on large capacity file memories like mageto-optic disks, which permit medical image processing and large scale simulation. Research on material characterisation is done by utilising techniques with electron beams, X-rays and ion beams. The discovery of high-temperature superconductivity propelled the laboratory into new research which already included Josephson junction devices, superconducting transistors and quantum magnetic flux parametrons. Fundamental research is also being done on artificial intelligence (AI), the fifth generation computer, and Universal Representation of Real numbers (URR) which eliminates the overflow and underflow problem in computers.

Hitachi is involved in a number of national research projects which are directly or indirectly supported by the government. Sortec Corporation, sponsored under the Japan Key Technology Centre, belongs to the second category. Hitachi, together with other major semiconductor manufacturers, participates in Sortec which has the major objective of developing very compact synchrotron accelerators which will provide X-rays for writing the very fine pattern on future generation microchips. The total government funding to Hitachi amounts to 2.7 per cent of the company's total R&D budget

Table 10.1 Hitachi corporate research laboratories

Laboratory	Established	Location	No. of employees	Main research fields
Central Research Laboratory	1942	Kokubunji, Tokyo	1,300	Microelectronics, information technology and their fundamentals
Hitachi Research Laboratory	1934	Hitachi, Ibaraki pref.	1,280	Electric power systems and new energy resources, electronics, materials
Mechanical Engineering Research Laboratory	1966	Tsuchiura, Ibaraki pref.	640	Mechatronics, industrial machinery and basic mechanical technology (CAE)
Energy Research Laboratory	1971	Hitachi, Ibaraki pref.	310	Nuclear power plants, nuclear fusion and other energy sources
Production Engineering Research Laboratory	1971	Yokohama, Kanagawa pref.	550	Development of new production process, facilities and systems, productivity improvement
Systems Development Laboratory	1973	Kawasaki, Kanagawa pref.	390	Systems and software
Microelectronics Products Development Laboratory	1983	Yokohama, Kanagawa pref.	160	Equipment and peripherals for office automation
Design Centre	1957	Kokubunji, Tokyo	230	Human interface design, product design, visual design
Advanced Research Laboratory	1985	Saitama pref.	90	Biotechnology, software science, materials science

Source: Hitachi brochure

Figure 10.2 Organisation of Hitachi central research laboratories

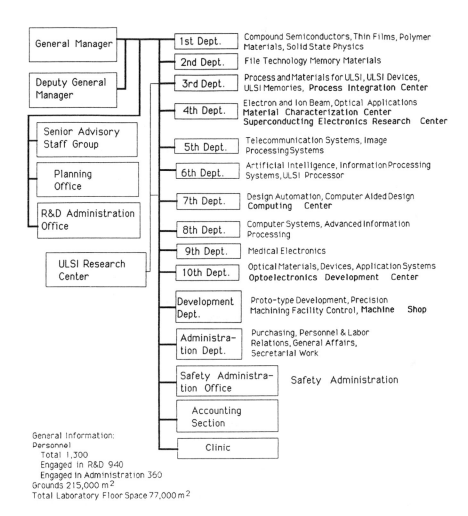

Source: Hitachi brochures and private communication

(1990) and involves between 100 and 200 researchers. The role of government funds is slightly higher in the Central Research Laboratory – around 5 per cent (1989). Considering that funds for national projects are generally of a long-term and exploratory nature it may be assumed that government funds are considerably more important for exploratory research activities where they may be in the region of 10-20 per cent.

The Hitachi Research Laboratory (HRL) develops new technologies in collaboration with the business divisions of Hitachi Ltd. The activities cover three major fields: electronics, energy conversion, and materials science. There are about 1,000 researchers from various academic backgrounds out of a total staff of 1,280. In electronics HRL is undertaking research on advanced technologies for a distributed computer system, information processing, VLSI, communication devices and sensing and control technology. One example is a multi-colour laser-addressed liquid crystal projection display which has already been developed.

HRL is also playing an important role in the development of new ceramics for the Hitachi Group. Recently, a special emphasis has been placed on developing thin film materials and related process technologies. Highly functional and large-scale thin film devices have been realised by utilising the fine patterning method of VLSIs. New devices, such as amorphous silicon photoreceptors, electro-luminescent displays, and thin film alloys for optical recording, are being developed with thin film technology. HRL has developed SIC ceramics with high thermal conductivity and is also researching near-net-shape ceramics.

HRL is involved in several national projects for the development of fuel cells, coal utilisation, and superconducting technologies and concrete results have already been obtained in the areas of high power lasers, and ion sources for plasma. Application of plasma technology has been expanding into many fields, including thin film fabrication, surface modification, etc. Consequently HRL carries out research on plasma generation, ion beam, laser beam and their applications. A Coal Technology Centre has been established inside HRL to investigate a wide variety of coal utilisation technologies as well as the basic research science of coal. Clean combustion of coal is being studied by a laser diagnostic method of the flame, with the purport of minimising NOx emissions.

The Energy Research Laboratory (ERL) which is also located in Hitachi City has a total staff of 310 and is mainly involved in research and development related to nuclear energy. ERL currently puts emphasis on the development of the advanced boiling water reactor (ABWR). It also carries out research on the fast breeder reactor (FBR) and the fusion reactor. ERL has four main departments specialising on light water reactors, nuclear fusion, fuel cycle and reprocessing, and advanced reactors systems (including new energy systems). See also Chapter 11 on energy.

The Mechanical Engineering Research Laboratory (MERL) is conducting research on basic engineering science such as heat transfer, fluid mechanics, vibration,and strength analysis. MERL has also been expanding its research into interdisciplinary areas of mechanical engineering, electronics and physics. A major objective of MERL is to contribute to the development of new products and R&D is generally organised in collaboration with manufacturing units and other laboratories. MERL is organised into seven laboratories with different specialisations.

The Production Engineering Research Laboratory (PERL), which was established in June 1971, is active in research and development of production technologies required in the Hitachi Group. Investigated topics include automated assembly, semiconductor production, high-density electronic circuit fabrication, and precision machining technologies. PERL is engaged in the development of fine motion mechanisms and their control, and sensor-interactive robot control with vision and tactile sensors. The laboratory is establishing its expertise in areas such as control of minute movements, plasma control, and laser/ion beam processing to cover the whole range of production processes and equipment for VLSIs including lithography, deposition, etching, and inspection. PERL is also investigating sub-micron machining of disks and dies for lenses, as well as pursuing research and development on thin film deposition of organic and inorganic materials, metals and semiconductors. New analysis and evaluation technologies are being pursued for the evaluation of materials and processes and for the reliability of products. PERL

Figure 10.3 Organisation of Production Engineering Research Laboratory (PERL)

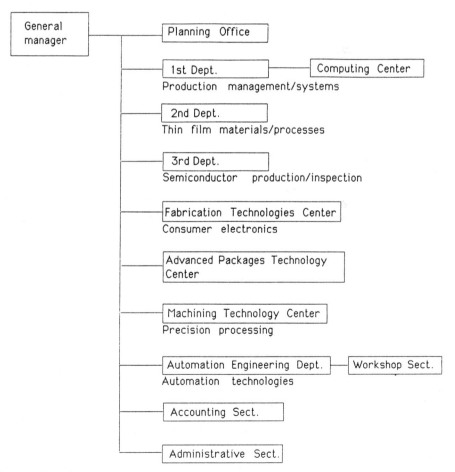

Source: Hitachi brochures and private communication

has a Ultra-Precision Machine Centre which provides a window to micro-machining in terms of nanometers. The laboratory also has large clean rooms for extensive research on thin-film materials and depositions, fine patterning etc.

The Systems Development Laboratory (SDL) was founded in February 1973 with the aim of developing new systems and software which can be incorporated into new products or find applications in new areas. The laboratory is organised in three basic groups: Systems Development; Systems and Software Engineering; and Computer Software. SDL functions as the Hitachi centre for developing software technologies and systems. The research activities are varied and include the following fields: basic computer software, communications and network engineering, software engineering, natural languages and image and information processing.

The Micro-Electronics Products Development Laboratory (MPDL) was established in 1983 and is the smallest in terms of researchers, aside from the more recently created Advanced Research Laboratory. MPDL is basically active in three areas: personal computers and wordprocessors; strategic subsystems such as diskdrives and printers; and specific LSIs for various applications.

The Advanced Research Laboratory was established in April 1985, on the 75th anniversary of the founding of the Hitachi company. Originally it was located adjacent to the Central Research Laboratory but has recently been relocated to Saitama prefecture north of Tokyo. The ARL researchers decide what areas to investigate and there are very few if any restrictions on the range of fields which can be explored – as opposed to the Central Research Laboratory which is focused on micro-electronics and information technology. However, there may be a basic difference between ARL and a university setting in that the management is likely to have an idea of potential applications of the research being carried out. The management also puts a strong emphasis on gaining patents and information about research results is only released after careful filtering. Areas of emphasis include electron-beam radiation physics, advanced materials based on man-made lattices, software and biotechnology. In sum, ARL may serve the very important function of identifying and researching emerging technologies which become the roots of Hitachi business in the future.

The Consumer Products Research Centre (CPRC) is an interesting feature of the Hitachi research organisation which has its parallel in several other companies with a strong orientation towards the consumer market. CPRC was earlier under the Business Groups but is now part of the Corporate Laboratories and apparently has a strong orientation towards technological research. Its task is to anticipate the future needs of the consumer and to develop new electronic products that can be introduced to the public at the most opportune time. CPRC co-operates closely with other laboratories and is involved in the development of basic devices, processes and components. The laboratory, for example, has done research on all fields for optical disk system from disk material to application systems. In the related field of semiconductors, CPRC pushed forward with the development of new system LSIs, the design of photomask patterns and the development of video signal processing and analogue circuit technology.

The Hitachi research activities, which have been briefly outlined above, are almost completely located inside Japan. A couple of embryonic research groups have been established in Cambridge (UK) and in Dublin (Ireland) attached to existing university institutions. The team at the Cavendish Laboratory in UK will undertake research in the micro-electronics field while the Hitachi Dublin Laboratory will concentrate in information science with the O'Reilly Institute. Two similar research teams have been established in the USA – in San Fransisco to work on high-speed signal semiconductors and image processing for computer graphics, and car electronics in Detroit. Each team will have about ten members, both Japanese and locally recruited researchers, and the latter will increase as the scale of each operation expands. At present the teams are much smaller. Hitachi allocates 0.2 per cent of its R&D budget (Y500 million) to the four teams.

Judging from the more or less clearly announced plans from other Japanese electronics companies it may be assumed that this is only the beginning. Hitachi could by the end of the century have at least 10 per cent of its total R&D capacity outside the country and possibly one third of central research capacity in overseas locations. Hitachi Chemical, in which Hitachi Ltd has a majority stake, has already established a major biotechnology laboratory on the Campus of the University of California – with a total investment of US$20 million. Hitachi Chemical is a comprehensive producer of synthetic resin with an orientation towards electrical and electronic applications. In early 1989 Hitachi and other semiconductor manufacturers announced plans for fully integrated manufacture of silicon wafers in Europe. The Japan Times commented at the time that a next logical step would be the conducting of wider research and development activities in Europe to take advantage of the broad pool of scientific skills of the region's specialists.

Conclusion

Hitachi, which used to be a manufacturer of electrical equipment, has increasingly become an electronics company, which is reflected in the ongoing transformation of the R&D structure. Changes are basically carried out twice a year which coincides with the rotational transfer of engineers, managers and higher executives. In the semiannual alteration in Autumn 1990 two new development centres were created directly under the divisions. See Figure 10.1 on Hitachi R&D organisation. The new centres are the Business System Development Centre and the Office System Design and Development Centre which reflect the attention to strategic product development for the near future. Considerable organisational changes were at the same time carried out in the Central Research Laboratory. The earlier opto-electronics laboratory became a separate department. Design automation and computer-aided design became integrated with the activities for supercomputing, vision, information environment (SVIE). At the same time research on ULSI memories and processors were transferred to the third and sixth departments, respectively. See Figure 10.2.

Research and development at Canon

Canon was in the past basically a camera manufacturer. The company first diversified into calculators then into copiers, to be followed by a broader entry into business machines like fax machines and laser beam printers and also into semiconductor-manufacturing equipment. The present company originated in 1933 when the Precision Optical Research Laboratory was established. The company produced Japan's first 35 mm focal-plane shutter camera in 1935 and branched out into other optical products with X-ray cameras in 1940. The company changed its name in 1947 to become the Canon Camera Co. which reflected the dominance of camera manufacture at the time. The name again changed in 1969 and the company became Canon Inc. to mirror the fact that the firm had increasingly become more broadly based in business machines. Total sales in 1989 amounted to Y1,300 billion and the number of employees in the same year was slightly above 16,000 with an average age of 32 years (*Japan Company Handbook*, Spring 1990).

Today Canon is active in three major product areas: cameras including video systems; other optical products like mask aligners and wafer steppers for IC production; and business machines, which is the major activity. The three areas are organised in some 20 business groups, which each has a development centre with a total R&D staff of approximately 4,000. Furthermore, Canon maintains four research centres which are organised by the R&D Headquarters and employ almost 1,000 people (1990). The four main centres are:

1. Components Development Centre, Hiratsuka, established in 1980.

The centre, which has a total staff of 270, is oriented towards research on devices and components with specific performance characteristics. This includes development of amorphous silicon contact sensors and image sensors like CCD.

2. Information Systems Research Centre, Kawasaki-Shi,established in 1987.

The centre, which has a staff of 100, is responsible for research on advanced software which includes various approaches to artificial intelligence (AI). The centre is also doing research on new telecommunication systems – e.g. based on optical beam transmission.

3. Future Products Centre, Kawasaki-Shi, established in 1989.

The centre, which has a staff of 170 people, is responsible for research and development on products which may or will constitute new business opportunities. This includes projects such as electronic notebook and laser rotary encoder.

4. Canon Research Centre, in Atsugi, established in 1969 and the oldest of the corporate research laboratories.

The centre, which currently has a staff of 310 people undertakes research on advanced technologies which are important for future business oppor-tunities, or may generate new possibilities. The research fields include new materials, biotechnology, etc. See below for more details.

The R&D Headquarters have two major tasks – to support ongoing business areas, in terms of future development, and to create the technological basis for completely new business opportunities. The character of the Canon Research Centre will be briefly described as it constitutes a central part of the resources which are directed by the R&D Headquarters.

Canon Research Centre

The Centre has three major activities: research organised in projects; research in six leading-edge technology fields; and research on future technologies. The project groups are basically organised to raise the technological level and competence – aiming at future products. This would for example include research on optical communication systems and information display devices.

A considerable part of the Centre's resources is taken by the research groups in the six leading-edge technology fields which are: optics, nano-meter technology, biotechnology, super materials, electron beam technology and printing technology. The biotechnology group researches recombinant DNA, bacterio-rhodopsine and genetic engineering while the group for super materials studies ultra-fine particles, superlattice structures and superconductors. Each of the six groups has an average of 30 researchers who are also participating in various project groups – according to a matrix organisation. In addition the Centre also has some 20 people organised in a Future Technologies Group. This may serve as the nucleus for a completely new product or technology.

A significant new addition to the Canon corporate laboratories is the Global Exploratory Open (GEO) Centre for "mind communication and ecology" which is being planned to be established as a new research entity in Kansai Science City (Kansai Bunka Gaku Jutsu Kenkyu Toshi). The new Centre, with a staff of 100 at the time of opening, will eventually increase its staff to 200 people. Major themes will cover clean energy, bio-recycling and what Canon refers to as "mind communication". The latter can be understood as new means for enhancing communication and understanding among human beings.

The Canon Research Centre, which has its parallel in other Japanese companies, should be seen as an attempt to keep a wider and more open window to identify and understand future technologies and their consequences for present products and possibilities for future products. The company allocated Y100 billion to R&D in 1990 (*Nihon Keizai Shinbun*, July 2, 1990) which is an increase of 16 per cent over the preceding year and Canon belongs to the league of top R&D spenders in Japan. The Canon Research Centre and the new GEO which represent exploratory and long term research efforts may in the future require approximately 6 per cent of Canon's total expenditure on R&D.

Technology strategy

Canon is a good example of a company which has quickly and successfully diversified away from its traditional product line – cameras – which today constitutes less than 15 per cent of sales. The company has followed a basic philosophy of vertical integration which has two main pillars – upstream and downstream integration. The upstream integration aimed at the integration of materials and device technologies, exemplified by the upgrading and new developments for ink and heads used in ink-jet printing, photo-sensors based on amorphous silicon and magneto/optical memory discs.

The increasing proportion of devices and their costs meant an erosion of added-value. The company decided early on that this was not acceptable as the devices dominate the product performance. Furthermore, Canon found it necessary to develop its own components and devices in order to maintain or improve the competitiveness of its products. With this notion in mind Canon decided that component and device technology should be an integral part of the company's strategy with organic consequence for internal research and development. The other pillar, downstream integration, has meant that Canon has broadened its scope to incorporate the dimension of system technology – basically computer and telecommunications technology in various kinds of system configurations.

Canon is now facing the challenge of subsequent transformation of the company to remain competitive for products and technologies which will emerge in the coming ten to twenty years. In the following text an attempt will be made to outline the planning process for the future research and development strategy at Canon to handle the expected new situation.

The company already has major activities in office equipment and video systems. In order to strengthen the competitive situation, in particular vis-a-vis the major electronics makers in Japan, such as Hitachi, Toshiba, NEC, Matsushita, Mitsubishi Electric, Sony Sharp etc., it was necessary for Canon to develop long-term strategic planning for research and development. The Canon R&D strategy for the next century, which is basically completed in its main features, has already greatly changed the research orientation within the company.

The planning has basically been done in three stages. The first stage followed from a recognition among the top managers of the corporation that a long range technology strategy was needed – with some of the reasons already stated above. The preparatory process was rooted in informal meetings which were organised every month. The members were directors from the four corporate research laboratories and one director from the Production Engineering Research Centre. The discussions focused on general market and technology trends and what technologies would be important for the future of Canon. These meetings were initially very informal, which is generally the case for similar activities in Japanese companies, and discussions were often continued late in the evenings in the relaxed atmosphere offered by bars and restaurants.

The members were, after approximately a year, able to clearly indicate 21 technologies or areas which are essential for the Canon Corporation at the turn of the century. These can be classified into the following main groups.

1. Basic technologies
– optical technologies
– opto-electronics
– new functional materials
– "super-materials"
– biotechnologies
– nano-meter technologies

2. Product technologies
– high quality printing
– high quality image processing
– large area display technologies

3. System technologies
– next generation computer system technologies
– artificial intelligence
– next generation telecommunication technologies

4. Device technologies
– advanced semiconductors
– high density memories

5. Production technologies
– advanced production methods
– high density assembling
– high efficiency software development
– R&D support technologies

6. Other strategic areas
– research on trends in life styles – social/humanities research
– analysis of forms of strategic co-operation

In the second stage Canon organised working groups for each of the 21 technologies or areas. More than 200 people became involved in the working groups for a period of approximately six months. Members included people from the R&D headquarters, from development centres and from the planning divisions of the various groups. Each group investigated the technological trends, the competitive situation and market trends, and the relative strengths and weaknesses of the Canon Corporation. These preparations formed the basis for making a plan for technological development within Canon which also included suggestions for the necessary organisational reforms.

In parallel, the corporate planning division organised working groups to cover the various business areas in order to identify the direction of Canon's future diversification. Naturally, some people would participate in the working groups for both areas, technological development and business diversification.

Previously the business areas were organised according to the three main product groups: cameras, other optical products, and business machines. Canon is now starting to implement a restructuring plan based on proposals from the working groups which intends to organise business operations according to various markets such as home consumers, office users, industrial applications and societal demands.

In a third stage the technology strategy and the business strategy are being integrated – under the responsibility of the R&D Headquarters and Corporate Planning Division. Some of the proposals on the technology side have already been implemented. One example is research on optical communication systems which is carried out at the Canon Research Centre. Canon views optical transmission technology as a key technology as it is an extension of traditional optical technology and lens design for cameras and other optical products in which the company has maintained a leadership.

Furthermore, high definition television (HDTV) has been identified as a key business area because of its expected wide application in various types of home-based equipment. Canon has identified the need to combine optical communication technology with the expected breakthrough in the use of HDTV which is expected after the launching of a HDTV satellite in 1997. Following that, Canon perceives that communication systems, at home and in the office, will be multimedia systems in which high definition video signal will be a pivotal characteristic. The hammering out of new technology strategy and new business strategy, as outlined above, has the purpose of converting the existing competitiveness in traditional optical technology and high precision technology to a similar strength in communications technologies in the next century.

Globalisation of research

In 1987 Canon established its first laboratory abroad which is located near the University of Surrey in UK. A second one was established in 1990 in Silicon Valley. Both laboratories are focused on software development and computer applications and each are expected to have a staff of 30 people – in three to five years.

In 1988 Canon announced its Global Corporation Plan – Phase One – which extends to 1992. The company states that it will make a contribution to the countries in which Canon is active. As a consequence Canon will relocate manufacturing and increasingly its research and development activities. The company in mid-1990 announced that the design and development activities overseas for compact cameras will follow the reallocation of the manufacturing to countries in East and South East Asia. Similarly Canon in 1989 moved its Electronic Typewriter Business Group, including development from Japan to Southern California.

Canon is a rather exceptional company in Japan as it obtains approximately 70 per cent of its revenue from sales abroad. The Corporate Technical Planning and Operation Centre in early 1988 announced that Canon plans to globalise its R&D activities both in product development and basic research. For basic research the company will pursue two parallel strategies – strengthening ties with companies abroad and setting up overseas research centres, mainly staffed by local researchers.

Research and development at Nippon Telegraph and Telephone Corporation (NTT)

The predecessor of the present NTT is the Nippon Telegraph and Telephone Public Corporation which was inaugurated in August 1952 with international communications transferred to Kokusai Denshin Denwa Co., Ltd (KDD) in April 1953. Telecommunication had previously been operated as a public monopoly and the transformation was done in order to improve efficiency and inject vitality in the telecommunications sector which had a long history since a first link between Tokyo and Yokohama started in 1869.

NTT remained as a public corporation and enjoyed a monopoly situation until 1985 when it was privatised following the new Telecommunications Business Law. For reference it should be noted that radio broadcasting started in Japan in 1925 and Japan Broadcasting Corporation (Nippon Hoso Kyokai – NHK) maintained a monopoly until 1947 when broadcasting was opened to other private companies.

NTT is one of the largest companies in the world and has a work-force of 266,000 (1990), which is slowly decreasing, and is expected to be down to 230,000 by 1995. Total income in 1990 amounts to Y5,796 billion (March 1990 estimate) and ranks in the telecommunications industry second in size to AT&T in the USA. Its income is mainly generated through its telephone services – 82 per cent – with another 6 per cent for leased circuit services. Its telephone network consists of 51 million lines which are used for telephone, fax and data, and 6,700 ISDN (Integrated Services Digital Network) lines (March 1990).

NTT is among the five largest spenders on R&D development in Japan – after Hitachi Ltd, Toyota Motor, NEC, and Fujitsu. NTT plans to allocate Y260 billion to research and development in 1990 which is an increase of 9 per cent over the preceding year (*Nihon Keizai Shinbun*, July 2, 1990).

About 40 per cent of the total research budget is allocated to the Centre of Network Systems and the Centre of Software Engineering and development sections in business units. See Figure 10.4 on R&D organisation. The total staff of research organisations is 7,300 of which 3,000 are researchers in the NTT laboratories and the remainder engineers in the development organisations.

Figure 10.4 R&D organisation at NTT

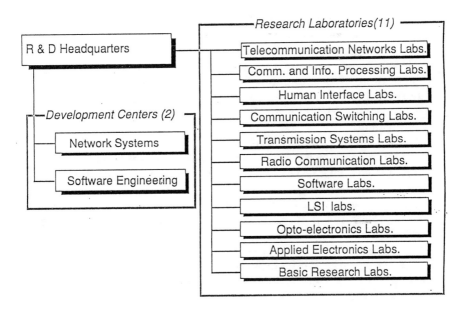

Source: NTT brochure

The research activities of NTT have in the past served two different functions, one of which is embedded in the development of new services and support of existing ones. In the other function NTT research was to a large extent oriented toward raising the technological level of the Japanese telecommunication industry including four major suppliers of telecommunications equipment – NEC, Fujitsu, Hitachi Ltd. and Oki Electric – a task which has been successfully accomplished.

The latter task is no longer relevant and the situation for NTT research activities has shifted in three major ways. First, the Japanese telecommunication equipment companies have become increasingly competent and maintain large and independent research facilities which are generally on a par with NTT. Second, the demands from foreign makers and governments has created a situation of a more open competitive market in which NTT is one among several actors. Third, the privatisation of NTT in 1985 signified a new situation in which other companies can compete in the telecommunications market by providing cheaper, alternative or new services. Thus, the R&D resources of NTT are in a narrow sense no longer a national capital but instrumental assets for the future of NTT itself. In the new situation it may be expected that the R&D facilities will increasingly be reoriented towards providing the underpinning for a rapid development of new services and the required network facilities.

The main competitors are Daini-Denden Inc. (DDI), Japan Telecom and Teleway Japan Corporation. Their share of total telecommunications services in Japan can be estimated at 3 per cent.

R&D organisation at NTT

The present research laboratories have expanded from the Electrical Communication Laboratory, located in Musashino in the western part of Tokyo. This laboratory came into existence after dividing an earlier government laboratory with the other half remaining as the Electrotechnical Laboratory (ETL) at the time of forming the present Ministry of International Trade and Industry (MITI) in May 1948. A new laboratory specialising in basic research on material and components was set up in Ibaraki in 1960 to be followed by a complete reorganisation of the R&D structure in 1971. In 1973 one more laboratory for information processing, and cable and radio communication systems was added, with a final addition in 1983 of a laboratory specialising in VLSI, nano-technology and opto-electronics. The privatisation of NTT, in 1985, had far-reaching consequences for the R&D structure at NTT.

A major reorganisation was implemented in 1987 partly based on recommendations contained in a study on research management carried out by the US consulting company McKinsey and Co. The change included the following main shifts. First, the various research stations within the four physical laboratories were reorganised into eleven research laboratories in order to strengthen both basic research and development capabilities. See Figure 10.5 on NTT research organisation. Second, each business division has its own R&D team so that it can directly and efficiently relate both to the changing R&D scene and the changing competitive situation for services and equipment. Third, the R&D functions that support work-site operations were strengthened. Fourth, two development centres – Network Systems and Software Engineering – were established.

The changes meant that that the R&D activities became much more closely integrated with the business activities of NTT and that the earlier close relations with Japanese makers of telecommunications equipment became much looser and no longer preferential to the exclusion of foreign suppliers.

Another important structural change is the increasingly important role given to in-house software development which is exemplified by the creation of the

Figure 10.5 R&D mechanism in NTT

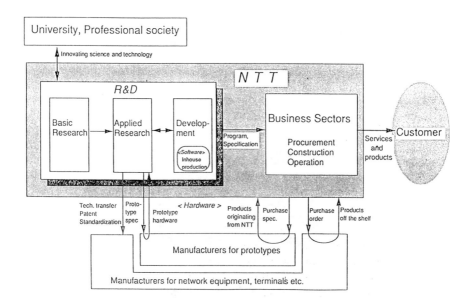

Source: NTT 1990

Centre for Software Engineering. The growing attention to software development inside NTT is a consequence of a growing need to develop operation software systems for the increasingly complex transport networks and management systems for developing high level application software in order to be able to offer high-quality services.

The new organisation has meant that the R&D projects are more carefully planned, executed and monitored. Similar to the planning in many other companies, as exemplified by Hitachi, NTT flexibly allocates R&D funds and researchers to what are termed important tasks.

NTT laboratories
The various laboratories are briefly described below, according to information in Nikkei Communication. See also Figure 10.6.

Telecommunication Networks Laboratories
The total staff is 200 and the main task of the laboratories is to investigate advanced network technologies. This includes research on network operations, network architecture, telecommunication quality and private communication systems.

Communications and Information Processing Laboratories
The total staff is 500 and the main task is to investigate information processing technologies for intelligent communications. This includes research on

Figure 10.6 Laboratories and development centres at NTT

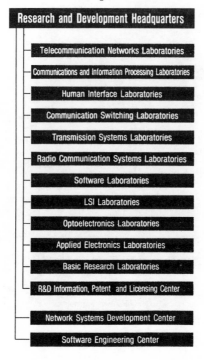

Source: NTT 1990

communication and information systems for new services, message processing systems, information systems such as Multi-vendor Integration Architecture (MIA), Knowledge Base Management System (KMBS), and advanced information processing systems.

Human Interface Laboratories
The staff is 250 and the main task is to investigate human interface technologies for research on visual and intelligent communications services. This includes research on human and communications systems, visual communication systems, visual perception technologies, speech recognition and synthesis technologies, autonomous robot systems.

Communication Switching Laboratories
The staff is 250 and the main task is to investigate advanced communication switching systems. This includes research on transport network systems such as Asynchrous Transfer Mode (ATM), transport switching software technologies, intelligent network systems, and photonic switching system technologies.

Transmission Systems Laboratories
The staff is 200 and the main task is to investigate optical fibre transmission systems. This includes research on coherent optical transmission systems, optical subscriber loops, optical fibre cables, high speed MODEMs, cross-connect systems, and high speed digital signal processing technologies.

Radio Communication Systems Laboratories
The staff is 200 and the main task is to investigate advanced radio communication systems. This includes research on personal communication systems using very small portable telephones, mobile communication systems, satellite communication systems, and monolithic microwave integrated circuits (MMICs)

Software Laboratories
The staff is 150 and the main task is to investigate advanced software technologies for improving software quality and productivity. This includes research on software production support tools such as Software Design Automation (SoftDA) and Software Production and Circulation Environment (SPACE), and software fundamental technologies.

LSI Laboratories
The staff is 400 and the main task is to investigate advanced LSI technologies for high performance communication systems. This includes research on computer aided design (CAD) systems for application specific integrated circuits (ASICs), integrated circuit technologies, LSI manufacturing systems such as synchrotron orbital radiation (SOR) lithography, super-large scale integrated circuits (SLSI) fabrication technologies, ultra-high speed GaAs ICs, and quantum effect electronic devices.

Opto-electronics Laboratories
The staff is 200, the main task is to investigate opto-electronic devices and materials for advanced communication transmission and switching systems. This includes research on semiconductor laser sources, photodetectors, opto-electronic integrated circuits (OEICs), photonic functional devices for switching systems and computers, planer light wave circuits, and photonic materials.

Applied Electronics Materials
The staff is 300 and the main task is to investigate advanced energy and opto-mechatronics technologies, This includes research on telecommunications energy systems such as very small batteries, visual I/O devices such as large liquid crystal display devices, high performance optical disk memories, and material characterisation technologies.

Basic Research Laboratories
The staff is 150 and the main task is to play a leading role in the global science and engineering community. This includes research on communication, physical science such as quantum optical communication, physical science such as quantum effects in mesoscopic size semiconductors, and material science such as Tc superconductors.

The LSI laboratories and part of the Opto-Electronics Laboratories are located in the Atsugi research facilities which were inaugurated in 1983. Total staff in this location is 500 of which 400 are engaged in the LSI field. The research areas include ultra-large scale integrated circuits, post-silicon devices and molecular electronics, all of which could also be termed nano-electronics. The most important research areas are: thin-film materials, techniques for growing such films, self-aligned technologies, device isolation technologies, and methods for perfectly planerizing entire chip surfaces. Through experimental fabrication of large scale ICs the various technologies are tested and verified.

The Atsugi Centre is also pursuing superfine processing in a number of research projects: synchrotron orbital radiation (SOR) lithography, electron-beam direct writing methods for transferring computer-designed patterns directly to a silicon wafer; methods of growing superior-quality thin films using plasma; and patterning methods using new photo-sensitive materials and methods. The Centre is also doing research on Optical Semiconductor Technology and a range of devices are studied. These include semiconductor laser sources, photodetectors, opto-electronic circuits (OEIC) that integrate optical and high-speed electronic elements, and devices that offer new functionality by exploiting the quantum effect.

Research co-operation

NTT has in the past co-operated closely with the private sector in developing advanced telecommunication technology. This is still done because NTT has no manufacturing facilities for network products. However, the procedure to invite makers for joint development has now become fully open. The approach is that NTT publicly announces specifications for a certain device, equipment or system and asks for tenders for the development to be carried out.

NTT does not participate in any national joint research projects which are directly sponsored by MITI, the Science and Technology Agency (STA) and the Ministry of Education. However, NTT maintains many direct university contacts with both domestic and foreign universities. NTT is also an active member in a number of the R&D companies which have been established with capital investment from the Japan Key Technology Centre (JKTC). NTT has sent 40 of its staff (Summer 1990) to the four laboratories of the Advanced Telecommunications Research Institute (ATR), discussed in Chapter 9. In fact, JKTC owes its existence to the privatisation of NTT which provided the opportunity to set aside capital for the new organisation coming from the sale of NTT shares. The Advanced Telecommunications Research Institute (ATR) with its four integral laboratories is highly significant for NTT as aural and visual recognition research, at ATR, is very relevant for the future development of NTT services.

Future of telecommunications and the role of research at NTT

The Atsugi Centre is one of the major research laboratories on VLSI and opto-electronic technology in Japan and remains in the forefront. The justification for the substantial research efforts, NTT staff explain, lies in the advantage that the company has an advance knowledge of possibilities for designing and developing systems and services. Another important factor is that NTT also wants to accelerate technology by providing NTT technological solutions and designs, which requires very advanced knowledge and preceding research. On a minor scale NTT is also involved in the manufacture of VLSI which is organised within a subsidiary – NTT Electronics (NEL) – at Atsugi. Whether justified or not it should be noted that NTT at its Atsugi Centre is in the frontline of developing compact SOR machines which are expected to replace optical lithography printing chip wafers after the mid-1990s.

The justification for the research efforts can be better understood when looking at the expected developments within the telecommunication services which has three major constituents. First, the services will be increasingly portable as exemplified by mobile/car telephony and personal pagers, integration of various services like data and voice and increasing demands for user-friendliness. Second, the telecommunications systems will change as optical transmission will become more prevalent, as terminals become increasingly complex and intelligent and as the control and management systems become more intricate. Third, all development will be based on systems using devices which must be semiconductors with constantly increasing levels of integration, consuming little power and operating at high speed.

Figure 10.7 Digitisation and expansion of high-speed network in Japan

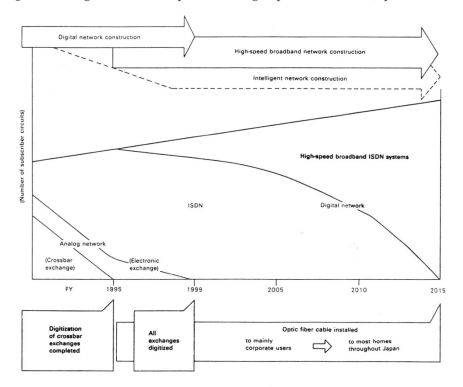

Source: NTT 1990

These developments are further strengthened by the forecasts that Japan, will by the year 2005 have 70 million telephone subscribers of which 20 million will be ISDN subscribers. Japan may have as many as 5 million videophones, telecommunications companies may be in the position to offer three-dimensional-screen video communications, and also translation services may also be available over the normal telephone system. These services will require major changes in the telecommunication systems and NTT expects that high speed broadband connections will be available to 30 per cent of all subscribers by 2005 and a complete coverage achieved by 2015. See Figure 10.7. According to present plans all electromechanical exchanges will be replaced by 1995 and the Japanese telephone system fully digitialized by 1999.

Chapter 11

Energy

No other advanced industrialised country is so dependent on imported energy as is Japan. During the past two decades Japan produced only about 10 per cent of its primary energy supplies and relied on imports for the remaining 90 per cent. Oil, which is by the far the most important source of energy, is almost completely imported with less than 1 per cent produced domestically. The major domestic sources of energy are hydraulic power, coal, some natural gas and geothermal power. In order to reduce its dependence on oil Japan has made major efforts to develop alternative means to secure the country's energy requirements. Such efforts have naturally been intensified after the two oil shocks in 1973 and 1979.

Today Japan has R&D programmes in all energy fields which include the development of fossil energy, natural energy, nuclear energy and energy conservation. At present more than 50 per cent of all energy R&D expenditure goes to the nuclear sector, a situation which has prevailed for a long period of time. Nuclear energy has in the past appeared to promise an almost unlimited supply of energy which would provide Japan with the underpinning which could secure long-term prosperous development.

With virtually no other major energy options nuclear energy has been embraced as a national credo and given the highest priority in the search for alternatives to oil. However, the high expectations have diminished as safety and proliferation concerns have become acute. So the role of nuclear energy has in Japan, as in most other industrial nations, become a central public issue. Polls in the late 1980s indicate that the public majority support for nuclear energy has vanished.

Conservation has been also been given dominant attention and constitutes one of the pillars of Japan's energy policy. However, the potential for savings are lower than in many other industrialised countries as the per capita energy consumption is relatively low. Very considerable energy savings have already been accomplished in most industrial sectors. It is obvious from these introductory remarks that no single alternative will provide an answer to the problem of reducing the dependence on oil imports. Thus, Japan will have to to pursue a comprehensive alternative energy policy and nuclear power development remains a very important element – although its future is being increasingly questioned.

This chapter will mainly discuss the nuclear energy research which dominates to be followed by two major government programmes – Sunshine to enhance energy resources, and Moonlight to conserve energy – before finally providing information on some additional research activities in oil exploration and sundry other energy areas.

Nuclear energy development

The research and development on nuclear energy in 1988 received Y450 billion of which the government paid Y354 billion for its nuclear research institutes/corporations, the private industry paid Y73 billion, mainly for nuclear plant technology and the remainder was spent at the universities.

The installed nuclear capacity in June 1989 amounted to 29,280 MW which corresponds to 17 per cent of the installed electricity-generating capacity. In meeting the actual demand for electricity the present 37 nuclear facilities provide 27 per cent. An additional thirteen plants are under construction which will add another 13,000 million kW when commissioned. Preparations are also being made for the construction of three additional nuclear power stations which would give Japan a total installed capacity of 45,900 MW.

All the Japanese commercial reactors have, so far, been of the light water type, except the first one which is the gas-cooled type imported from the United Kingdom. Boiling water reactors have proved the most popular, contrary to the world trend to give first place to pressurised water reactors – although the utility companies are now more intent on diversifying their reactor types. All reactors except the first have been built by Japanese companies which include Hitachi, Toshiba, Mitsubishi Heavy Industries and Ishikawajima-Harima Heavy Industries.

The faith in nuclear power has its roots partly in the discovery that nuclear power can be generated more cheaply than by using imported oil or coal. With construction costs rising the electric utility companies are finding that nuclear power is less favourably priced. Another discouraging factor is that they are finding the construction of new nuclear energy facilities problematic as public protests about them rise.

Long term plan

The research and development for utilisation of nuclear energy follows the "Long Term Programme for Development and Utilisation of Nuclear Energy" which was set by the Atomic Energy Commission in mid-1982, and revised in June 1987. The programme contains five major approaches:

1. strengthening of nuclear safety measures;

2. establishment of an independent nuclear fuel cycle;

3. development of new types of nuclear reactors;

4. research and development on nuclear fusion; and

5. facilitating the siting of nuclear energy installations.

The programme states that light water reactors are to continue to be built and are expected to provide 30 per cent of generating capacity by the year 2000. Attempts will be made to participate in overseas uranium development projects, to promote domestic uranium enrichment, stockpile nuclear fuels and develop domestic reprocessing facilities. Plutonium obtained by reprocessing will be used by the fast breeder reactors which will come into commercial use from about 2010. While research is still going on into the commercialisation of fast breeders, plutonium will be used as fuel for thermal neutron reactors (heavy water reactors). For this purpose, research on advanced thermal reactors will be carried out with the aim of incorporating them into power generation systems. At the same time, efforts will be made to use plutonium in light water reactors.

The Power Reactor and Nuclear Fuel Development Corporation (PNC) and other key actors argue that in order to realise the full potential of nuclear power, it is essential to utilise plutonium and establish a balanced fuel cycle. To utilise plutonium as an energy source, Japan is pursuing a basic strategy of shifting from light water reactors (LWR) to fast breeder reactors (FBR).

Increasing attention has been given to safety research on new types of reactors such as light water reactors and fast breeder reactors as well as into nuclear fuel cycle facilities like reprocessing plants. This work is mainly carried out by the Japan Atomic Energy Research Institute (JAERI) and the Power Reactor and Nuclear Fuel Development Corporation.

The fuel cycle

As nuclear power generation in Japan has entered the stage of large-scale commercial use it has become essential to establish a nuclear fuel cycle consisting of a secure source of natural uranium, uranium enrichment, reprocessing, treatment and disposal of radioactive waste. Japan has to rely upon foreign countries for uranium supply. PNC has been prospecting and exploring uranium deposits in Canada, Australia, Africa and China. PNC is also operating the Pilot and Demonstration Plant for Uranium Enrichment, with 7,000 centrifuges, at the Ningyo-Toge Works, started in 1981. The private sector plans to construct a commercial plant, and several research projects are underway to explore laser enrichment technology.

PNC has a key role in the development of a wide range of plutonium utilisation technologies. This involves carrying out extensive R&D programmes in various stages of a complete fuel cycle: reprocessing light-water-reactor (LWR) spent fuels; co-conversion of uranium-plutonium mixed oxide (MOX) and fabrication of MOX fuel; development of the fast breeder reactor (FBR) and the advanced thermal reactor (ATR); and reprocessing of FBR spent fuel. PNC also has a leading role in R&D on uranium exploration, uranium enrichment and treatment and disposal of high-level radioactive waste.

PNC is also active in developing reprocessing technology installed a Chop-Leach Head-Enf and Purex Process facility at the processing plant of the Tokai Works. The plant is designed to produce uranium trioxide powder and plutonium nitrate solution as its final products, from spent fuels from light water reactors. The construction of the facility started in 1974 and it began operating in 1981. PNC is also giving support to the plans of the private sector to build a commercial reprocessing plant.

PNC has also, at its Tokai Works, started development of plutonium fuel fabrication technology as well as fuel assemblies for the heavy water reactor – Fugen – although fuel has so far been imported. The original nuclear energy approach in Japan envisaged a closed-fuel-cycle in which plutonium generated by the first nuclear energy reactors would feed a following generation of fast reactors which have the ability to "breed" more plutonium than they consumed. The expected consequence was that nuclear-based power generation would lessen its dependence on the limited resources of uranium. However, less costly and more easily available uranium has for the time being eroded the basis for such a vision as fast reactors have proven very costly to build. Thus the need for reprocessing plutonium has lost much of its urgency although Japan is committed to reprocessing at Sellafield in the UK and La Hague in France.

PNC is developing methods both for sea-dumping and land-based disposal. Japan expects that it will be possible to obtain approval from parties both inside and outside the country for sea-dumping disposal of low-level radioactive waste. PNC is doing research on the vitrification of high-level radioactive waste and finding relevant methods for geological disposal. Temporarily PNC is developing a Storage Engineering Centre where high-level radioactive waste will be stored and where research will be carried out to find the best geological disposal techniques in deep underground foundations.

Reactor development

PNC is the central organisation for development work on new reactors and is simultaneously carrying out research on several different reactor types: advanced thermal reactors using heavy water, and fast breeder reactors. JAERI is responsible for the development of very high-temperature helium-cooled reactors – and fusion reactors, to be discussed further on.

The fast breeder reactor programme is far the most ambitious national project that Japan has undertaken. The project is an attempt at a very big step forward into new technology, particularly as the need for fast breeders is being more and more questioned outside Japan and national schemes in other countries are being delayed or even abandoned. A first experimental fast breeder reactor, Joyo, reached criticality in April 1977 and has been operating with a thermal power of 100,000 kW since July 1983. It is a sodium-cooled, loop-type reactor using plutonium oxide-uranium oxide fuel and has during the 1980s been used to provide technical data for the prototype fast breeder reactor Monju, which is a medium-scale reactor. These have included irradiation tests of fuel and materials, test of decay heat dissipation by natural circulation in the event of a total power failure and various types of failure simulations.

The advanced thermal reactor (ATR), using heavy water, is ahead of the fast breeders in its development and was originally intended to fill the gap between the closure of some of the light water reactors currently in use and the start up of the fast breeder reactors to be constructed early in the next century. Despite such plans, it seems likely that the heavy water reactor will not be ready early enough to be useful in the transition period to fast breeders. The project has not been abandoned, however, for the following three reasons. First, there may be unforeseen delays in the fast breeder programmes. Second, it may pay a dividend to build and operate a variety of reactors. Third, the heavy water reactor can make effective use of different fuels.

Fugen, an advanced thermal reactor (ATR) developed exclusively in Japan, can use both uranium and plutonium fuel and has been a vital link in the development of new uranium-plutonium mixed oxide (MOX) fuel. Thus ATRs can also help utilise stockpiles of plutonium from spent LWR fuel that will accumulate in the years before commercial FBRs are operating in Japan. After having provided valuable experience the ultimate goal of the Fugen ATR is to shift from research to commercial application. The Electric Power

Development Co. has in co-operation designed a 600 MW demonstration ATR for which the construction, in Northern Japan, will start in 1993 and is expected to be in operation by 1999.

The design of Monju is basically the same as that of Joyo although its thermal output has increased seven-fold and it has a different steam generating system. Monju differs in its technical designs from other FBRs being built abroad. One special concern for Japanese reactor plants is earthquakes, so Monju has been designed to withstand an earthquake three times as powerful as the strongest that has ever hit Japan. The reactor building, which houses the reactor containment vessel, internal structures and shielding, is supported by the reactor auxiliary building, which stands on bedrock and accommodates expansion of components during operation whilst also absorbing earthquake shocks.

The construction of Monju, located on the Japan Sea coast, was started in 1985. The reactors' criticality is scheduled for 1992 and will then, it is officially expected, serve as the stepping stone for future commercial reactors.

Research on a novel type of reactor being carried out by the Japan Atomic Energy Research Institute (JAERI). The very high-temperature gas-cooled reactor (HTGR) is designed to use the heat generated in the reactor process as a direct source for a number of temperature for the reduction of steel – a MITI national project – for the production of hydrogen by thermochemical water splitting, for coal gasification and for the generation of electricity by a helium gas turbine, and several other possible uses.

A design for a high temperature engineering test reactor (HTTR) with capacity of 30 MW and an outlet gas temperature of 900°C has been thoroughly revised in the late 1980s and will serve as basis for a first reactor. The role of the HTTR is to establish a technological base and upgrade the technology. According to original plans it was expected to have been completed by 1994 and make a major contribution to the development of nuclear power applications.

Fusion research

Nuclear fusion has its centre of research and development activities in Japan Atomic Energy Research Institute (JAERI), aside from important activities carried out in several of the national universities. National fusion development has in Japan been carried out as a national project. A major object of the programme is to achieve a break-even plasma condition by a large tokamak device – the JT-60 – which started its operation in April 1985 and reached its first target in September 1987. Since then experiments have been carried out to develop higher plasma core performance.

Great faith is expressed in Japan in nuclear fusion as the energy source of the future, and the Japanese believe they will be the first to produce a commercial reactor. Since 1968, when nuclear fusion research was made a special national research project, JAERI has been carrying out plasma research. Its main experimental contrivance JFT-2 has allowed detailed studies of plasma confinement and heating techniques in the tokamak configuration. The JT-60 programme was begun in 1975 with the objective of achieving the breakeven condition, which is the important barrier where the system supplies as much heat as it consumes.

To achieve the breakeven temperature of 100 million degrees, both neutral ion beam and radio frequency heating are being used. High-speed hydrogen atom beams are fired into the plasma from fourteen injector units which provide a total of 20 megawatts, and are being supplemented by another 30 megawatts of radio frequency heating. For the development of reactor core plasmas JAERI is also carrying out plasma experiments with the modified JFT-2M and Doublet III, the latter under a US-Japan joint research programme.

Alongside such development the design work for the next stage experimental fusion reactor has been made with the objective of realising a self-ignited, long-burning DT plasma, and developing new reactor technologies – the fusion experimental reactor (FER). The FER may be completed in the first years of next century, to be followed by Demonstration Fusion Reactor (DEMO) which could possibly enter into operation around 2015 – according to present plans.

JAERI is also participating in the conceptual design of the International Thermonuclear Fusion Reactor (ITER) with EC, USA and USSR under the auspices of the IAEA. Eventually, large-scale international co-operation between the countries concerned may in fact overcome some of the difficult engineering problems which still remain unresolved.

In order to facilitate the siting of nuclear power installations, public facilities required for the welfare of residents in areas adjacent to nuclear power stations are established. Public education activities are being carried out in order to gain the understanding and co-operation of the people with regard to the use and development of nuclear power.

Budget and major research institutes

The nuclear energy research activities described above are in the main carried out by two main research institutes: the Power Reactor and Nuclear Fuel Development Corporation (PNC) and the Japan Atomic Energy Research Institute (JAERI).

PNC in 1989 had a budget of Y230 billion and a staff of slightly above 3,000. It was established in 1967 with the objective of developing, on its own, fast breeder and heavy water reactors and the technologies for a complete fuel cycle. PNC maintains plants and research laboratories at a number of different locations. Apart from the reactors mentioned above, the institute also operates a centrifugal uranium enrichment plant, a plutonium-uranium re-conversion plant, a fuel fabrication plant, and a waste vitrification plant. PNC is also directly involved in uranium exploration aboard while ore milling and conversion plants are operated in Japan.

JAERI in 1988 had a budget of Y107 billion and a total staff of around 2,500. The institute was established in 1956 to promote the research, development and peaceful use of atomic energy in Japan and is now responsible for a wide range of activities from environmental safety to nuclear fusion. JAERI has most of its activities in three major locations. One is the so-called "nuclear village" at Tokai-murai in Ibaraki prefecture which houses the traditional research reactors as well as experimental facilities for research on nuclear fusion. The second is the Radiation Chemistry Research Laboratory at Takasaki in Gunma prefecture. The third large establishment is the Engineering Research Centre at O-arai, Ibaraki prefecture, where irradiation tests of reactors materials and fuels are carried out. The Plutonium Fuel Research Laboratory at this centre is developing new fuels for fast breeder reactors.

The main R&D activities at JAERI are the very high-temperature gas-cooled reactor and the JT-60 fusion project. Other activities include reactor and environmental safety. JAERI conducts simulation tests on loss-of-coolant accidents in light water reactors, the safety and integrity of reactor fuels and reactor boundaries, to mention some of the research topics. Fundamental research on a wide range of topics relevant to, and supportive of, the development of nuclear reactors is also carried out. Such studies include reactor physics, reactor engineering, irradiation research on fuels and materials, compilation and analysis of nuclear data, physical properties and reactor chemistry.

Mutsu – the nuclear ship

The Japan Nuclear Ship Research and Development Agency was created in 1973 as a government-funded special organisation and merged with JAERI in March 1985. Its main purpose was to carry out research and development necessary for the use of nuclear energy in ships. The nuclear ship *Mutsu*, the main project of this agency, started construction in 1967 and was launched in 1969, and a pressurised water reactor installed in 1972 in the home port of Mutsu City in Aomori in 1972.

While commercial nuclear ship projects have been abandoned in other countries *Mutsu* is still officially proclaimed as a project of importance to the national policy. It is Japan's only nuclear-powered vessel and has a light-water reactor with a nominal capacity of 36,000 kW and an expected speed of 16.5 knots.

The major contribution of *Mutsu* has been to stimulate the anti-nuclear protest movement in Japan. Already in 1972, local protest groups in Mutsu City feared that radioactive leakage could damage local scallop fisheries prevented early sea trials. Only after massive compensation in the event of an accident had been promised and a timely typhoon dispersed a local fishermen's blockade did the *Mutsu* finally set sail in August 1974. Almost as soon as the reactor was brought to criticality, however, a gamma ray radiation leakage was discovered.

The announcement of the reactor leakage enraged protesters and only after lengthy negotiations was the ship allowed to return to Mutsu City – on condition that it left within six months and all nuclear installations were removed from Mutsu City. Shielding repair work was subsequently carried out in another place, Sasebo Harbour, and the project stalled for more than a decade. *Mutsu* has port facilities in Sekinehama and the project was again revived in the fiscal year 1987 when inspection of fuel and equipment of the reactor began. Reactor and other testing was carried out in the late 1980s and *Mutsu* again set sail in July 1990 to begin nuclear-powered sailing tests for the first time since the ship was built more than 20 years ago – only to meet with a series of new problems.

To pacify the protesters the *Mutsu* was powered by a spare boiler and will only start its reactors when it is in the Pacific Ocean – far from its home port. After return it may be sent on a year-long experimental voyage to the South Pacific – before retiring permanently. So far the Mutsu project has expended more than Y100 billion which includes some Y13 billion for repairs after the reactor accident.

Nuclear energy research at universities

The universities are involved in nuclear research in a major way and information is given below for some of the important university institutes. Almost all university nuclear research is located at national universities and with a heavy concentration of activities in the Kansai region.

The Institute of Atomic Energy at Kyoto University covers a wide variety of fields in nuclear science and engineering and is also responsible for the teaching of nuclear engineering in the Faculty of Engineering and the Graduate School of Engineering. Research is carried out in nuclear reactor engineering, magnetohydrodynamic (MHD) electric power generation, nuclear reactor materials and solid-state physics, plasma physics associated with nuclear fusion engineering and reactor accident analysis. The institute is collaborating with Department of Nuclear Engineering of Kobe University of Mercantile Marine where a pulsed high-current light-ion beam has been built.

The Plasma Physics Laboratory at Kyoto University is the main institute for nuclear fusion for fusion research at Kyoto University and makes a major contribution to the national efforts in this area. The laboratory runs a heliotron project and has designed and built a series of devices. The heliotron, also known as the torsatron, is one of the five main plasma-confining field approaches being tried out in Japan.

The Research Reactor Institute at the University of Kyoto was established in 1963 and its main installation is a light water moderated tank-type reactor of 5,500 kW which reached criticality in 1967. Facilities include a 46 MeV electron linear accelerator. The demands from the scientific community to have a high flux reactor will be realised at Kyoto University. The reactor will have a thermal power of 30 MW and provide greater opportunities for neutron beam experiments among other things. The institute is an Inter-University Research Centre.

The Institute of Laser Engineering at Osaka University was established in 1972 for research on high power lasers and expanded in 1976 to become the centre in Japan for research in laser fusion. The institute carries out research on a radically different approach to nuclear fusion – the "Kongoh Project" – which aims at achieving breakeven condition in inertial confinement fusion. Instead of the conventional approach of confining a plasma by an intense magnetic field and then heating it until fusion begins to produce energy, a tiny pellet of tritium is bombarded with laser beams. Related to this approach, the institute is carrying out research on high-power lasers, tritium pellet target design and fabrication, and the development of new approaches for diagnosing fusion plasma.

From the foundation of the institute, basic research on the laser-plasma experiment has been performed with the glass lasers Gekko II, Gekko IV and Gekko MII, magnifying the scale of laser systems. In March 1983 the twelve beam laser system, Gekko XII, which is the world's largest – was completed and an advanced implosion experiment started. Experimental data such as a plasma temperature of 100 million degrees, a compressed core density 50 times solid density and a fusion neutron yield of 1.25×10^{12}/shot are the highest in the world, and indicate the potential of achieving inertial confinement fusion. The institute is one of the most advanced in the world for the research of inertial confinement as well as laser technology. New fields related to laser technology such as X-ray laser, laser acceleration, free electron laser and X-ray lithography are also studied.

The Institute of Plasma Physics at Nagoya University is studying the confinement of plasma in four different configurations of fusion reactors which include three toroidal forms – tokamak/stellerator, a bumpy torus and reversed filed pinch – and also an "open bottle" system. The tokamak systems are essentially very similar and differ only in the pitch of spiralling magnetic field that surrounds the plasma and in how the pitch varies away from the centre of the plasma. Thus significant differences can be created in the time the plasma can be confined, its density and the efficiency of the magnetic field. The main areas of research at the Nagoya institute are basic research on plasma behaviour, vacuum and surface technology, strong magnetic fields, plasma electronics and high-temperature plasma diagnostics. In 1989, the status of the institute was changed to provide for joint use by all universities and renamed the National Institute for Fusion Science. Under construction at Toki, Gifu prefecture, is the world's largest helical fusion machine, designed on the basis of research carried out on the heliotron at Kyoto University. The machine will use superconducting magnets and begin operation around 1995.

The Research Laboratory of Nuclear Reactors at Tokyo Institute of Technology has a total staff of 55 (research staff 32). The laboratory, which was re-established in 1956, conducts research in nuclear science and technology related to nuclear fission and fusion reactors, and research includes activities in nuclear fuel and tritium chemistry. The main function of the laboratory is to provide laboratory training for graduate students.

The Plasma Research Centre at the University of Tsukuba was established in 1976, and was the first in the world to construct and operate a tandem mirror plasma confinement device – Gamma 6. A larger machine, Gamma 10, has been completed and is rivalling similar efforts in the USA. The tandem mirror design is an open-ended fusion device where magnetic field lines enter at one end of the plasma bottle and leave at the other. At each end of the bottle the field lines are constricted into a tight bundle by magnetic fields, to form "mirrors" and the charged plasma is forced to oscillate back and forth between the two end regions. Machines of this kind and those used in research at Nagoya (see above) indicate that the overall fusion programme in Japan is structured in such a way that options are kept open in order to identify the eventual best configuration for a fusion device.

The Research Institute for Atomic Energy at Osaka University carries out basic studies in theoretical physics, atomic energy and nuclear fusion. Osaka University is often judged to have the most important institute for nuclear research, a major reason being the creative and unique approaches in its Institute of Laser Engineering.

The University of Tokyo has a small fast neutron source reactor in the engineering research laboratory in the Faculty of Engineering.

Outside the group of national universities there are three universities which maintain small research reactors: Kinki University, Musashi Institute of Technology and Rikkyo University.

Nuclear energy development in industry

More than 150 companies are involved in Japan's atomic energy programme. Most of them are grouped around one of the five big suppliers: Mitsubishi Heavy Industries; Hitachi Limited; Toshiba Corporation (a group including Ishikawa-Harima Heavy Industries); Fuji Electric Company (including Kobe Steel and Kawasaki Heavy Industries); and Sumitomo Atomic Energy Industries Limited. Brief information for Hitachi will be given in order to illustrate the involvement of private industry.

In August 1987 the Fukushima Dai-Ni Nuclear Power Plant, belonging to Tokyo Electric Power Company put a fourth unit into commercial production. The latest addition consist of a Hitachi-built boiling water reactor (BWR) with an output of 1,100 MW. Construction of the unit was started in December 1980 and full loading was completed in October 1986, with a start-up test a couple of months later. The start of commercial operation had to be delayed for nineteen months because of a decrease in demand for electric energy.

The new unit features a number of improvements in comparison with the second unit of the same power complex, also designed and constructed by Hitachi on the same site. Aside from the overall changing requirements laid down by the government, a new central monitoring and control system with improved man/machine interface has been developed and introduced. The plant's reliability has been enhanced by adopting one-piece forged low-pressure turbine rotors. The radiation level in the reactor cooling water has been reduced by injecting iron into the feedwater, which has an effect on the behaviour in comparison with the earlier Hitachi reactor on the same site, in order to improve reliability and and improve the capacity.

Hitachi has, aside from modifying existing designs, in partnership with Toshiba Corporation and General Electric Co in the USA developed an advanced boiling water reactor (ABWR) which has a number of new features. The design has been simplified through the application of more compact systems. The reinforced reactor containment vessel is integrated into the reactor building itself, thereby significantly reducing the size. The unit has been built to withstand the thermal hydraulic dynamic loading conditions that would follow an accident involving the reactor. Water circulation can quickly respond to unintended changes in power demands during plant operation. New control systems can more flexibly and precisely control the reactor and also assure finely-tuned power response and fuel reliability.

Hitachi also supplies major components to the prototype fast breeder reactor Monju, and is also participating in a major way in the demonstration (ATR) project for advanced thermal reactor. The company provides project co-ordination for the joint group of five plant manufacturers and is carrying out basic plant design. Finally Hitachi is contributing to the conceptual designs studies and research programmes for a demonstration fast breeder reactor.

Hitachi has also been involved in a major way in fusion research and has built a number of experimental devices. In March 1988 Hitachi completed the construction of the Compact Helical System (CHS) which is installed at the Institute of Plasma Physics at Nagoya University.

Toshiba is another of the major actors in nuclear energy development and has been involved in the design and construction of boiling water reactors (BWR) for more than 20 years. The company is also engaged in the development of fast breeder reactors (FBR) and advanced BWR. Toshiba plays an important role in the Joyo FBR project as the principal manufacturer and is also responsible for the design and manufacture of key reactor components, secondary sodium loops and turbine/generators for the larger Monju FBR.

The Nuclear Energy Laboratory is the core of Toshiba's development activities in the field. Most projects are undertaken through co-operation with Toshiba's other laboratories and with those of other companies. With respect to light water reactor technology, the laboratories of Toshiba are working closely with the Isogo Engineering Centre in order to improve reliability, safety, efficiency and economy. In developing FBR, nuclear fuel cycle, and fusion, Toshiba is participating in a number of national projects – in collaboration with other companies.

Boosting and conserving energy – non-nuclear research programmes

In the 1970s – following the first oil crisis MITI established two large energy research programmes – Sunshine and Moonlight – which began in July 1974 and 1978 respectively. These programmes were in 1980 transferred to the New Energy Development Organisation (NEDO) which itself underwent a major reorganisation in 1988 by incorporating three other major research programmes which are supervised by MITI. The objective of using NEDO as an umbrella organisation is to foster closer and more flexible contacts with the private sector.

In 1982 MITI's Advisory Committee for Energy declared as a long-term goal that dependence on oil should be reduced to 49 per cent by 1990; and that the new energy services research in the Sunshine Project should provide 2 per cent of Japan's energy supply by 1990, and 7 per cent by 2000. Japan is still far from these goals but is undertaking major research programmes into both nuclear and non-nuclear energy. There is a growing belief, in certain quarters, that nuclear energy is not the answer for Japan's long-term energy balance. However, the Science and Technology Agency and the Atomic Energy Commission are pressing ahead with costly nuclear power research projects that may yield far less than is promised which may be true for the Monju fast breeder reactor and and the experimental plutonium-burning facility in Fukui. The energy-conservation critics argue that estimated Y700 billion to complete the Monju fast breeder reactor project might better go into the development of alternate energy sources.

Sunshine Programme

The Sunshine Programme was established in the fiscal year 1974 in order to improve Japan's energy balance through the development of new energy technologies. It can be seen as the first large-scale, long-term effort which deserves to be to be designated as a national project. It has as its object all aspects of new energy technology, with the exception of nuclear power technology. Major development targets have been set in four fields: solar energy, geothermal energy, gasification and liquefaction of coal, and hydrogen energy. Research and development encompasses the development of these resources, their transportation and storage and their use. In addition, research and developments have been begun on such subjects as wind and ocean energy.

The basic studies have in the main been completed and the projects have entered into the phase of plant development. The projects are now in the stage of developing large-scale test plants. This partly explains the creation of NEDO, in 1980, which plays the main role in constructing and operating the large scale test plants – to promote the development of the new energy technologies.

Development of solar energy technology

The activities include two different approaches: the development of photovoltaic power generation technology and the development of industrial and other solar thermal application systems.

At present, large-scale use of solar cells cannot be justified because the cost of manufacturing them is far too high, and major research efforts are thus aimed at finding new and less costly methods of mass production, although considerable cost reductions have already been achieved. The cost for 1 watt capacity was in the region of Y20-30,000 when the project started and is now down to Y800 (1990). In order to compete with coal it is necessary to come down to Y200 per installed watt.

Attempts are being made to save costs by recycling the process chemicals used in the manufacturing process for semiconductor solar cells and also by attempting more direct and less costly production methods. Improvements are also being sought for casting and splicing techniques and in a direct method of continuously growing a ribbon of silicon. One approach is the development of amorphous-crystalline stacked-structure solar cells to achieve almost as low cost as amorphous solar cells and higher stability.

The other major line is the development of industrial and other solar thermal application systems. This includes the construction of big solar collectors with panels able to deliver 200 kW or more. It also includes hybrid systems which combine the solar thermal systems with solar cells to maximise the use of solar energy.

Development of coal energy technology

This is, in terms of R&D budget, the major part of the Sunshine Programme and has been so throughout the 1980s. It comprises two major approaches – coal liquefaction and utilising coal for the production of hydrogen for use as automobile and aircraft fuel. In the first project technology is being developed for the liquefaction of bituminous coal and brown coal to produce liquid fuel to replace oil. Originally four different methods were being developed which included extractive coal and solvolysis coal liquefaction. At present direct liquefaction and brown coal liquefaction methods are pursued.

In direct hydroliquefaction coal is directly hydrogenated in the presence of an iron catalyst at high temperature and pressure and the process is achieved in a single step. A demonstration plant with a capacity for a few tons per day has been completed, and a pilot plant for bituminous coal liquefaction with a capacity of 150 tons per day – using the NEDOL process – was completed in 1987. Redesign of this plant will provide the basic design for another stage plant for which construction will be completed in 1994 after which testing will follow until 1997.

Brown coal liquefaction requires two successive stages of catalysed hydrogenation, the first at high temperature and high pressure, to produce light and heavy oils. The laboratory stage research is now being followed by construction and test operation of a pilot with a capacity of 50 tons per day – being built in Victoria in Australia, in co-operation with the Australian government.

Two methods are being tried to produce clean fuel gas from coal. In the hybrid gasification process coal and heavy oil are mixed in a slurry and gasified with oxygen and steam. In the hydro-gasification process products from hybrid gasification are hydro-gasified with hydrogen-rich gas to produce a fuel gas.

Development of geothermal energy
This part of the Sunshine Project includes two major components of which one is the development of technology for exploration and extraction of geothermal resources and the other development of the hydrothermal resources. The development of new technology for exploiting geothermal energy is being conducted in parallel with large-scale surveys to find the most promising areas for exploitation. Geothermal energy derives from three sources: shallow hot water and steam of volcanic origin; deep non-volcanic hot water and steam which is widespread but hard to exploit; and hot and dry rocks which are located at considerable depth.

A nationwide survey to identify new regions that might contain geothermal resources has been carried out by using satellite data and microwave imaging flight data to identify the promising structures. These explorations also include a search for crustal heat anomalies as magnetism disappears above 560°C, and regional gravity surveys which reveal changes in rock density. New exploration methods are being exploited through rock fracturing methods.

The utilisation of hot water is relatively easy although wider commercial application by having it distributed or converted into electricity is not easily achieved, considering the economic factors. The exploitation of hot dry rocks requires the digging of two deep holes, spaced apart, and the opening of cracks in the rocks by a controlled explosion or by hydraulic fracture. Water can then be pumped down one hole and will emerge in the other after being heated by its passage through the rocks.

Development of hydrogen energy technology
This project aims at manufacturing hydrogen by hydrolysis and developing technology for the storage and transport of hydrogen. Four main types of hydrogen production have been studied: water electrolysis, thermochemical processes, direct thermal decomposition of water and photochemical processes.

Hydrogen can, in the future, be obtained through electrolysis using excess electric power available during off-peak periods, and will thus provide an economical means of storing electric power. Research is being carried out on two types of electrolysis: the high-temperature, high-pressure process and the solid electrolyte process. The former can achieve a high conversion ratio while the latter requires more research on different cycle options.

Hydrogen might, once produced, be more easily stored in the form of metal hydrides such as that of magnesium, than in pressurised vessels. Research is under way on reversible hydride compounds to find systems which can easily store and release the hydrogen.

Other Sunshine projects

The programme also includes research on ocean thermal heat to utilise the temperature differential between surface water and the deep water beneath. Large-scale power generation systems using wind energy are also being researched. Other projects include research on fuel cells that can generate electricity directly by an electrochemical reaction and research on advanced battery systems which can be used to store electricity when demand is low and return it to the grid at times of peak demand.

Moonlight Programme

The Moonlight Programme began in 1978 and is designed to search for new practical energy conservation methods. It complements the Sunshine Programme which searches for new energy sources. The development of energy conservation technology requires, in particular, the development of new generating methods with higher energy efficiency, and the development of energy storage systems that allow full use to be made of existing generation facilities when demand is low.

The large-scale research and development projects within the Moonlight Programme generally invoke the co-operation of industry, national laboratories and universities. Subsidies are also provided for the development of energy conservation technologies.

A practical waste heat utilisation system to recover heat from factories and use it for room heating or cooling and for hot water supply systems has already been completed.

The programme includes or has included three projects to develop more efficient engines or turbines, as well as projects for a new battery power storage system, fuel cell power generating system, super-heat pump energy accumulation system and more recently a superconducting power utilisation technology.

Engine and turbine projects

The Stirling engine which relies on external heat and can use various types of fuel and also waste heat from industrial processes, is highly efficient, non-polluting and quiet. The object was to develop a Stirling engine for practical use in industrial air conditioners and in small electrical power generators. Development also covered improvement of components, including heat exchangers, etc. The project, which was completed in 1988, was partly carried out in collaboration with similar research projects in the USA (Department of Energy), the Netherlands (Philips), Germany (MAN) and Sweden (United Stirling Inc.)

The project on an advanced gas turbine was intended to produce a combine-cycle power plant of 100,000 kW in which a repeat gas turbine system with low emission will drive a steam turbine by means of an exhaust heat recovery boiler. The objective was to achieve an overall thermal efficiency of 50-55 per cent. This required ultra-high heat resistant material for combustor and turbine blades to allow the turbine to operate at very high temperatures. This project involved several of the institutes which belong to AIST and was organised as an Engineering Research Association. It is now being followed by a Ceramic Gas Turbine project which was started in 1988.

The favourite technique for levelling electricity loads has been the use of pumped hydroelectric plants. There are, however, difficulties in finding suitable sites near cities and one aim of the Moonlight Programme is to find alternative energy storage systems. Three approaches are being pursued – flywheels, superconductive coils, hydrogen generation and electric battery storage, of which the first were investigated on small scale. Battery storage was thought to offer the best option and a major project has been carried out during 1980-90 to develop varieties types of batteries with diverse capacities.

The Moonlight Programme also includes research on fuel cell power generation. Fuel cells are, in theory, very efficient energy conversion devices and it is expected that fuel cell systems could replace power stations in cities where a pollution-free system is desired. Research has been carried out on four types of fuel cells – phosphoric acid, alkaline, molten carbide and solid oxide. The first one was initially developed. The second offers the advantage of low operating temperature, although it is less advanced, and commercialisation is possible as soon as pure hydrogen is available. Molten carbonate fuel cells can only be developed at a later stage but offer high efficiency. Solid oxide fuel cells are still the subject of basic research.

Work on magnetohydrodynamic power generation has been carried out at the Electrotechnical Laboratory since 1966. In an MHD system a very hot ionized gas passes through a channel in which a strong magnetic field is produced by powerful magnets. The movement of the ionized gas induces an electric current in electrodes in the channel and a thermal efficiency of 50 per cent can be reached. The discovery of high-temperature superconductivity has over the past years triggered an enormous interest in all industrialised countries. Thus it is not surprising that the Moonlight Programme quickly incorporated major superconductivity power technology projects – in the fiscal year 1988.

Petroleum research and development

Research in petroleum exploration and recovery can be divided into three broad areas. First, there is research intended to help improve understanding of the formation of petroleum and thus more easily identify the areas in which it can be found. Second, new methods are being developed by using increasingly detailed and sophisticated data from satellites specialised to provide data for resource analysis. Third, new methods for enhancing the recovery of oil from wells are being developed and tested. Research and development are being carried out along all three avenues but should be considered in the light of the fact that Japan has so far been able to identify only very limited oil resources.

The most revolutionary project is a subsea oil production system, a national project sponsored by MITI which was formally completed in 1984. Finally research is also being carried out to improve several different petroleum refining processes.

Chapter 12

Space and aircraft

Japan is today one of the major nations in space research and space rockets although its activities are dwarfed by those of the USA and USSR. In rocketry the country was handicapped by having no military experience on which to draw. The attempts to develop military rockets towards the end of the war naturally came to a stop and scientific research was not resumed until 1954.

The space programme is today influenced by two major and partly conflicting objectives. First, the Japanese companies in electronics, comm-unications and heavy engineering realised at an early stage that space activities might provide interesting new markets. Second, the users of communications and resources satellites, also at an early stage, became very interested in utilising the new technologies – a natural outcome considering the need for good communications and access to natural resources on which the tiny island country is very dependent. The situation is in many ways similar for South Korea which – at a later stage and from a smaller national base – has also decided to embark on a major space programme.

The present ten-year plan announced in June 1989, states three basic objectives:

1. the advanced information and communications needs of a mature industrialised society require satellite systems;

2. a major nation like Japan must have an independent technological base in order to participate in major international projects; and

3. there is a need to encourage the private sector to fully participate in future space activities.

In 1990 Japan is building its own satellites and rockets, independently launching them into orbit, planning for major efforts in building a space station and carrying out a number of space research activities. These achievements have basically followed a strategy used with considerable success in many of its other industries; licensing of foreign technology to learn basics, followed by often co-operative efforts by its own companies to grow from that basis, improve on its former teachers and take off in new directions.

Organisation

The technological landscape for Japan's space activities is rather complex and requires a brief explanation. Basically three groups of actors are concerned. First, there is the Science and Technology Agency, with other closely related ministries like Posts and Telecommunications, and Transportation. STA is the main provider of funds, most of which go to the National Space Development Agency of Japan (NASDA), the executive organisation. See Figure 12.1. NASDA has responsibility for planning and procuring satellites, launching vehicles into space and tracking the satellites.

Figure 12.1 Organisation of space research and development activities in Japan

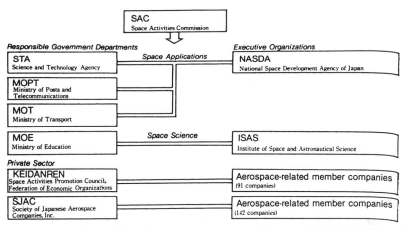

Source: National Space Development Agency of Japan (NASDA), Brochure 1989, p. 45

Second, the Ministry of Education plays an important role – mainly in scientific research – through its Institute of Space and Astronomical Science (ISAS) and its various funding programmes, although more modestly. ISAS has its own rocket range but depends on NASDA ground tracking stations to collect its satellite data. The present premier rocket used by NASDA, H-I, uses solid-fuel boosters for which the technology was developed by ISAS.

Third, there is a large number of private companies which are participating and supporting Japan's space activities with four main sub-groups – satellite companies, communications companies, rocket companies and fuel companies – together with a large number of other supporting companies. It is no exaggeration therefore to say that the space efforts are fully sustained by the industrial structure in Japan. The private companies are organised in one council under Keidanren and another organisation with a wider participation – the Society of Japan Aerospace Companies Inc.

Given the multitude of actors and their often conflicting interests it is natural that the Space Activities Commission (SAC) – the major policy organisation – eventually has to act as a referee.

Launching and tracking

In the early stage of development rockets were launched from the Takesaki Range in southern Kyushu where small rockets are still started. The nearby Tanegashima Space Centre is today the largest and most important launch site in Japan. The major tasks of the centre are to check, assemble and launch rockets, and to perform tracking after launch. The centre has two rocket launch complexes – the Osaki Range and the Yoshinobu (H-II) Launch Complex. The latter will be completed in 1992. Major facilities will include a building for assembling and checking launch vehicles, a mobile launcher to move and launch the vehicle, a pad service tower to make final check-out, etc.

NASDA maintains a number of tracking stations to control flight paths and collect data. See Figure 12.2 for names and locations. Furthermore, Tsukuba Space Centre (TSC) performs a major role as the nucleus of the space tracking and control network in Japan and has three functions. First, TSC processes satellite orbit data, obtained from the tracking stations, and provides calculations for determining and forecasting satellite orbits. Second, the centre evaluates the functions and performance of satellites and also provides control and command plans for satellite orbits. Such information is then passed to the relevant organisations. Third, TSC also does research on advanced tracking and control systems.

Figure 12.2 Location of major space activities in Japan

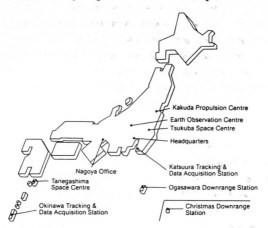

Source: "20 Years of Space Applications" in *Science and Technology in Japan,* October/December 1989, p. 23

Launch vehicles

Japan and its space agency, NASDA, have been developing and executing four launch vehicle programmes – since its first N-I launch vehicle in 1975. The N-I rockets had a gross weight of 90 tons and a payload of 130 kilograms. In the subsequent N-II series the payload was increased to 350 kilograms with a rocket weight of 135 tons. Altogether fifteen vehicles in the N series were launched before the programme was terminated in 1987. During the early phase of the the programme three satellites were also launched by NASA in the USA. See Figure 12.3.

The N-Series launch vehicles were replaced by the H-I rocket which was only slightly heavier but had an increased payload of 550 tons. The H-I vehicles are presently the workhorse of the Japanese space programme but are intended to be replaced by the H-II vehicles in 1992. However, several fires during engine tests for the H-II have delayed the programme and it is unlikely

Figure 12.3 Satellite developments programmes in Japan

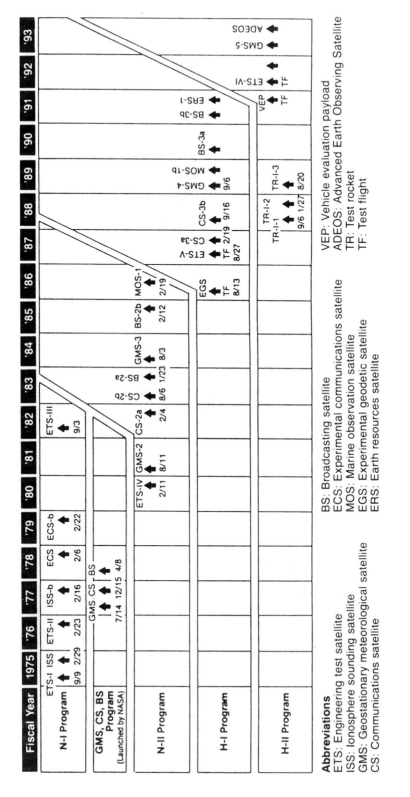

Abbreviations
ETS: Engineering test satellite
ISS: Ionosphere sounding satellite
GMS: Geostationary meteorological satellite
CS: Communications satellite

BS: Broadcasting satellite
ECS: Experimental communications satellite
MOS: Marine observation satellite
EGS: Experimental geodetic satellite
ERS: Earth resources satellite

VEP: Vehicle evaluation payload
ADEOS: Advanced Earth Observing Satellite
TR: Test rocket
TF: Test flight

Source: "20 Years of Space Applications" in *Science and Technology in Japan*, October/December 1989, p. 20

to be complete before 1993 at the earliest. The H-II has a gross weight of 256 tons and, after a recent redesign, will acept a payload of up to 2,000 kilograms, 200 kilograms less than announced earlier. All the payload figures relate to satellites placed in geostationary orbit (GEO).

The H-II vehicle compares favourably with the Ariane 4 which can lift the same payload into GEO. The Ariane 4 has a payload capacity of 8,000 kilograms for low earth orbit (LEO) which is also the same as H-II. However, the more recent Ariane 5 has a payload capacity of 4,000 kilograms for GEO and 15,000 kilograms for LEO. The corresponding figures for the US space shuttle are 2,400 and 29,500 kilograms respectively. The poorer performance of the H-II in comparison with Ariane 5 has caused some consternation in Japan – although the vehicle was redesigned to accommodate a considerably increased

Table 12.1 Characteristics of the H-II launch vehicle

Item		Dimension	Remarks
Total length		49 m	
Diameter		4 m	
Lift-off mass		260 t	
Payload Mass (GTO)		4 t	
	Propellant	LOX/LH	
	Propellant mass	85 t	
1st	Thrust	93 t	At sea level
stage	Burning duration	316 sec	
	Specific impulse	449 sec	In vacuum
	Total mass	97 t	
	Propellant	Composite	
Solid	Propellant mass	118 t	
rocket	Thrust	320 t	At sea level
booster	Burning duration	95 sec	
(x2)	Specific impulse	271 sec	In vacuum
	Total mass	140 t	
	Propellant	LOX/LH	
	Propellant mass	14 t	
2nd	Thrust	12 t	At sea level
stage	Burning duration	527 sec	Restart capability
	Specific impulse	452 sec	In vacuum
	Total mass	17 t	
Payload	Diameter	4.1 m	Payload envelope
Fairing	Length	12 m	3.7 mØ x 10 mL
	Guidance system		Strap-down inertial guidance

Source: "Hardware for the Coming Age – Rocket/Satellite Technologies" in *Science and Technology in Japan*, August/September 1988, p. 19

payload, to the present level. The main characteristics of the H-II vehicle are shown in Table 12.1.

Research on xenon ion engines for geostationary satellites provides an interesting insight on Japanese satellite research. It is important to be able to increase the weight of the payload and life expectancy of a geostationary satellite. One promising means is to use an ion engine instead of using small rockets which use chemical propellants to correct the position of the satellites. The ion engine generates thrust by accelerating and jetting propellant using electrical energy: it produces an extremely large force per unit of propellant and thus requires less fuel to be carried. Ion engines have no history of operational application and only Japan and the USA are carrying out tests in space. Japan's research on ion engines started around 1970. Tests with mercury propellant were carried out on the ETS-III satellite in 1982. The first operational system will be installed on the ETS-VI, to be launched in 1992.

The Institute of Space and Astronautical Science (ISAS) left the University of Tokyo in 1981 with the same status as a university and with all its facilities open to all other universities. Its early history in space research and its influence as the premier university in the country enable it to maintain an exceptional status in the field of space research. With the organisation of NASDA in 1966, the institute was allowed to develop rockets with a diameter of less than 1.4 metres. All its rockets had to be launched from the national space centre, and all research was to have an exclusive academic orientation.

The size restrictions, and budget constraints, have forced ISAS to become more innovative and it has developed a series of rockets, the latest of which, M-3SII, has a payload of 770 kilograms for a rocket weighing 61 tons. In upgrading its programme ISAS argues that it should be allowed to build the M-V, which would be similar to the H-I but less costly. A reason for the high cost of the NASDA rocket is that the liquid propellant is transferred from the USA, and it is also based on US licensed technology, although built in Japan. If successful ISAS would launch the first M-V satellite in the fiscal year 1994 which would be carrying the world's first satellite specifically designed for very long baseline interferometry (VLBI).

Scientific satellites

The Institute of Space and Astronautical Science (ISAS) has been developing the M-series of solid propellant rockets to launch scientific satellites – the last model being M-3SII. ISAS is planning to launch four more satellites in the early 1990s – EXOS-D, Muses-A, Solar-A and Astro-D. In addition, ISAS is scheduled to launch the Geotail in July 1992, using a Delta-class rocket from the USA.

EXOS-D will study the effect of solar wind on the earth's magnetosphere in the uppermost atmosphere above the polar regions. The satellite will observe and measure electric fields and plasma waves and capture auroras unfolding.

Muses-A, an engineering test satellite, was launched successfully in January 1990. The 182 kg satellite, renamed "Hiten" (Angel), was pulled out of Earth orbit in March by the gravity of the approaching Moon as planned, and then began a series of complicated loops around the Earth and Moon. As it swung by the Moon, it dropped a mini-satellite the size of a baseball into lunar orbit. Unfortunately, communication with the mini-satellite was lost but the success of the fuel-saving 'slingshot' approach using gravity assist to reach the Moon was proven. The same method will be used in future lunar and planetary probes, starting with the observation satellite Geotail.

The observation satellite Geotail will be launched in July 1992 as part of an international programme of joint research on solar wind and and the magnetosphere during the 1990s, involving the NASA in the USA, the European Space Agency and ISAS. The main objective of Geotail will be to examine the mechanism of accelerating ions and electrons in the tail of the magnetosphere.

Solar-A originally to be launched in the Summer of 1990 is designed to study high-energy phenomena involved in solar flares. To permit comprehensive observation, the satellite will be equipped with two telescopes, one for soft X-rays and one for hard ones, to take two-dimensional X-ray images at an an angle of a few seconds. The satellite will also carry a detector which can measure precisely over a wide range of wavelengths. The soft X-ray telescope is being manufactured jointly by Japan and the USA, and one of the X-ray spectrometers jointly by Japan and the UK.

X-ray astronomy has become as important as optical astronomy and radio astronomy as a means of explaining the mysteries of space. Japan assumed world leadership in the field with the launch of the first X-ray astronomical satellite, Hakucho, in 1979 followed by Tenma in 1983. A third X-ray satellite, Ginga, was launched in 1987. Astro-D, to be launched in February 1993 as the successor to Ginga, will have extremely sensitive detection capabilities and will be able to detect almost all quasars in our universe. When all these quasars have been identified it will be possible to measure correctly the true X-ray background radiation from beyond the quasars.

Commercial and other satellites

There are basically four different types of satellites, apart from those with military applications: engineering test satellites; communication and broad-casting satellites; and meteorological and earth observation satellites. Satellites consisting of a huge number of parts must be 100 per cent reliable and must withstand severe conditions such as vibration and shock at launch, and later on vacuum, radioactive radiation and thermal stress in space. Thus engineering test satellites are important to clear the way for the commercial ones. NASDA started its test series in 1975, the next one, ETS-VI, is planned for 1993. The purpose is to confirm launch vehicle performance and to establish basic technology for 2-ton geostationary three-axis satellite bus systems. The long-range purpose is to develop large-scale telecommunications satellites and to carry out technological development and experiments on advanced satellite communications.

Communications satellites act as international communication stations in space and are important for relaying television programmes and international telephone calls, although optical fibre lines in the ocean and on the continents may provide a serious challenge in the future. The Yuri BS-2 broadcasting satellite is today in operation to be followed by two BS-3 satellites to be launched in 1990 and 1991 respectively.

The CS Sakura satellites are communication satellites and a first experimental one was launched in 1977, another two in 1983 and still another two in 1988 – which are all used for practical purposes such as emergency communications and communications with remote islands. The last ones, Sakura CS-3, were developed to lead the way for advanced communications satellites to meet an increasing and diversifying demand for communications and to develop communication satellite technologies for the future.

The ambitious plans for space communication satellites, with the Sakura CS-4 to be launched in 1995, have been opposed by the USA. The US Department of Commerce argues that the satellite is an attempt to use government funds to exclude US companies from a profitable market in supplying commercial satellites. The US government has in fact listed satellites under the Super 301 clause of the 1988 Trade Act, with the purpose of reserving the market for US companies which for the time being have a definite lead. There can be little doubt that the struggle will continue as Japan clearly has the ambition to build an independent capability in all major fields of space technology. It was in fact the concern over possible US restrictions on technology exports, following from the controversy over joint US/Japan development of the FSX fighter plane, which prompted Japan to increase its funding for space research – including communications technology. It is worth noting that five US-made communications and broadcasting satellites were added to the Japanese satellite network in 1989, which substantially increase satellite services in Japan. However, there is little doubt that Japan is bent on establishing a technological base for the design, manufacture, and maintenance of at least the major components of space systems. This is needed, it is claimed, to enable Japan to retain the capability to conduct a wide range of space activities with consistency and independence.

Meteorological and earth observation satellites are important for Japan since the country is surrounded by oceans and its weather is directly affected by them. Marine observation satellites provide detailed information on high tides, coastal disasters, sea currents and temperatures, plankton concentration and other information which is useful for fishery activities. The first geostationary meteorological satellite, GMS Himawara, was launched in 1977, followed by several during the 1980s.

The first marine observation satellite, Momo, was launched in 1987. The first earth resources satellite, to be launched in 1992, is mainly aimed at collecting global land data (including Antarctica) and at exploring natural resources. Finally the Advanced Earth Observing Satellite – ADEOS – will be developed not only to contribute internationally to observations of global environmental changes but also to develop the platform technology required for satellites in the future and the inter-orbit communications technology required for relaying earth observation data. It is expected to play an important role in observing oceanic climate, ozone contents in the atmosphere and gases causing the greenhouse effect. It will be launched in 1995.

Future plans and research activities

Space communications are considered an integral part of the communications infrastructure in Japan. So Japan has intensified the development of space

186 SCIENCE AND TECHNOLOGY IN JAPAN

communications technologies and is paying special attention to geo-stationary platform satellites, large deployable antennas, and satellite-based switching. It is often stated that Japan is pursuing the development of original technology in order to be able to freely conduct space development.

There can be little doubt that space activities will increasingly become an internationally organised area. This is exemplified by the permanently manned station for which the assembly work in space will start in 1995. Underpinning this ambitious project is the Space Station Intergovernmental Agreement (IGA) which has been signed by the USA, Japan, Europe and Canada. Japan's main contribution to the Space Station will be the Japanese Experiment Module (JEM) which is expected to cost Y310 billion.

The experiment module consists of a Pressurised Module, an Exposed Module, and an Experiment Logistics Module. The Pressurised Module is a multipurpose laboratory for performing material processing experiments, life science experiments, etc., under microgravity conditions. The Experiment Logistics Module is a container which is used to store and resupply specimens, various gases and other consumables and to transport these materials between the JEM and the ground. This module will make it possible to carry out a large number of experiments and satisfy the needs of space utilisation in a wide range of fields. The exposed module is for support purposes.

The Tsukuba Space Centre, responsible for tracking and mentioned above, also has a research and development section which plays an important role in developing fundamental technologies required for space development. This includes, along other things, work on structure technology and thermal control technology for launch vehicles and satellites. The Kakuda Propulsion Centre also belonging to NASDA, has an important mission in carrying out tests on the high performance upper-stage in a simulated space environment.

Space research sponsored by the Japan Key Technology Centre (JKTC)

In 1986 and 1987 JKTC invested in two R&D companies which are oriented towards space development and exploitation. One is the Space Technology Corporation, focusing on the processing of materials under micro-gravity conditions – or more specifically "studies on the crystal growth of semiconducting materials using space environment", including studies on crystal growth of compounds such as PbSnTe (from melts), GaAs (from solution) and InP (from vapour). The company has a total budget of Y5.6 billion over a period of seven years and includes the following six company members: Ishikawajima-Harima Heavy Industries, Toshiba Corporation, NEC, Hitachi Ltd, Fujitsu Ltd and Mitsubishi Electric.

The other JKTC R&D company is the Space Communications Research Corporation, founded in 1987 to undertake the research and development programme on communications payload of a Japanese Geostationary Communications Platform which is intended to come into existence in the late 1990s. The corporation will work for a period of seven years and will focus on three related issues:

1. frequency structure and use for land mobile satellite communications;

2. development of large satellite antennas, and millimetre-wave personal satellite communications (handheld micro-terminals); and

3. enhanced direct broadcasting satellite services.

An important idea voiced in this and other contexts is the replacement of conventional onboard satellite processing with a system which offers sophisticated on-board routing and reconfiguration which would enable dyamic channel re-allocation between different multiple access schemes. The corporation will partially carry out such studies before its folds. The founding members are NTT, KDD, NHK, Toshiba Corporation, Mitsibishi Electric, Hitachi Ltd, Jujitsu Ltd, NEC, Toyota Motor and Tokyo Electric Power Inc.

The major companies in satellite communications are NEC, Mitsubishi and Toshiba, as well as service providers such as NTT and KDD.

Aircraft industry

Rapid development of aircraft technology in Japan did not start until after the First World War as the country was not compelled to develop military aircraft. There was rapid progress in the 1920s following the introduction of European framemaking techniques and engines. With manufacture under licence companies started to develop their own designs. The development came to be oriented increasingly toward military needs.

By 1935 the Japanese aircraft industry had begun to produce mainly indigenous designs often with features not found in European and American aircraft. During the Second World War Japan surprised the world by developing some of the fastest propeller-driven engines known. These included the famous Zerosen (Zero-fighter) and Hayabusa (Falcon) fighter planes. At the very end of the war – in March 1945 – the first Japanese aircraft with a jet engine was tested. The engine had been made according to blueprints secretly obtained from Germany. A few months later the Imperial Navy tested its new high-speed bomber, Kikka, which was equipped with a jet engine. The war came to an end a few days later.

The Japanese aircraft industry today is struggling along and would hardly have existed if it were not for military orders which provide three quarters of the income. A major reason for the present weakness is the ban which the Allied Occupation imposed on Japan in 1945. Until April 1952, when the peace treaty was signed, Japan was completely banned from the production and use of airplanes, and all facilities for aviation research and the manufacture of aircraft were either dismantled or transferred to other purposes. In the years of inactivity there had been a switch from propeller to jet planes, and aircraft construction altered greatly in almost all areas, including performance. structure and equipment.

With the handicap imposed by the Allied Occupation Japan had no choice but to start rebuilding its technological and industrial base. It did so by importing technology, offering repair and maintenance services to the US forces and starting production under foreign licences. The decades which followed demonstrated that this approach was successful – as far as technology is concerned. The Japanese aircraft industry can be rated as one of the best and most reliable in the world. The supporting evidence is fivefold:

1. it has built aircraft, including advanced fighters, under licences and has also built business jets and helicopters of many types;

2. it overhauls the engines of US commercial aircraft;

3. it developed a medium-range passenger aircraft, YS-11, with turbo-prop engines;

4. it developed its own experimental engines for a STOL (short take-off and landing) aircraft; and

5. started, with foreign collaboration, to develop and manufacture a successor to the YS-11 engine.

In engine technology the Japanese industry is on a par with almost any other country. This provided the opportunity for the three Japanese companies, Ishikawajima-Harima Heavy Industries, Kawasaki Heavy Industries and Mitsubishi Heavy Industries, to join forces with Rolls Royce in the UK to develop and manufacture a jet engine, RJ500, for a 150-seat plane. The engine later came to be known as the V2500, and Pratt and Whitney also joined the joint development consortium. In Japan, Ishikawajima-Harima Heavy Industries, Kawasaki Heavy Industries and Mitsubishi Heavy Industries, organised as the Japanese Aero Engines Corporation, are taking part. The corporation, which is an administrative co-ordinating body for the three companies, had a 23 per cent share of the total V2500 engine work, with Rolls Royce and Pratt and Whitney each sharing 30 per cent and the remainder taken by MTU of Daimler Benz (11 per cent) and Fiat (6 per cent).

The Japanese consortium was given the responsibility for the design and production of the fan section. The V2500 engine project was significant for the Japanese makers as this was the first time that they had contributed to a standard jetliner engine.

However, the complexity of entering the market for civilian aircraft becomes evident when one traces the Japanese efforts since the YS-11. This twin-turbo-prop 60-seat commuter plane was a technical success but a commercial failure. The costs were borne by the Japan Development Bank, which covered both direct subsidies and losses on loans. The next major aircraft project was YX, in which Mitsubishi, Kawasaki and Fuji took a 15 per cent share and Airitalia of Italy another 15 per cent with the major part - 70 per cent - taken by Boeing for what was eventually to become Boeing 767. The Japanese consortium produced body sections which represent 15 per cent of the value of the aircraft - a co-production rather than a co-development project.

The experience of collaboration with Boeing was the basis for an active solicitation for joint development and production of another aircraft, and led to discussions with all major producers. As a result the Japanese companies eventually entered into an agreement with Boeing which contained full participation for development, production, sales, and services of the 7J7 - corresponding to 25 per cent. The funding on the Japanese side was provided by the Japan Development Bank, rather than direct subsidies, with the condition that the capital had to repaid even if the project was a failure while the interest would be paid back from revenues generated from sales.

Responding to criticism that Japan is "targeting" the aircraft industry, MITI at this time (1987) changed the funding mechanism by establishing the non-profit International Aircraft Development Fund. This organisation provides funds for aircraft development, but these can only be used for international projects, wholly domestic projects are excluded.

Given the strength of the Japanese industry in engineering and electronics it would be reasonable to expect that Japan would be among the world leaders in the design and manufacture of aircraft. The brief description above has clearly indicated that this is not the case, and Japan still lags far behind the international leaders in the field. There are several reasons. First, Japanese industry has only limited experience in large systems integration. There is a considerable difference between building a supertanker, a large petrochemical plant or a supercomputer and developing and building a modern aircraft.

The size of the domestic market may be a more important factor. Having entered the field relatively late, a Japanese aircraft – even if successful – can only capture part of the Japanese market. So a break-even point cannot be reached by relying on the domestic market which has generally been the case for cars and most electronic products. So the only possibility for Japan and its aircraft companies is to enter into collaboration for production and joint development of succeeding generations of aircraft.

However, the belief that Japan is secretly targeting the aircraft industry has had a bad impact on US-Japan relations, in particular as regards the joint development of the FSX fighter – a modification of the F-16 of General Dynamic – to become the mainstay of the Japanese airforce. The two governments had in principle reached an agreement, but US public and Congress criticism all but led to a cancellation of the agreement. The effect has been to make Japan consider domestic independence or collaboration with European companies in other technological areas, such as space technology.

The major research centre for aircraft technology is the National Aerospace Laboratory, which was founded in 1955. Its mandate was widened in 1963 to include rocket and space technology. The institute has a total staff of 450, of whom 330 are researchers and an annual budget of Y10 billion (1988). Its major research areas include: STOL aircraft; innovative aerospace transportation technologies; space transportation system, utilization of space environment and satellite systems.

An experimental STOL aircraft, ASUKA, has been developed by the institute. Development continued for many years with the ultimate aim of establishing all the necessary technologies for developing a domestic quiet fan-jet STOL aircraft which could meet future demand for commercial transport. However, the project was cancelled towards the end of the 1980s. The institute is also investigating the key technologies of a spaceplane and hypersonic airplane which are considered essential for autonomous space activities and to meet the need for hyperspeed air transportation. Innovative aerospace transportation technologies need to be established and the institute is investigating laminar flow control, new composite materials and structures, ultra-high bypass ratio engines of variable geometry, airbreathing engines etc.

Research is also being carried out to improve rocket engine performance, and a high pressure LOX turbo pump for the LE-7 engine that is used in the first stage of the H-II is being developed. Studies on bi-propellant apogee engines are also being conducted. Ways are being studied to apply rocket technology to recovery, rendezvous and docking techniques. The institute has also carried out the research for the xenon ion engine used to control the position of geostationary satellites mentioned above. Finally, the Kakida Research Centre for Rocket Propulsion, mentioned above, is operated by the National Aerospace Laboratory.

Chapter 13

Defence

Defence, like aviation, is a high technology industrial sector which has remained undeveloped in Japan, and in which the country remains thoroughly dependent on imports from the USA and Western Europe. The reasons why Japan's defence industry still remains tiny are easy to find. The post-war constitution imposed by the Allied Occupation contains a clause that prohibited the maintenance of armed forces.

It is often assumed that General MacArthur, the Supreme Commander of the Allied Powers (SCAP) intended to completely wipe out the military forces and industries in Japan and transform the country by a complete commitment to peaceful activities. The emergence of the Cold War and the Korean War in 1950 altogether changed the situation and the necessity arose not only to prevent Japan from gravitating towards the Soviet faction but also to enable Japan to participate in its own defence. So in 1950, after the outbreak of the Korean War, a national police reserve force of 75,000 men was formed. This corps, together with maritime and air forces, became the National Safety Forces at the time of the United States-Japan security treaties in 1952, and was reorganised as the Self Defence Forces in 1954.

Until now, the Self Defence Forces and the security treaty with the USA have remained the fundamental framework of the military component of Japan's national defence. In the early days of the Cold War the USA consistently requested a considerable degree of Japanese rearmament, which was rejected at the time by the Prime Minister Yoshida Shigeru, who argued that this would not only be detrimental to the economic development of the country but also jeopardise political stability in Japan.

The Basic Policies for National Defence, declared by the cabinet in 1957, recognised Prime Minister Yoshida's tack. Japan has subsequently followed a policy aiming at economic development through free trade and peaceful co-existence, although the USA has insisted on increased Japanese military activity – until the downfall of Soviet might in early 1990.

Additional policies have supported Yoshida's early stance. These include the principle of not exporting arms and the position that the costs for maintaining the Self Defence Forces may not exceed 1 per cent of the gross national product (GNP). The government has, since 1976, prohibited the export of any kind of weapon or weapon component to any country, friendly or unfriendly, although this position has since the mid-1960s been eroded by the insistence of the US government.

Funding

Total government expenditure on research and development for its Self Defence Forces has been as low as 0.01 per cent of GNP, or even lower, in the 1970s. This should be compared with defence R&D spending in the US, which has been close to 1 per cent during part of the 1980s, and with figures for France and UK being in the interval 0.5-0.7 per cent. However, Japan's spending on defence R&D has gradually increased since the mid-1970s and is now approaching 0.025 per cent of GNP or 2.5 per cent of total costs for the Self Defence Forces. See Figure 13.1. The amount is still small and amounts to 1 per cent of total national R&D expenditure or some 5 per cent of government expenditure in R&D. For easy comparison, Japan's annual expenditure on military R&D – Y103 billion in 1990 – roughly corresponds to the annual R&D budget of Canon and is much less than the annual budget of any of the major companies – say NEC and NTT. The official defence R&D expenditure is only slightly larger than that of Sweden.

Figure 13.1 Funding level for defence research in Japan

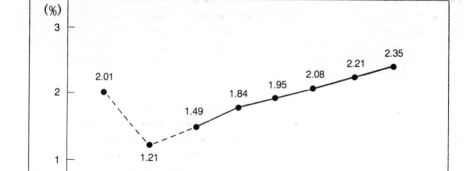

Source: Defence White Paper (Boei Hakusho). Compiled by Defence Agency, Tokyo 1990. Printing Bureau, Ministry of Finance, p. 161

Total procurement from the Defence Agency totalled Y1,500 billion in 1989 which is approximately one third of the total defence budget. When comparing the defence R&D budget with the budget for defence procurement the ratio turns out to be 7 per cent. The same ratio in Sweden is of the order of 25-30 per cent, which is heavily influenced by a level of high domestic development and major systems development. However, it may be assumed that the private companies in Japan also fund defence-related research. This is for example true for radar research, where Mitsubishi Electric has undertaken its own research on phased-array radar. However, even adjusting for privately funded defence R&D does not change the overall character of industrial R&D in Japan which has a very small percentage of military activities.

Procurement and Japanese defence contractors

The Defence Agency has three ways of obtaining advanced hardware and systems: design and development in Japan; licensed production of American (or European) hardware; and imports directly from arms manufacturers abroad. The approach would naturally differ from area to area. The needs of the army for vehicles, including tanks and armoured vehicles, have basically been met by indigenous design, development and manufacture. The same is true for the navy, where Japan has been able to draw on its excellent shipbuilding capability. However, for the airforce Japan has been much more dependent on foreign technology and foreign suppliers. This is also true for missiles and, to some extent, for military communication systems.

The major items in defence procurement (1989) are as follows. The ground forces obtained 56 tanks and 71 armoured personnel carriers, nine anti-tank helicopters (AH-1S), five transport helicopters (CH-47J) and one group of Hawk surface-to-air guided missiles.

The navy obtained two destroyers and submarines, ten fixed-wing anti-submarine patrol aircraft (P-3C), twelve anti-submarine helicopters and four mine-sweeping helicopters (MH-53E). The airforce acquired eleven fighter-interceptors (F-15), two transport aircraft (C-130H), two transport helicopters (CH-47-J), twenty medium training aircraft (T-4) and one group of surface-to-air missiles (Patriot)

A very large part of the defence procurement contracts goes to Japanese companies – either for licensed products or their own hardware and systems. There is a heavy concentration of military production in a limited number of companies. Half the defence equipment deliveries in 1989 – at Y1,500 billion – came from five companies: Mitsubishi Heavy Industries (MHI), Kawasaki Heavy Industries, Mitsubishi Electric Corporation, NEC and Toshiba. MHI is by far the most prominent supplier, accounting for 24 per cent of the value of the Defence Agency procurement contracts, which in 1989 amounted to approximately 20 per cent of the company's total sales, or Y363 billion. The defence procurement budget in 1989 was roughly Y500 billion for the airforce, Y500 billion for navy, Y400 for ground forces and the remainder, Y100 billion, was allocated to the Technical Development and Research Institute which is directly supervised by the Defence Agency. See below.

Mitsubishi Heavy Industries is the main contractor for Japan's next generation fighter, the FS-X, designed to replace the present F-15 which is still being produced by MHI. MHI, and the major collaborating companies – Kawasaki Heavy Industries and Fuji Heavy Industries – in early 1990 sent a joint task force of 100 engineers and other staff to the USA where they are working together with General Dynamic on the Japanese modifications of the F-16 to produce the Japanese FS-X. At its peak the joint task force will involve 300 people from the Japanese and American companies.

The main fighter aircraft in Japan are the F-15(J), F-1 and F-4(EJ), and all carry American as well as Japanese air-to-air missiles. The FS-X fighter will also have air-to-ship missiles. The missile arsenal also includes Raytheon Sparrows (AIM-7F), Sidewinders (AIM-9L) and Hawks – all made by Mitsubishi under licence. Today the most important part of the missiles is the sensors and electronics system to seek the target and guide the missiles, considering the high value-added for sensors and electronics.

Given Japanese industrial competence in these fields, it is not surprising that the Japanese defence industry is trying to capture a large share. The Harpoon Aircraft Command and Launch Set (HACLS) provides a good example. The missiles themselves are being imported and installed on submarines, destroyers and anti-submarine planes (PC-3). However, the important control and guidance system is almost completely manufactured by Mitsubishi Electric – although under contract with McDonnel Douglas and Westinghouse Electric. Similarly NEC through a subsidiary – Japan Aviation Electronics Industry Ltd – is building defence electronics and draws on its American partner, Hughes Aircraft Co. The inferiority of the Japanese defence forces, in terms of number of aircraft and ships, over a likely adversary has given an added impetus to missile development to partly compensate for the imbalance.

MHI is heavily involved in the civilian aviation projects discussed, such as the Boeing 767 (the medium-sized civilian YSX plane), and is also participating in the MITI-sponsored project to research the high speed HSCT commercial transport aircraft. MHI is also involved in a major way in the development of the rocket launcher H-II, with a first launch scheduled in 1992.

The dispute between the USA and Japan over the FS-X plane, with the US side accusing Japan of surreptitiously acquiring technology to outcompete the US aircraft manufacturers in the future, may have prompted MHI to look for alternate partners hereafter. The indicated background may be part of the explanation why Mitsubishi Group and Daimler Benz AG in Germany in 1990 reached an agreement to enter into a still loose relationship. The major companies interested in the Mitsubishi Group are MHI, Mitsubishi Electric and Mitsubishi Motors. Daimler Benz for its part already has a strong interest in both aero-engines and aircraft/space through MTU (engines), and through Messerschmitt-Boelkow-Blohmn, which was acquired in 1989.

Kawasaki Heavy Industries also plays an important role in Japan's defence industry and is particularly strong in aircraft and submarines. The Fuji Heavy Industries is expanding its aircraft activities with its participation in the FS-X project and has inherited the tradition of the former Nakajima Aircraft. The remaining major heavy industries company – Ishikawajima-Harima Heavy Industries – is more active on the civilian side of aerospace equipment although it manufactures the Pratt and Whitney F-100 engines which are installed on F-15(J) fighter-interceptors.

The interests of defence contracts are discussed and occasionally promoted in various organisations. One is the Defence Production Committee of the Federation of Economic Organisations (Keidanren), which in 1988 was chaired by the Chairman of Mitsubishi Heavy Industries Ltd. Keidanren also maintains a small office which has the responsibility of serving another related committees active in science and technology matters. The other is the Japan Ordnance Association.

In the early 1990s Japan has embarked on four major development projects of which the most prominent is the FS-X fighter. A second is a comprehensive communication system at the level of division (*shidan*). A third project is the development of a short-range SAM attack missile, while the fourth is GRX-4. The Defence Agency has in its long-term plan indicated that Japan should acquire a number of AWACS (airborne warning and control system) aircraft, although with an indication that they should be produced in Japan.

Technical Research and Development Institute (TRDI)

The Japan Defence Agency maintains major research facilities in its Technical Research and Development Institute (TRDI), which was originally established in August 1952. TRDI has since expanded and been reorganised and at present has a total staff of 1,181 (May 1990). This includes 548 researchers, and 262 officers from the three forces. Most of the staff seconded from the various forces are qualified researchers. The remainder provide a substantial number of administrative and supporting staff. TRDI has five research sections, of which four are located in Western Tokyo and another at the Yokotsuka naval base, and test ranges in various part of the countries. It handles a total research budget of Y103 billion (1990). In 1987 the institute completely reorganised its Sections 1 and 2. The first section specialised in research on firearms, ammunition, armour materials, antiballistic structures, protection against chemical weapons, and human engineering.

Section 2, which previously focused on food, clothing, gas-proof masks, etc., has now become a Defence Optical and Electronic Laboratory and also incorporates electronic warfare (previously conducted inside Section 1). One of the first tasks of the reorganised section was a basic project-technology study related to the FS-X fighter plane. Following from that Section 1 is currently involved in the active phased-array radar system, for the FS-X, to be completed by 1995.

The new Section 2, which has a total staff of 140, has three subsections: information and communication systems; electric wave systems; and optical wave systems. The section has one of the biggest anechoic chambers in Japan which can also be used for testing radar under simulated tactical electronic warfare situations. Research on excimer laser beams and forward-looking infrared (FLIR) imaging devices had been studied. The FLIR device which is used for imaging objects by detecting infrared rays will be installed, among other places, in the new 120-mm tank for which development was completed in 1990. The institute has also been studying the possibility of using excimer laser beams for laser radar to detect objects more precisely than is possible with conventional radar.

Section 1, located on the same ground as Section 2, has major research projects on penetration phenomena in armour materials. The aim is to develop lighter and stronger composite materials by combining ceramics and steel at different intervals. Section 3 specialises in aircraft, aircraft engines, missiles and rocket engines. Section 4 is focused on vehicles and engineering equipment while Section 5 is dedicated to research on underwater acoustic systems, underwater weapons, magnetic equipment and mine sweeping equipment.

Japan-USA co-operative relations in defence equipment and technology

Japan is dependent for its national military security on the USA, for which the responsibility and consequences are spelled out in the 1960 Treaty. Furthermore, Japan is dependent on the USA for procurement of whole equipment and integral technologies used in domestically manufactured equipment. The related issues are discussed in the Japan-USA Systems and Technology Forum, an informal forum for working-level officials which meets once or twice yearly. The forum discusses, among other things, joint research on equipment and technology. The Defence Agency announced in early 1990 that it would shoulder half of the research expenses of Japan-USA joint weapons research projects which will follow the joint development of the FS-X fighter plane.

The "Mutual Assistance Agreement between Japan and the U.S.", signed in 1954, is instrumental for the transfer of defence equipment and technologies in Japan. Certain equipment, like the portable SAM missiles, have been procured as Military Foreign Sales (MFS) while others like the F-15 interceptor-fighter plane and Patriot surface-to-air guided missiles have been produced in Japan under licence agreement.

In 1983 Japan decided to open the way for its transfer of military technologies to the USA as an exception to the Three Principles on Arms Export formulated in 1967, which became even more restricted by the Government Policy Guideline on Arms Export of February 1976. The transfer of military technologies to the USA covers articles which are necessary to make the transfer effective and fall under the category of arms. In response to the US request for technology transfer, and after careful studies, the Japanese section of the Joint Military Technology Commission decided in 1986 that it was appropriate to approve the transfer to the USA of three military technologies.

The first case was the joint development of the FS-X fighter plane, and a Memorandum of Understanding was signed in November 1988. The US side – after political turbulence in the USA on the issue of technology transfer and joint development – again requested the Japanese to clarify their position. It was confirmed again that the governments of the two countries had a strong desire to bring the co-development of the FS-X to success. The concern in the US may not have been completely unfounded, as a group of the main Japanese contractors in 1987 argued that it was imperative for them to design, develop and manufacture the new plane domestically in order for the aircraft industry to raise its overall capacity.

The Strategic Defence Initiative (SDI) also posed problems for the Japanese government. In a public statement in September 1986 it was declared that it is appropriate to handle Japan's participation in SDI research within the framework of the existing domestic laws and the Japan-USA agreements – similar to the exchange of defense-related technologies. As a consequence those bodies in Japan desiring to take their place in SDI research will participate in individual SDI research projects under separate contracts with the US Department of Defence or with participating enterprises. In 1988 the USA initiated a SDI research project for a missile defence system to cover the Western Pacific. This has brought about the involvement of Japanese companies, which have generally been lukewarm to the SDI projects – partly because of perceived or real restrictions on the use of the results of the developed technologies.

The lively debate on defence technology between the USA and Japan has its roots in two closely related factors. First, Japan (or rather its companies) is constantly gaining over the USA in areas such as semiconductors and semiconductor materials, photonics, machine intelligence and robotics and superconductivity – areas in which its success is partly explained by the dual-purpose nature of many technologies with the cutting edge shifting towards the civilian side. US companies still have the edge in large scale integration of complex systems and AI and in many specific technologies. Second, it is feared in the USA that Japan may be shifting its defence purchases and its technology collaboration to European companies, which may be logical given some of the experiences in the past.

Chapter 14

Transportation and construction research

During the National Seclusion *(Sakoku)* policy which was in force from 1639 to 1853 no Japanese were allowed to travel abroad and only the Dutch and the Chinese were allowed limited trading in Nagasaki. However domestic travel expanded and coastal shipping moved the major part of an expanding commodity trade. Although there were no modern means of transportation at the time of the Meiji Restoration it took only until 1872 for the first train to run between Tokyo and Yokohama. The first electric trolley operated in Kyoto in 1895, the first automobile was imported four years after and the first airplane was produced in 1911.

The railways played a very major part in the communications system in the the period between the two world wars and continued to do so for a number of years after the end of the Second World War. Passenger air lines were prohibited by SCAP until 1951, and then took off to a slow start. The inauguration of the high speed passenger train service – Shinkansen – in 1964 was a severe blow to the air industry.

Private cars formed the fastest growing segment of transportation in the 1960s and there were three contributing factors. First, the rapid growth of income enabled people to buy cars. Second, the domestic car industry was responding to Japanese demand by providing small and low-cost vehicles. Third, there was a rapid and considerable improvement of the road system. As a consequence car ownership increased from 331,000 vehicles in 1960 to over 19 million in 1979.

Shinkansen, the most famous part of the Japanese railway system for a considerable period of time, changed the whole transportation system. Shinkansen provided safe, reliable and very speedy transportation which was eventually extended beyond Osaka to the South and also to the North. The development was triggered by the transport problems in the Tokyo-Osaka corridor where almost half the population and two thirds of industry is located on only 16 per cent of the total land area.

The existing double-track system could not increase its capacity, so Japan National Railways established a committee in 1956 to look for different solutions and came up with the idea that the existing two-track should be converted to a four-track system. However, a second committee two years later suggested that a high speed railroad should be built on a separate double track. The committee estimated the cost at Y198 billion with a construction period of five years. The decision was taken in 1959 and the line was completed on schedule in time for the Olympic Games held in Tokyo in October 1964.

Superconductivity for transportation

The race for superconductivity applications entered a new phase in 1987 when the awareness spread, after the discovery by two IBM scientists, that superconductivity can be achieved at temperatures considerably above absolute zero. This was an important stimulant to the technology-driven groups of engineers working on various projects in Japan, of which the Maglev train is one.

The Shinkansen train has already been overtaken by the French TGV, which attains speeds higher than those of the Tohoku Shinkansen which runs between Ueno in Tokyo and Morioka in Northern Honshu. A competing approach for a Maglev train has reached an advanced stage of development in Germany. The Transrapid Versuchsanlage in Emsland is using a levitated train powered by a linear synchronous motor and has reached speeds of more than 400 kilometres per hour on a test track of 31.5 kilometres.

The Japanese effort to develop a Maglev train started at approximately the same time as the first Shinkansen line was completed. Efforts have been pursued by two groups of companies. The first has been led by the former Japan National Railways (JNR), which has become known as JR after its privatisation. The other group, originally led by Japan Air Lines (JAL), is now controlled by High Speed Surface Transportation (HSST) Corporation, a subsidiary of JAL. The airline's interest focused on the possibility of providing a high speed service from downtown Tokyo to Narita airport, while the JR interest lies in upgrading technology in the Tokyo-Osaka corridor and possibly providing new services in other areas. The industrial companies participating in the projects are naturally also viewing the potential in export markets. HSST Corporation signed a memorandum in Summer 1990 to sell the technology for a high-speed train line which would serve the Sheremetyevo Airport in Moscow.

Today the JR Group is operating a Maglev train on an 8 kilometre test track in Miyazaki prefecture on Kyushu. The total expenditure for the Miyazaki test track, which is based on low temperature super conductivity, has reached approximately Y50 billion. Hitachi has been the main developer throughout the period. A first test vehicle, the ML500, was delivered in 1970 and reached a speed of 517 km/h in 1979. A second test vehicle, MLU001, which consisted of three sections, was completed in 1980 to be followed by MLU002, delivered in 1987. The present JR Maglev vehicle, the MLU002, is a prototype of a real train with comfortable seats and a lightweight body. A real Maglev train between Tokyo and Osaka would possibly carry 1,000 passengers in fourteen cars and cover the distance in approximately 60 minutes.

There is now a desire to ascertain the technical and commercial viability of this dream. So the Ministry of Transportation in 1990 made a decision to build a 43-kilometre experimental track in Yamanashi prefecture, between the two villages Akiyama and Sakaigawa. The new test track, which has been given a budget of Y304 billion for a test period to end in 1997, will be completed in 1993. The location was chosen so that the test track could be incorporated in a possible new Maglev Chuo Line running between Tokyo and Osaka which would become operational around 2005. However, the costs for such a Maglev line have been estimated to reach Y3,000 billion which is fifteen times more than the original Shinkansen line.

The introduction of Maglev trains faces three major difficulties. First, the terrain necessitates the use of tunnels, which pose serious air suction problems when trains pass. Second, soaring land prices in Japan make it difficult to achieve economic operation in serving the capital investment. Third, the operating costs for the trains themselves have not yet been clarified. So the JR Group has asked three major electric machinery manufacturers – Toshiba Corporation, Hitachi Ltd and Mitsubishi Electric Corporation – to individually develop superconducting systems. An agreement to this effect was reached between the JR Group and the three companies which were given all the necessary specifications.

The SCM (super-conducting magnet) system has three main components: a coil made of niobium-titanium alloy and copper; a supercooling device; and an outer vessel. The cooler contains liquid helium, to bring the coil temperature close to absolute zero, making the coil superconductive. The problems to be solved include making the superconducting device small enough to be contained in the undecarriage of the train and keeping the magnets permanently cooled to ascertain the commercial viability of the technical possibility.

Efforts to apply superconductivity technology for ship propulsion are also under way. *Yamamoto 1*, a small ship of 280 tons, was launched in Summer 1990 by a consortium to demonstrate that superconductivity can be used to power a ship. Superconducting coils of niobium and titanium in thrusters under the ship are used to create a magnetic field. That field is repulsed by an electric current in the water circulating through the thrusters, producing the force to propel the ship. The co-ordinator of the consortium is Mitsubishi Heavy Industries with Japan Foundation for Shipbuilding Advancement also participating. The Ministry of Transportation is backing the project as part of an overall approach to support the development of superconductivity in the transportation sector.

A superconductivity catapult for rocket launching is another interesting and very novel way of applying superconductivity which has been proposed by a construction company, Taisei. The basic idea is to utilise linear-motor-car technology for providing the initial boost to a rocket and space shuttle by catapulting the vehicle toward the sky on the back of a car following a steeply inclined track. The space vehicle would be thrown off the car at an altitude of around 2,000 metres – with its engines firing. It has been estimated that this could reduce the fuel used by as much as 20 per cent, which would greatly increase the economic payload.

Major efforts are currently under way to develop and introduce various car navigation systems. Since the early 1980s Japanese automobile and electronics manufacturers have been interested in the development of a navigation system for automobiles. Such a system would identify the location of the vehicle while travelling and assist the driver to find the best route in an unfamiliar area. An intelligent system would require a number of components which include: a cd-based map data system to be displayed in the car; an interactive system using satellites or roadside transmitters to pin-point the location of the vehicle; and information systems to notify the driver of traffic and road conditions.

Development projects have followed two different approaches. The major one is the Advanced Mobile Traffic Information and Communication System (AMSTIC), which is supported by the Ministry of Posts and Telecommunications and the Metropolitan Police Department – with participation by the major manufacturers of equipment. The AMSTIC, which was ready for testing in Tokyo in 1989, and in Osaka in 1990, already provides information, added to the CD-ROM data, through messages sent from police traffic control centres.

The other project Driver Information and Guidance System Using Car Communication (DIGSUCC) is supported by the Japan Digital Road Association in which the Japan Highway Public Corporation plays an important role, with an overall backing from the Ministry of Construction. In this system the drivers are provided with information transmitted from roadside beacons. The project has also in major ways involved the car and electronics makers with the Public Works Research Institute providing a coordinating role.

The two ministries and the National Policy Agency have, after the initial experiments in 1990, decided to develop jointly a communication system that will help to guide drivers while travelling. The organisations will study the current traffic communication systems with a view to developing a new system which will be easy to use. Finally, the makers are organised in the Navigation System Researchers' Association in Japan in which Mitsubishi has taken a leading role.

Construction research

In land development, the attention has shifted away from the metropolitan areas where land for development is no longer available. Building giant structures in the ocean, along the coastal areas, poses major technical and economic problems – with anchoring and chaining, or constructing a seabed – and are increasingly studied and researched. One possibility is control configured and functionalized structures (CCFS). In such structures large cylindrical legs are placed at fixed intervals. The submerged portions of these legs form ballast tanks, each equipped with an automatic pumping and draining system. Sensors placed on these cylinders detect the upper load of the structure and feed information to a computer-based control system. Such systems could be constructed as modules and be functionally divided. A lower level would contain city service functions with business in the following, then housing and finally an international airport for hypersonic transport at the upper level.

Another tack is the intelligent building which already exists in some places. The most important feature of such a building is the integration of the telecommunications and building maintenance systems within the building and their link-up with a host computer, mainly through a digital PBX, which controls the local area network through optical fibres. The occupants of such an intelligent building can use multifunction telecommunications equipment both for inside and outside contacts. They can also have direct access and control of lighting, renting meeting rooms and making reservations.

The concept can be extended to build intelligent cities. In such a city general information centres and intelligent buildings will perform the role of both central and relay stations for various types of information networks. They will also provide access points for open information from shared supercomputers and various types of databases. The continued development of information technologies will, according to this concept, include the provision of road and traffic information systems, disaster information systems, etc.

With the introduction of an information-oriented society it may be possible to take advantage of the potential of such systems to meet regional needs. There are already plans in Oita to turn the prefecture into an information-oriented prefecture. Basing this scheme on the presence of electronics industry and the emergence of a software park, the two major cities Oita and Beppu will develop municipality facilities as an information base for the whole prefecture.

Chapter 15

Research in life sciences and new materials

Efforts to promote research on life sciences in a more systematic way started in 1971 following the Science and Technology Agency (STA) enquiry into Japan's comprehensive science and technology policy the preceding year. Much of the effort during the 1970s was directed at solving pollution and energy problems. STA had already in 1968 indicated that biotechnology research promotion should follow its efforts to launch marine engineering. STA stated at the time that efforts in the biotechnology field should aim to clarify the mechanisms of life phenomenon of biorganisms and apply them to solve various problems concerning human life. Later on research fields also included the health and medical sectors as well as agricultural and industrial production. After replacing biotechnology with life sciences, and after considerable promotion and awareness creation, it became clear that Japan should mobilise considerable research resources in the sector.

One of the important documents was the "Views on Life Science Promotion" released by the Science and Technology Council in August 1980. Life sciences research is defined as scientific and technical research which uses knowledge from various disciplines such as biology, medicine, agriculture, engineering, physics, chemistry, etc. to clarify life phenomena as well as the the multiple functions of living organisms. Throughout the early period as now the government sector and the national research institutes play a more significant role than in other scientific fields.

Support for life sciences research

The Japanese government has provided support in a major way for biotechnology from the fiscal year 1981 with the aim that this new field will become a leading technology in the next century. The research and development expenditure for life sciences almost doubled between 1981 and 1986 – from Y510 billion to Y918 billion. Life science research amounts to approximately 10 per cent of all R&D expenditure in Japan. The expenditure reached Y1,115 billion in 1988, with industry spending Y561 billion. The university share is almost 40 per cent, with the majority being allocated to health and medicine. Adding private industry and private university funding would indicate that the private sector finances approximately two thirds of life science research in Japan.

Classified by kind of research, organisation expenditure on life science research represented about 20 per cent of the total science and technology expenditures of universities, some 10 per cent of those of research institutes and 7-8 per cent of those of corporations. Classified by research purposes, research expenditure in 1988 for health and medicine totalled Y773 billion or 69 per cent of the total, followed by Y103 billion (9.2 per cent) for life phenomena and biological functions, Y87 billion (7.8 per cent) for food resources, Y52 billion (4.7 per cent) for manufacturing industries and Y44 billion (4.0 per cent) for environmental protection.

Two major approaches have provided the support for the rapid development of life sciences during the 1980s. One is contained in the STA document "Views on Basic Policy for Cancer Research" which was released in July 1983 following the Cabinet document "Comprehensive 10-Year Strategy for Cancer Control". This considerably boosted cancer research through using recombinant DNA technology, DNA base sequence determination and other methods from molecular biology. Progress has been made in illuminating the cancer mechanism at the molecular level. The curing rate of cancer patients has constantly increased as a consequence of research on diagnostic and treatment techniques.

The other major approach is an outgrowth of the ageing of the Japanese society. Two major reports were published in 1986. One was a government report, "General Policy Rules for the Ageing Society" and the other, "Views on Basic Science and Technology Policies in an Ageing Society". The views in these documents have provided additional support for research efforts in life sciences.

Industrial research

Furthermore, the government, which has not only announced polices but also established new laboratories and R&D companies, has influenced private industry, which has increasingly seen more commercial possibilities and consequently allocated substantial R&D amounts to life science research. The lead has been taken by the pharmaceutical, textile and food industries, followed by many electronics and steel companies, etc., which are also quite active in pursuing life science research. Recombinant DNA technology has, in particular, found rapid application in the food and pharmaceutical industries. Growth hormones have already been marketed by both Eli Lily Japan and Yamanouchi Pharmaceutical Co. The Central Pharmaceutical Affairs Council have already approved gamma-interferon which is a cancer control agent, and the blood forming agent erythropoitetin (EPO). The market for the latter is expected to grow very rapidly and Kirin Brewery and Chugai Pharmaceutical have already started production in 1990. A wide range of diagnostic drug products is being marketed. Research is very intensive on drugs for diagnosis and treatment of non-A and non-B hepatitis and DNA probes are scheduled to be marketed in 1990.

Several companies are engaged in developing detergent enzymes. Toyobo and Hokkaido Sugar are planning to start commercial production of a recombinant protease. The application of bio-reactors in the food industry is also being intensively researched. Kao Corporation is marketing a special type of emulsifying oil for use in the making of bread. Biotechnology is already being aggressively applied in agriculture and Japanese businesses based on indigenous plant tissue culture are already emerging.

Bioindustry Development Centre (BIDEC) serves as a common organisation for the biotechnology-related interests in Japan. BIDEC owes its existence to the Japanese Association of Industrial Fermentation (JAIF), which traces its origin to an organisation established in 1942 to secure the country's supply of liquid fuels. The membership of BIDEC indicates the character of industrial development in the biotechnology sector. Approximately one fourth of the members are mainly active in the chemical industry and another one fourth in food industry. Surprisingly, one fourth of the members have their main activities in electronics, engineering and construction and the remainder is found within the petrochemical industry, steel industry, textile industry and so on.

Genetic engineering research was in Japan, as in most other countries, postponed until rules for laboratories were established. Such guidelines were eased through an amendment in August 1982 which further activated research both in industry and in universities and government research institutes. The original guidelines were issued by Monbusho in March 1979 and by STA in August the same year. Prior to the revision about 30 of the 200 major drug, chemical and food companies had already started research on genetic engineering.

There is growing public concern about the activities of biotechnology institutions such as those having P4 or P3 laboratories in Tsukuba, Suita, Takatsuki (Osaka, Japan Tobacco Corporation), Oiso (Kanagawa, Showa Denko Co.), etc. This concern will require more attention by the companies to alleviate public concern about their research activities.

Support by the ministries

The narrow biotechnology applications – as opposed to the overall support for research in life sciences – are considerably buttressed by the various ministries. The total support in 1990 amounts to Y90 billion, while the biotechnology related budget of the private sector is of the order of Y200 billion. MITI allocates Y84 billion, most of which in 1990 has been set aside for global environmental measures, which includes support for the Global Environment Industrial Technology Institute. However, MITI is indirectly supporting the Marine Bio-Technology Institute (MBI) which was established in 1988 with the participation of 24 private companies. The aim is to develop fine chemicals from marine organisms, which is part of the Large Scale Projects – now under NEDO. The sea is home to a number of organisms which subsist in environments characterised by low temperature, high pressure and high salinity. The plan is to use marine organisms to manufacture biologically active substances and industrial products such as enzymes, raw materials for paints and cosmetics etc. Another goal is to integrate the unique functions of marine organisms into products such as biosensors and biochips.

Monbusho has been actively promoting basic and clinical studies on cancer at universities, and its research has recently begun to progress rapidly with the new technologies of recombinant DNA and cell fusion. Following the government report mentioned above, the Monbusho Science Council formulated its own long-term plan which proposes priority research into the true character of cancer. As a consequence Monbusho now awards research grants for "Priority research of cancer based on the development of biosciences" and also for overseas scientific surveys of cancer research.

MITI is also providing support to develop technologies for the biological mobilisation of CO_2. MITI argues that the reduction in consumption of oil and coal may be satisfactory as a short-term solution despite having serious economic repercussions. So, according to MITI, biotechnology should be applied to breed new plants by controlling them at the molecular level. Such plants, which will be more resistant to aridity, salt and acids, will be capable of immobilising large quantities of CO_2 and can also be used for the greening of deserts.

The Ministry of Agriculture, Forestry and Fisheries (MAFF) has allocated Y3.9 billion – out of a total of Y7.9 billion for the development of advanced technologies for the food processing industry. The biotechnology-related budget of the Ministry of Health and Welfare is the largest – Y35 billion in 1990 – and also includes an allocation for advancing co-ordinate research on problems associated with the ageing society. The biotechnology budget of STA is the next largest among ministries – Y20 billion – which includes additional funds for the biotechnology-related projects within the ERATO programme. STA has also stated that it will increase its budget for promoting public acceptance of new technologies and products. Monbusho in 1990 allocated Y14 billion to bio-science and biotechnology of which biotechnology is only a minor part. Finally (although this is not an exhaustive listing) the Ministry has set aside a small amount, Y0.2 billion, for biotechnology research on waste water treatment.

Another example is the plans announced in late 1988 by Japan Tobacco Co. to establish a biotechnology laboratory. Preparations are (mid-1990) well under way to set up a research laboratory for bio-sciences, at Takatsuki between Osaka and Kyoto, which will have a research staff of 100 people.

In the following sections a few examples will be provided to illustrate various forms of organising research in life sciences or more narrowly within the biotechnology area.

Institute of Physical and Chemical Research (RIKEN)

RIKEN is a non-profit research organisation supported by STA. The research at the institute covers wide areas in the physical, chemical and biological sciences and engineering, and includes science, applied science and industrial applications. The institute is a research complex which consists of some 50 laboratories devoted to specific research under autonomous management. Research is often conducted through active collaboration with university laboratories and other research institutions, including those belonging to private companies.

When necessary, RIKEN organises a group of laboratories to conduct comprehensive and often interdisciplinary research projects. Thus, six laboratories have formed what is now the Tsukuba Life Science Centre, established for research on recombinant DNA. In 1986 RIKEN established the Frontier Research Programme (FRP) – not to confused with the Human Frontier Science Programme, although both have a life science and basic research orientation. FRP is a novel way of organising research in a flexible way for conducting long-term leading basic research. FRP has three major characteristics:

1. Researchers in various disciplines and with different backgrounds are invited to participate.

2. About one third, including team leaders, are invited from abroad.

3. The research teams remain for long period of times although the service of individual researchers may be relatively short.

The projects are likely to last for fifteen years, divided into three periods. Three projects are presently under way (1990): Bio-Homaeostasis Research, and Frontier Material Research, both started in 1986, and Brain Mechanisms of Mind and Behaviour, which started in 1988. The first project will provide an important basis for research on the ageing process which can be interpreted as indicative of the breakdown of the homoeostatic function. It has four laboratories: Molecular Regulation of Ageing; Ageing Process, Intestinal Flora; and Plant Biological Regulation. The latter aims to explore the molecular and cellular mechanisms by which light signals are received and transduced to produce homoeostatic responses in plants.

The Frontier Material Research Project, which aims to clarify various phenomena exhibited in ultra-fine structures of proteins, polymers, metals, etc., has three laboratories: Quantum Materials; Non-Linear Optics and Advanced Materials; and Bio-Electronics Materials. The latter has many research targets such as short-term research on biosensors and long-term research on bio-computers. One goal is to form molecular aggregates consisting of proteins in a state of close packing or two-dimensional crystals as a basic technique for bio-electronics devices.

The Brain Mechanisms of Mind and Behaviour Project, which aims to understand functional and structural principles of the brain through anatomical, physiological and theoretical approaches, has three laboratories: Neural Networks; Neural Information Processing; and Neural Systems. The latter will make detailed structural analyses of complex and highly integrated neuronal networks of the brain, and of the variability of the network structure related to functional localisation and activity levels of the brain. The goal is to elucidate the principal structures of the brain essential for an algorithm of thinking.

Protein Engineering Research Institute (PERI)

PERI is a R&D company which was founded in April 1986 under the sponsorship of the Japan Key Technology Centre (JKTC), which together with fourteen private companies, has provided the necessary capital. The total planned research fund amounts to Y17 billion over a period of ten years – of which JKTC has provided Y12 billion. The research laboratory for PERI was completed in 1988 at Senri in Suita City in Osaka prefecture. Before its completion, research was carried out at six laboratory annexes atttached to the research institutes belonging to some of the contributing firms, to which researchers were seconded from the participating companies, as well as from universities. Certain research tasks of PERI are being carried out at universities.

The number of researchers in the laboratory is approximately 60. They work in five divisions: structural analysis of proteins; structure-function correlation and design of new proteins; protein synthesis; isolation, purification and characterisation of proteins; and database and computer analysis. The first step in protein engineering is the structural analysis of natural proteins. The accumulation of data relating the structure to the function and mechanism of a large variety of natural proteins will allow proteins with specifically desired functions to be designed. The design technology will be developed by repeating the three research steps indicated by the divisions listed above.

The institute boasts that it is the first integrative organisation for protein engineering. It has been established for the purpose of developing the technology required to design proteins possessing specifically designed functions. In doing so it may be able to provide basic technologies which can be used for applications such as bio-functional membranes, high-functional enzymes (bio-reactors), biosensors, biochips etc. PERI is located in the Kansai Science City, and nearby related institutions include the Senri Life Science Centre and the Osaka Bioscience Centre. See also the discussion on the Kansai Science City in Chapter on 18.

Bio-Oriented Technology Research Advancement Institution (BRAIN)

Similar to the Japan Key Technology Centre (JKTC), BRAIN has been created as a specially approved corporate body (*Tokubetsu Ninka Hojin*) and it is not a quasi-governmental special corporation as is RIKEN, discussed above. Its main purpose is to promote research and development in areas of particular relevance to the Ministry of Agriculture, Forestry and Fisheries, which is the supervising ministry.

BRAIN, which was established in 1986 as a result of the reorganisation of the Institute of Agricultural Machinery, supports research and development activities for bio-oriented technology, by granting subsidies for the establishment of corporations. It also extends loans to industries involved in bio-oriented activities. The R&D corporations must be formed by two or more companies and BRAIN can provide up to 70 per cent of the required capital. The financial resources of BRAIN are much smaller than those of JKTC.

BRAIN created seven research corporations in the fiscal year 1986, three in 1987 and four in 1988. Those established in the fiscal year 1986 are:

Hokkaido Green-Bio Institute, Inc. (research for the development of cold-resistant plant resources by biotechnology).

Okinoerabu Bulb Bio-Research Institute, Inc. (studies on biotechnological breeding of florihorticultural bulbs and on their high-volume and high-speed culture).

Nursery Technology Inc. (research and development of mass production systems for seeds and seedlings).

Iwate Bio-Research Centre Ltd. (studies on effective utilisation of wooden biomass materials for use as animal feeds and other purposes).

Research Institute of Brewing Industries (developmental research on genetic resources of brewing organisms).

Marine Culture Centre (developmental research on feed for fish aquaculture).

Seatex Co. Ltd. (developmental research on marine culture systems for "high class" fish yet to be developed).

Finally, it may be noted that BRAIN also offers mediation services for private groups who want to obtain genetic resources such as seeds, seedlings, parts of plants or micro-organisms. Such material is available in gene banks which are maintained by MAFF. The main centres are: National Institute of Agrobiological Resources (Tsukuba) (Plants and Micro-Organisms); National Institute of Animal Husbandry (Animals); Kanto Forest Tree Breeding Institute (Forestry resources); National Research Institute of Aquaculture (Fishery Resources).

Exploratory Research for Advanced Technology (ERATO)

ERATO has several projects within the life sciences, two of which will be mentioned here. One is the Nagayama Protein Array Project (1990-95). Proteins in this project are not viewed as biological substances but purely as engineering materials. The interesting aspects are their physical and chemical properties as objects somewhere between atoms and macro-objects where the molecular recognition is determined by the surface structures of the proteins. This project will take proteins as the elements in which selective interactions among molecules can be controlled. Dr Nagayama, the project leader, considers that this research is a first step toward reproducing biological objects through engineering. The results are expected to become the basis for future materials such as molecular devices and highly functional films.

Another project is the Shinkai Chemirecognics Project (1990-95), which will explore the relationship between the molecular structure of the host and its recognition properties. Living organisms contain chemical reaction mechanisms, such as enzyme reactions, which are highly efficient and highly selective. The basis for these mechanisms is thought to be recognition through complex host-guest interaction. Efforts to artificially construct systems which show a high degree of recognition and establish methods of molecular design could possibly generate entirely new recognition mechanisms and new recognition targets. The project will seek to make recognition systems with special selectivity towards metal ions and organic molecules.

Material research

The behaviour of matter at a scale of nano-meter is becoming a major theme in physics, chemistry and increasingly in materials science. The proficiency to design and manufacture devices which are only tens or hundreds of atoms across will become increasingly important in many technological and industrial fields. There are two approaches to the manipulation of matter at the nano-meter level. One way is to start with a relatively large piece and carve out the required shape and size. The other way is to control the process from the bottom up which will require both advanced scientific knowledge as well as engineering skills. The Agency of Industrial Science and Technology argues that advanced materials can be created based on molecular manipulation which will have a great influence in many sectors. However, Japan lags behind the developed countries, according to AIST, and must take energetic steps not to be left further behind.

Research and development on materials during the 1970s was mainly influenced by demands in certain industrial sectors like semiconductors, space and aircraft. Still earlier the government established national institutes for metals (in 1957), for polymers and textiles (in 1969) and for inorganic materials (in 1966). RIKEN was all the time active in the field of material science. Later on sections for ultra-high pressure and ultra-high temperature were added to the National Institute for Research in Inorganic Materials, and a section for low temperature research was added to the National Research Institute for Metals. The latter institute has been reorganised to develop basic and composite materials technologies. The ceramics sections at the two Government Industrial Development Laboratories in Osaka and Nagoya were also strengthened. Several projects within the ERATO are focused on various aspects of material science. Finally there was also a shift at the universities where metal engineering started to incorporate material engineering.

New project initiatives

The shift in material science and technology followed from recommendations made by a Committee on Aircraft and Electronics Technology in August 1980. The report emphasised the need to do more research on high and low temperatures and on high pressures. MITI initiated its Future Generation Basic Technologies Programme (1981) which, among other projects includes a major one on fine ceramics, another on separation membranes and still another on conducting polymers. Industry also followed suit and new materials were targeted in newly created business divisions. A number of investigations followed and the more official reports have throughout prompted the research community to move more extensively and more quickly into advanced material research. A few examples will be given to illustrate new activities before presenting more details on the organisation of extreme ultrahigh vacuum technology.

Research for Metal Surface of High Performance (RIMS)
RIMS is a R&D company for which the Japan Key Technology Centre and participating companies have provided the investment. The main aim is to carry out research to improve resistance against corrosion, heat and wear in materials used for aerospace equipment, chemical plant, marine structures, automobiles, etc. New technologies have made it possible to apply high performance films at high speed to metals of complicated shape. This is being done through various processes such as vacuum evaporation, sputtering and ion plating/implantation and various ways of chemical vapour deposition. The technologies covered by the RIMS research activities imply substantial improvements of functions of metal materials which are expected to lead to important improvements in reliability, quality, stability and costs.

The total funding for the RIMS amounts to Y4 billion for a period of seven years. RIMS have three laboratories which are located in Tokyo and Chiba prefecture, employing 20 full time staff and several more on a part-time basis. The participating companies are mainly heavy engineering companies and metal companies.

Ion Engineering Centre

The Centre is being established in Kansai Science City and will be open for research in 1992. A major purpose is to provide research facilities which are important for future generations of integrated circuits, superconducting materials and other new materials. Establishing the Centre will carry a total cost of Y7.8 billion and facilities will include ion implantation devices, ion vapour deposition devices and electron microscopes.

The centre has been promoted by MITI through its new NEDO branch and is basically financed by private companies with additional investment coming from Osaka prefectural government.

Ultra-High Temperature Materials Research Centre

The Japan Ultra-High Temperature Materials Research Centre was established in March 1990. The Centre will carry out development and testing of materials for use in ultra-high temperature applications such as gas turbines and the proposed space plane. The Centre has been established jointly by private companies and governmental organisations, which include Nippon Steel among a total of 45 companies, NEDO of MITI and two prefectural governments, with a total cost of slightly less than Y1 billion. The Centre, which has two laboratories, will be open both for the private and public sector. It will start operation in the fiscal year 1991 and will work in close collaboration with the Japan Ultra-High Temperature Materials Research Institute which has been established simultaneously – with participation of private companies only.

More advanced projects are being carried out in some of the AIST laboratories. One is basic research on the sensing capabilities of molecular complexes. One objective is to develop molecular sensors which have the ability to identify other molecules. This would open the way for synthetic molecular membranes. Another aim is to understand electron transfer in enzymes and develop sensors based on enzymes. A related project is being carried out at the Industrial Products Research Institute in Tsukuba. Here research is focused on designing an artificial biotic system in which molecules or clusters of molecules react with each other in a controlled succession with an obvious application as sensors. In a third and related project the aim is to design and synthesise molecules which could selectively form clusters with specific ions or other molecular compounds. This would, if successful, mean that the engineering process could take place at the molecular level – at least for certain materials and applications.

Exploratory Research for Advanced Technology (ERATO)

Several of the ERATO projects actually cover advanced research in material science. This applies to the Yoshida Nano-mechanism Project (1985-1990). This project focuses on the physical actions and mechanical properties of material in the nano-meter region, while investigating new measuring and processing methods. To this end selected research topics are being carried out in the fields of basic analysis, measurement and control, as well as processing. The Kuroda Solid Surface Project (1985-90) is also closely related to material science. One of the research areas involves a search for methods to modify single-crystal surfaces in order to form ultra-thin layers or multi-layer systems, such as super-lattices. To deposit such layered systems under well-controlled conditions, various forms of UHV systems were designed and constructed. Further, the chemical reactions of solid surfaces are being studied in a search for methods to modify them by specific reactions with absorbed material, such as those involving organo-metallic compounds. A third project is the Hotani Molecular Dynamic Assembly Project (1986-91). This undertaking aims to understand why supramolecules function properly in thermally fluctuating environments, and fundamental studies are being carried out on the motions of such supramolecules as flagellar motors by direct observation. By utilising the self-assembly function of supramolecules, attempts are being made to create macrostructures whose sizes and shapes can be controlled freely and very precisely by varying thermal, light and other inputs.

Technological landscapes: Extreme Ultrahigh Vacuum Project

Thus there emerge what can be termed technological landscapes which embrace a number of closely related activities. A technological landscape represents the arena in which R&D activities, bearing on a certain technological field, are carried out. This includes activities in university departments on basic research, government research institutes and company laboratories working on both product development and long term research, and finally production. The landscape is characterised by its size, number of actors, linkage among actors and overall activity within the arena. In understanding the efficiency or results it is essential to identify not only bursts of activity in one particular part of the landscape but also its linkages to earlier ongoing activities and its trigger effects in other parts of the landscape.

The cognizance of an activity in one part of the landscape, revealed through one piece of information, is usually not enough to comprehend the full significance of that particular activity. Thus it is essential to select an approach which makes it possible to grasp the contours of the landscape even if a number of pieces of the jigsaw puzzle are not available.

Japan is a country of electronics products, electronics industries and electronics technologies. Vacuum technology is a key basic technology throughout the field of electronics, especially in its development and in several of its applications. When manufacturing integrated circuits, for example, vacuum technology is necessary to control processes and to realise surface structures in order to meet particular characteristics. The following pages attempt to trace emergent developments in the field of semiconductor technology and identify some important actors in one particular field, vacuum technology.

The strategic plan for the development of extreme ultrahigh vacuum technology in Japan provides an illustration. The Science and Technology

Agency (STA), which supports the project, is reported to believe that Japan now lags behind the US and Europe in the development of extreme ultrahigh vacuum technology. In five years, when the project is to be completed, STA believes that Japan will be the world leader in vacuum technology assuming that the planned results are attained.

Among the participants are IC equipment manufacturers who naturally have much to gain from major scientific advances in this technology. Today's sputtering and CVD (chemical vapour deposition) processes, which both use ultrahigh vacuum, are currently vital for the manufacturing of semiconductor devices. Reportedly "extreme ultrahigh vacuum technology would mean that electronic devices more powerful than HEMT (high electron mobility transistor) could be developed." The project member companies include Hitachi, Ulvac, Anelva and Sukegawa Electric Industries which will work with, it appears, highly knowledgeable professors from a number of national research institutes and university departments rather than whole departments.

The Science and Technology Agency is funding the vacuum project under a programme called "Special Co-ordination Funds for the Promotion of Science and Technology" which started operation in 1981. The project is to be funded over a period of five years starting in 1988, with an annual budget in the region of Y250 million (US$2 million). There is a co-ordinating committee of eleven members from the following institutions:

Institute of Physical and Chemical Research (RIKEN)
National Institute for Research in Inorganic Materials (NIRIM)
National Laboratory for High Energy Physics
Electrotechnical Laboratory (ETL)
National Research Institute for Metals
Toho University
Tokyo University (2 members)
Hitachi Ltd
Ulvac Corporation (2 members)

In addition, there are two subcommittees. The first is involved in research on ultra high vacuum (UHV) generation and has nine members from the following institutions:

Institute of Physical and Chemical Research (RIKEN)
National Research Institute for Metals
Tokyo University (3 members)
Hitachi Ltd
Ulvac Corporation
Anelva Corporation
Sukegawa Electric Corporation

The other subcommittee is responsible for research on measuring UHV and has five members from the following research institutions:

National Institute for Research in Inorganic Materials (NIRIM)
Electrotechnical Laboratory (ETL)
Toho University
Waseda University
Kobe University

The leaders of the three groups come from Toho University, RIKEN and Electrotechnical Laboratory respectively. Through contact with Professor Chuhei Oshima, the measurement specialist from the Department of Applied

Physics at Waseda University, part of the origin of the project can be explained. A group of three people (himself and two researchers from ETL and RIKEN) started five years ago to discuss the need to engage in more future-oriented research on UHV. The group prepared a proposal suggesting that UHV should become a national research programme because of its importance and the lack of active company involvement due to the presently small market. The original proposal was not accepted, but their work stimulated discussion within private vacuum companies who eventually proclaimed a positive attitude. An evaluation study then followed, financed by a public foundation, and the project was accepted as a candidate to be included in the category of national research projects. The selection was finally made in 1987 and funding started in 1988.

A closely related project is found in the private sector. The evaporation from the inner walls of the vacuum vessel is a concern with the development of an extreme ultra-high vacuum. Apparently, the Science and Technology Agency has proposed replacing stainless steel, the material currently used in conventional vacuum vessels, with aluminium. To this end a research foundation has been established under the name "The Vacuum Science Laboratory Foundation," also known by the acronym ALVALAB, which indicates that its main task is to be a laboratory for research on aluminium and vacuum technology. One of its brief brochures notes that the aluminum-alloy ultra-high vacuum system will draw on knowledge from particle accelerators, plasma nuclear fusion equipment, semiconductor manufacturing equipment and superconductivity technology.

The foundation, it is said, is receiving co-operation in all fields from companies striving for the development of an aluminium-alloy ultra-high vacuum system. The list of members includes a wider participation of university departments than in the committees discussed above and there is some overlapping membership.

Before looking more closely into the participation of industrial actors, I will turn to the basic aims of the Special Co-Ordination Funds for the Promotion of Science and Technology. These include:

1. to pursue state-of the art basic research;

2. to pursue R&D that requires co-operation with multiple organisations; and

3. to enrich organic collaboration between industries, universities and government.

Which are then the participating industries? Hitachi Ltd is well-known as a highly diversified electrical engineering company. Ulvac Corporation and Anelva Corporation are not listed on the stock exchange and information cannot easily be found on them. A company brochure obtained from ULVAC says that each company within the ULVAC Group is dedicated to vacuum technology and that this technology is indispensable in many fields of industry and science exemplified by the manufacture of integrated circuits.

It is possible to identify a wider network of interaction between industrial development and institute research than was indicated by only looking at the STA-sponsored project. Additional information searches may even reveal a considerably wider network of actors and possibly their contributions to further the development of extreme ultrahigh vacuum technology.

Participation in the STA-sponsored project includes three of the major electronics companies – NEC, Matsushita and Hitachi. The potential for practical application of any of the results of the project is great. It was mentioned that "if the project succeeds, extreme ultrahigh vacuums would provide great power to a wide range of fields, including the development of the next generation of electronic devices". It would also propel Japan into the lead in international extreme ultrahigh vacuum technology. The stated goals of the project is to attain a pressure of 10-11 pascal, which corresponds to that found at the centre of the Milky Way galaxy – an improvement over the present threshold by a factor of 100. Considering the implications for IC manufacturers it may be worth mentioning that the same three major electronics companies, together with Fujitsu, Toshiba, Sumitomo Electric Industries and others, are engaged in research and development to establish industrial technology for constructing synchrotron radiation facilities. One of their main goals is to develop an industrial technology for making fine patterns on future generations of integrated circuits.

Chapter 16

Marine research

Japan has always been dependent on the sea for its supply of fish, seaweed and other marine resources, and has also been exposed to nature's caprices through weather conditions and through earthquakes caused by the movement of the crustal plates along the seabed. Covering 70 per cent of the earth's surface, the oceans are today considered as the last frontier. With their vast size and enormous resources they hold a great potential which has to be meticulously explored and carefully exploited. As Japan is a small nation with limited resources, the development of marine sciences and technologies is becoming important. The interest of Japan and many other countries focuses on the utilisation of diverse metals and minerals, including manganese nodules and crust rich in manganese and cobalt – and the almost unlimited marine energy resources.

The international recognition of the rights of coastal countries to have exclusive control of the development of natural resources within a 200-mile economic zone followed from "The Law of the Sea" adopted by the United Nations in 1982. Under the new Law Japan's exclusive economic zone ranks sixth largest in the world. With its land area added, Japan's zone is estimated to be the tenth largest in the world. Thus, the era of of the 200 mile zone has dramatically changed Japan's area of administration.

The marine exclusive zone naturally poses a number of new challenges as the area is in many ways still unknown and tools for exploration and exploitation are still lacking. Marine exploration has taken on the character of big science and the mood in Japan is that the country should not trail behind the major partners, as is still the case in space exploration. Interest in expanding into marine areas, or rather coastal areas, is fuelled by the limited area of flat land and the construction of "floating cities" and sea-based airports has come to be regarded as a completely natural development in the next century.

The potential and interest in marine development existed before the UN adopted the "Law of the Sea" and research was carried out by several ministries and agencies throughout the 1970s. Thus, the Council for Ocean Development (also known as the Marine Development Council) was established in 1971 to co-ordinate activities and to advance a comprehensive marine development plan. The Council is an advisory body in the Prime Minister's Office and functions with the support of secretariat services provided by the Ocean Development Division within STA. The Council prepared two major reports: "Basic Concepts in Promoting Ocean Development from a Long-Term Viewpoint" in 1979 and "Measures to Promote Ocean Development on Long-Range Perspective" in 1980. These reports have guided the Japanese marine research effort throughout the 1980s.

Plans for marine development

A Liaison Committee for Ocean Development was created in June 1980 to direct development efforts by ministries and agencies. The committee, which represents eleven ministries and agencies, is responsible for formulating an annual Ocean Development Plan. The large number of actors involved in ocean research is shown in Figure 16.1.

There are three major areas of marine exploitation in which research and development is concentrated – biological resources, seabed mineral resources and marine space. For the first, the Ministry of Agriculture, Forestry and Fisheries have formulated a Marinovation Plan. This has been conceived with consideration given to the basic role which the fishing industry should play and also in recognition of the fact that the industry is facing major changes and diversifying needs for utilisation of the sea. The fishing industry expected to play the following basic roles: providing a stable supply of marine products; establishing efficient fisheries; and contributing to the formation of coastal settlements, partly based on marine traditions as a way of life.

Specific activities are spelt out in four subordinate plans. First, a Marine Complex Plan envisages the development of large fishing settlements, including industrial sites. Second, a Maritime Village Plan will promote breeding fisheries, to produce and supply middle and high class fish and shellfish. In this context it has been noted that it will be necessary to raise the technological level of the fishing industry and instil an understanding that fish are a national resource which must not be over-exploited. Third, a Marine Technology Plan will introduce high technology into the fishing industry. Finally, a Marine Culture Plan will protect and perpetuate maritime cultural assets and conserve the fishing ground environment.

The planned activities of MITI concentrate on exploiting manganese nodules and cobalt-rich crusts and prospecting for hydrothermal deposits. MITI has aims to start commercial extraction of manganese nodules early next century and already in 1981 had launched a project to develop the appropriate mining machinery. The project will be completed in 1992.

For a considerable period of time there was great uncertainty about the mining rights for mineral deposits outside the 200 mile exclusive national zone. The issue was not solved until 1987 when Japan was given the mining rights for sites which cover 75,000 sq km. See Figure 16.2.

Since 1987 Japan has been prospecting in the Central and Pacific oceans for cobalt-rich crusts. These crusts are deposits which measure from several millimetres to several centimetres in thickness and are attached to the sides of submarine mountains in the form of coal tar. They are considered to be an important deep seabed mineral resource. Aside from its own national interests Japan has also been engaged in a prospecting project – for manganese nodules and cobalt crust – together with Pacific nations, funded by the Overseas Development Agency (ODA). The third area of MITI interest is the exploitation of hydrothermal deposits which are found as ridges at depths of 2,000-3,000 metres. Such ridges are formed when water penetrates the seabed, is heated by magma and boils, extracting molten metals in the process which include copper, lead, zinc, gold and silver.

The Ministry of Transport has no less ambitious aims although focused more

Figure 16.1 Japan's ocean development promotion system

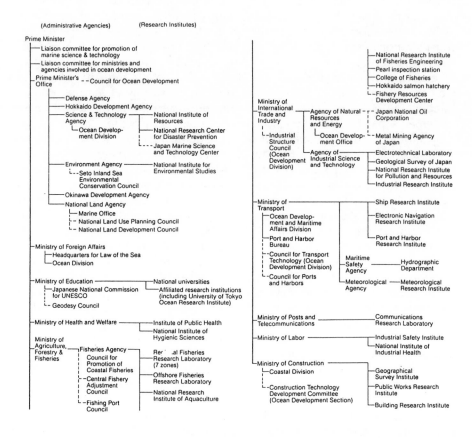

Source: "Ocean Development by Japanese Government" in *Science and Technology in Japan*, June 1988, p. 10

Figure 16.2 Distribution of deep seabed mineral resources

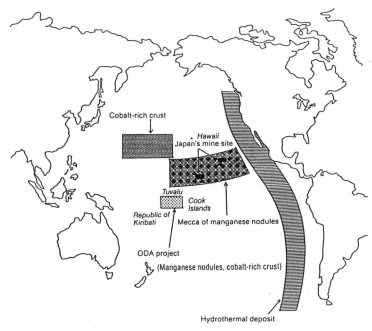

Source: "Ocean Development by Japanese Government" in *Science and Technology in Japan*, June 1988, p. 13

closely on the Japanese archipelago. The ministry envisages large-scale development of marine spaces and waterfronts. To raise the potential for exploitation of deep seas and coastal areas MOT is pursuing construction standards for floating structures, structures designed to sit on the sea bed, and wave-control structures. See Chapter 14.

MOT also has the goal of the development and construction of artificial islands. Early studies have already identified possible sites and surveillance of selected sites will follow. Part of the policy guidelines can be found in "Ports and Harbours for the 21st Century", considering the future needs of the water front when Japan is an ageing society. The policy guidelines for development suggest three different approaches, among other things. One is Port Renaissance 21 which aims at creating comprehensive port and harbour spaces through the joint efforts of private and public sectors. The second is the Marine Town Project which is intended to develop coastal areas for cruises and marinas. Third, the more ambitious Coastal Area Project aims to create large-scale recreation facilities around marinas.

The interests of the Ministry of Construction are in many ways complementary to MOT in that it wants to "Tame Wild Shores". All coastal sheltered zones such as Tokyo Bay and Seto Inland Sea are fully exploited. So, in order to exploit the exposed coastlines it will be necessary to handle nature's rage by controlling waves and coastal erosion. The ministry's Marine Multi-Zone Project aims at making it feasible to develop the coastlines. Together with the Public Works Research Institute, belonging to the ministry, a long-term plan was formulated. The plan identifies three major objectives for research and development: development of sea control structures; development of materials and management techniques for the harsh conditions; and research on marine conservation and utilisation technologies for marine vegetation.

Research on the first category will have to be most innovative. A new type of structure is being sought which is capable of withstanding the rigours of installation in deep water, in order to provide a broad expanse of calm water. Thus, development will focus on structures which are capable of controlling waves, currents and littoral drift in the depths. A number of different structures are being considered which include dissipators utilising swash plates, and piles and caissons to dissipate waves through turbulence and reflection.

Japan has for several decades been active in developing marine space. Port Island has so far been the most spectacular example, as the world's largest container port with a population of more than 20,000 people. Another example is the plant of Nippon Steel which was constructed on an island in Tokyo Bay designed and built for this specific purpose. So far, technology has been traditional and coastal extensions have basically taken place in areas where nature has been relatively mild.

The attention to coastal areas and development of new technologies may, together with the ageing society in Japan, change the nodal concentration of the population away from the Tokyo-Osaka corridor. The costs for artificial islands are still too prohibitive for anything like the new international airport being constructed in Osaka Bay. Construction of caissons have until recently been limited to water depths of no more than 30 metres – for cost reasons. However, the costs of reclaiming land in the Tokyo Bay will be considerably cheaper than buying land in Tokyo proper. So a combination of factors may propel the development of marine space. The Port and Harbour Research Institute in Kurihama in Kanagawa prefecture plays an important role in this development.

Marine development institutions

The description above indicates that marine development in Japan covers a wide range of activities and much effort in research and development needs to be expended before the fruits can be reaped. There is a need for gradual development of a large number of techniques. There is also a need to gain new knowledge in a number of fields and disciplines. The deep-sea exploratory vessels are among the more spectacular projects to gain new and necessary knowledge about the oceans. The deep sea is rich in minerals and biological resources for which the basic mechanisms have to be understood. Japan also has a keen interest in understanding the seafloor mechanisms which can facilitate the prediction of earthquakes and tidal waves.

Japan Marine Science and Technology Centre (JAMSTEC) is a semi-governmental organisation dedicated to marine science and technology. It was created in 1971 through co-operative efforts by the government, academic and private sectors. Its major research activities are in the areas of ocean floor surveys, ocean energy and undersea work systems. JAMSTEC has been involved in the successive stages of developing a deep sea submersible. The first system was Shinkai (Deep Sea) 2000, with its support ship *Natsushima* which was operational in 1981. The second and present stage is the Shinkai 6500 which during a test in August 1989 reached 6,257 metres below the surface. The total cost for developing and building the Shinkai 6500 has amounted to Y12.5 billion.

The Shinkai 6500, which can seat three people measures 9.5 metres long, 2.7 metres wide and 3.2 metres high and is equipped with a titanium antipressure cabin. The Shinkai 6500, based on the earlier Shinkai will be capable of exploring 98 per cent of the world's oceans as well as 96 per cent of Japan's 200-mile territorial waters. The submersible which has its support ship, *Yokosuka*, has three particular purposes: collecting data for precise earthquake predictions; exploring deep-sea natural resources; and finding yet undiscovered deep-sea life to enhance biology research. JAMSTEC has in this context started a research project on deep-sea microbiology called the Deep-Sea Environmental Exploration Programme, Science and Technology for Advanced Research (DEEP STAR).

JAMSTEC will in its next stage, starting in 1990, develop an unmanned deep-sea probe submersible which will be operational down to a depth of 10,000 metres. The probe, equipped with video cameras and manipulators, will be used to observe geographical features and collect living specimens from the deep sea. The probe will be ready in 1992, at a cost of roughly Y5 billion, and also serve as a scout for the Shinkai 6500 or as an emergency rescue unit – if the need arises.

The probe will be the first unmanned submarine capable of diving to depths of 10,000 metres – when it is fully operational in 1994. The remote-controlled submarine will consist of a launcher module suspended below a surface ship and the vehicle module itself linked to the launcher. The vehicle will be equipped with a wide-angle television camera and robot arms for collecting samples. Miniaturisation of components will be a high priority and a 1000 Mbit/second fibre optical communication cable will be used.

Marine biological resources

Japan is faced with a need to meet rising and diversifying demands for marine products, and to increase fishery resources in neighbouring waters in order to maintain a high degree of self-suffiency. Fish products at present account for about half the nation's consumption of animal protein.

In the decade following the Second World War Japan's fishing industry rapidly expanded its zone of operations, fish from coastal to offshore waters and the far seas. Japan catches more fish than any other country in the world – a total of 14 per cent of the world annual fish catch of 74 million tons is taken by Japanese boats. Only one third of this catch has in the past come from Japanese waters. With other nations introducing more stringent measures to guard their own 200-mile economic zones Japan will need to make increased efforts to promote fishing operations and to find new exploitable resources.

In anticipation of the 200-mile zone, Japan took two major steps to increase marine resources in its neighbouring waters. In 1963, the Seto Inland Sea Culture Fishing Centre was founded as a promotion organisation for culture fisheries, and in 1974 the Coastal Fishing Development Law was passed. Such efforts are now steadily bearing fruit as exemplified by a remarkable rise in salmon and trout returning from the open seas to Japan to spawn. In 1984 the production of marine culture as a whole exceeded one million tons for the first time. However, there is a need to recognise the limited nature of marine resources and the increasing scarcity of space on or near the coastal areas.

Of particular interest is the development of untapped marine resources, Antarctic krill being first and foremost among them. Bottom fish resources on the continental flats in the North Pacific including the Gulf of Alaska, which consist mainly of pollack, flat fishes and rock fishes, have been widely exploited by the Japanese and Soviet fleets since the late 1950s.

Stocks of fur seals were severely depleted but have recovered rapidly owing to conservation measures organised by the International North Pacific Fur Seal Commission. Recovery of whale stocks in the Antarctic and effective management of whaling in the North Pacific are decided at meetings of the International Whaling Commission. Japan is in fact one of the last countries to maintain a whaling fleet and has been subject – for many years – to great international pressure to abandon whaling altogether. This pressure is exercised not only by those who fear that whale stocks are poorly managed and that there is a danger of some whale species becoming extinct, but also by those who oppose whaling on moral grounds. However, Japan continues its whaling operations and whale is still being served (July 1990) in many of the fish restaurants in Japan where the customers consider it a delicacy.

The Ministry of Agriculture, Forestry and Fisheries maintains a group of seven fisheries research laboratories. The total staff was around 640 (300 researchers) in 1988 and the combined budget of the institutes Y5.3 billion. The largest of the institutes is the Tokai Regional Fisheries Research Laboratory which also maintains two biological stations – one for marine waters and the other for freshwater. Its main activities include stock assessment and prediction of fishing conditions on fisheries resources and mathematical ecology. Another area is oceanography for the fisheries environment which include utilisation of satellite data for fisheries. The institute maintains a research vessel – *Soyo-maru* – which serves as a platform for scientists who want to investigate oceanography, to conduct biological experiments at sea and to collect detailed biological information on size, composition, eggs and larvae of major marine resources.

Another laboratory is the Far Seas Fisheries Research Laboratory, established in 1967, which is responsible for assessing stocks of living resources in the waters covered by Japanese far sea fisheries and for providing scientific recommendations on management. Recent theoretical advances have widened the scope of the laboratory to include the effects of fisheries upon marine mammals and sea birds incidentally taken during operations and mutual relations with changes of species population in an ecosystem. Such studies form part of the scientific basis for Japan's administrative authority over fisheries and also contribute to the international community.

The other fisheries institutes have more specialised regional responsibilities. Finally the ministry maintains a National Research Institute of Fisheries Engineering and a National Research Institute of Aquaculture, both established in 1979. The former is mainly focused on engineering aspects of aquaculture, fishing boats and fishing gear. The latter conducts more basic studies on various aspects of aquaculture and has divisions for fish genetics, fish reproduction, fish nutrition, environmental management and fish pathology.

The Port and Harbour Research Institute, established in 1962, and already mentioned above, has a total staff of 205 (139 researchers) and an annual budget of Y2 billion (1987). The institute has been the source of expertise for solving engineering problems encountered at Japanese ports. Japan is exposed to severe attacks by the sea, strong depressions in winter and typhoons in the summer or autumn bring huge waves. Port construction works in Japan are being carried out under severe natural conditions which have become more severe with the expansion of facilities into deeper open sea. Thus the institute may be in a good position to take on some of these challenges to expand facilities in the exposed coastal areas in the decades to come. The institute has an offshore structure experimental basin with directional random wave generator and flow generator and also a 105 metre wave channel.

The University of Tokyo maintains the Ocean Research Institute which was established in 1962 on the basis of a recommendation made by the Science Council of Japan with the expressed purpose of intensifying the development of basic and comprehensive research in marine sciences. The institute, with total staff exceeding 200, has altogether fifteen research divisions, the most recently established (1975) being for Ocean Floor Geotectonics. The institute is attached to the University of Tokyo but open to scientists from all over Japan, providing them with access to research vessels and other facilities at locations in Tokyo and at the Otsuchi Marine Research Centre. The two research vessels, *Tansei Maru* with a gross tonnage of 469 and *Hakuho Maru* with a gross tonnage of 3,987, were launched in 1982 and 1988 respectively.

Chapter 17

Environment and research

Japan, which has become an economic giant, is gradually realising the urgent need not only to come to grips with simply domestic matters but to understand and treat the environmental problems in a global context.

Historically the early industrialisation of the Meiji period was accompanied by environmental degradation, and one of the earliest cases was the copper poisoning at the Ashio Copper Mine in Tochigi in 1878. The later development of textile, paper and pulp industries led to water pollution. However, it was not until the extremely rapid industrialisation of the post-war period that the pollution problems reached a crisis situation, with Japan – for a time – becoming one of the most polluted countries in the world.

For a considerable period of time ignorance was prevalent even if the mercury pollution known as Minamata disease was reported as early as 1956. By the late 1960s environmental degradation had greatly affected the national consciousness and a number of initiatives were taken. The fairly successful removal of toxic substances from the water and reduction of sulphur dioxide and carbon monoxide from the air temporarily reassured the population and clouded the urgency to continue the efforts.

The success in limiting pollution by sulphur oxide and carbon oxide can be seen in the greatly lowered figures for gas concentrations in the major cities. The sulphur dioxide concentration fell from 0.057 ppm in 1966 to 0.021 ppm in 1975, while carbon oxide concentration fell from 4.9 ppm to 1.4 ppm between 1968 and 1975.

However, nitrogen oxide concentrations were at the same time rising. The relative success in controlling the concentration of sulphur dioxide and carbon oxide reflects a strong commitment by the government to improve the situation. Measures included a switch to import of oils with lower sulphur content, de-sulfurizing heavy oil and stack gas and stringent requirements on car makers to lower the release of carbonoxide. Attention to nitrogen oxides came much later and emission standards were not adopted until 1973.

Organisation

The environmental crisis of the late 1960s prompted the government to institute a number of measures. One of the first and important measures was the Basic Law for Environmental Pollution Control, enacted in 1967 and subsequently strengthened in 1970. Although a Basic Law has no specific legally binding provisions it made possible the specific legislation which followed: the Air Pollution Control Law, the Water Pollution Control Law and much other legislation dealing with noise and vibration, waste management etc.

The Parliament (Diet) session in 1970 was deeply involved with environmental issues. Among other consequences was the establishment of the Environment Agency (EA) by a special law passed by the Diet in May 1971. The EA – in the Prime Minister's Office – is the central agency in the Japanese government with primary responsibility for national pollution control and environment protection. The establishment of EA was also accompanied by problems, as pollution control functions are distributed among a number of ministries and agencies.

A major reason for setting up the new agency was to comprehensively control pollution, promote administrative measures, set levels for acceptable pollution etc. These responsibilities had in the past been distributed throughout the administration and were only partly transferred to EA. The traditional ministry disputed their proposed loss of power and largely succeeded in restricting the agency's role to that of a co-ordinator, rather than a direct implementor of environmental policies, while holding on to a considerable proportion of regulatory power themselves. At the same time funding for the agency was severely restricted so that the environmental protection budgets of the traditional ministries often exceed that of EA itself. The budget of EA has remained at a low level and is Y9 billion in the fiscal year 1990, which is in fact almost a 15 per cent increase over the preceding year.

The Director-General of EA has the status of a minister and is a member of the cabinet. From outside the agency, advice is mainly received from the Central Council on Environmental Pollution Control, which basically replaced the earlier Pollution Commission of the Ministry of Health and Welfare. The EA Council has 90 regular members, the majority academics and scientists, although ex-government officials, local government officials and representatives from labour unions, private industry and various associations are also members.

The EA Council has a number of sub-committees and expert committees but has no secretariat of its own. The Agency generally asks for recommendations and advances on rather narrowly defined topics and it appears that the role of the EA Council in the past has been far from commensurate with the importance of environmental issues in Japan or world-wide.

Environmental research

The environmental research fields can be classified into the following five areas:

1. development of technology for pollution prevention;

2. development of monitoring and measuring technology;

3. interpretation and assessment of the effects of environmental pollution;

4. identification of the mechanisms of pollution; and

5. conservation of the national environment.

Pollution-related research in Japan and in most other countries has so far in the main been concerned with the domestic situation, at national or regional levels. However, environmental problems have taken on a global and comprehensive character. Thus Japan is, like other nations in the process of finding improved and more relevant research structures to deal with a new situation.

The Environmental Agency in March 1974 established the National Institute for Pollution Studies (*Kogai Kenkyusho*) to be followed by the National Institute for Minamata Disease in October – located at the Minamata bay in Kyushu where the disaster actually took place. There are two other organisations – National Research Centre for Disaster Prevention, belonging to STA, and National Research Institute for Pollution and Resources, belonging to MITI – which are also in environmental research. All the institutes with the exception of the Mimata disease institute are undergoing major changes.

The Environmental Agency had already in August 1988 announced that it would set up a group to promote measures to cope with global environmental problems such as the preservation of the ozone layer and the gradual warming of the atmosphere – acting on a proposal from the agency's advisory council. The EA will subsequently co-ordinate various research activities which also include attention to acid rain, depletion of tropical forests and desertification. It was at the time also decided that the National Institute for Environmental Studies should play an important role in studying global environmental problems. Some two years later, in June 1990, EA announced that it would set up a new task force to co-ordinate activities more strongly and take new initiatives. It was also officially announced that the institute would be renamed and take on a more important role for global environmental problems. Among other things, the institute will create a Global Environmental Research Centre with a database which includes up-to-date information on issues such as global warming, ozone layer depletion, acid rain etc., linked to similar systems in the USA and Europe and accessible world-wide.

The new name of the institute is the National Institute for Environmental Studies (*Kokuritsu Kankyo Kenkyusho*) and the organisation aims to achieve two major objectives. First, the institute will regroup various research divisions into two separate departments – one for interdisciplinary research and the other for basic research in conventional disciplines. Second, the institute will in October 1990 add the Global Environmental Research Centre, already referred to. The new global centre will, in addition to its own staff, also have visiting researchers from government laboratories and universities and in all likelihood also from foreign institutions.

In the reorganisation of this research institute, as in most other cases, the transformation takes place without increasing or reducing the staff and by retraining present staff. However, the Training Institute for Environmental Control Specialists, at present in Tokorozawa City near Tokyo, will in all likelihood be amalgated.

The National Research Institute for Pollution and Resources (NRIPR) has a major research interest in the exploitation and utilisation of mineral and energy resources. The institute, which is supervised by MITI was originally established in 1920, reorganised in 1970 and subsequently relocated to its present site in Tsukuba. Since its reorganisation the institute is also engaged in the development of environmental protection techniques such as technologies for air and water pollution control – at source. It also undertakes environmental assessments and pollution measurements.

In May 1989 the NRIPR formed a special task force to study pressing issues regarding the earth environment. This group will co-ordinate research in three fields. First, it will study pollution from factories by studying substances such as carbondioxide, chloro-fluoro-carbons (CFC), hydrocarbons (CH4) and nitrogen oxides (NOx). Subsequently, it will also look for methods of preventing emission of such substances at the source. Second, it will develop monitoring and analysing methods and compare data from a variety of sources. Third, it will attempt to evaluate the environmental effects of global warming, changes in ocean environment, desertification etc.

The MITI institute mentioned above will in the main retain its present functions. However, the Bureau of Industrial Location and Environmental Protection has set up a new environmental institue, named the Research Institute of Innovative Technology of the Earth (RITE), to be built in Kansai Science City. The institute is to be funded by more than 60 major companies and economic organisations which will contribute a total of Y50,000 million ($400 million), alongside Y70,000 million a year from the Ministry of International Trade and Industry (MITI). The institute will be responsible for the research and development of substitute CFCs, biogradable plastics, and technology to reduce carbon dioxide emissions or to absorb and utilise the gas. In addition to the money from MITI and industry, local prefectural and municipal governments will inject another Y30,000 million into RITE making the institute probably the best-funded national project ever in Japanese history. Around 80 researchers from MITI's national laboratories will be assigned to RITE when it opens in 1992.

In a single year the Environment Agency allocates grants to some 100 research projects amounting to Y2-3 billion. These projects are carried out throughout the total government structure and with only a single project in many of the more than 50 institutes which receive grants. The emphasis is on projects that not only have a bearing on urgent problems but also have positive effects on long-term pollution prevention measures.

Conflicting views are natural in any system, and this is also evident in Japan. The Ministry of Construction and MITI are both actively pursuing actual construction and future-oriented research to construct large-scale underground facilities for highway transportation and possibly also shopping and cultural activities. However, the National Institute for Environmental Studies in late 1989 warned that the development of structures deep underground may cause widespread surface sinking, water pollution and other problems. The institute's research, based on computer simulations, was in response to increasing activities of construction firms to launch below-the-surface projects as a way of coping with rocketing land prices in Tokyo and other major urban concentrations.

Environment-related research institutes

The Geological Survey of Japan, which belongs to MITI, has a total staff of 374 (246 researchers) and an annual budget of Y2.2 billion (1987). The Geological Survey of Japan began as the geological section of the Geographical Bureau in 1882. It has gradually evolved into an integrated scientific arm of the government and covers the entire spectrum of geo-sciences. Departments for Marine Geology and Geothermal Research have been added in recent years.

The institute is responsible for geological sheet mapping and for research on geology and various kinds of resources in the Japanese archipelago, adjoining offshore areas, and the ocean floors. Its work also contributes to environmental conservation and to the mitigation of damage by geological hazards such as earthquakes, volcanic eruptions and landslides.

The Survey has also participated in the MITI Sunshine Programme and has been responsible for carrying out basic research on geothermal systems. Techniques for assessing geothermal resources are being researched, including experimental work on rock specimens from geothermal areas, and the development of a passive seismic method that monitors microseismic activity common in some geothermal areas.

The Geographical Survey Institute, which belongs to the Ministry of Construction, has a total staff of 884 (46 researchers) and an annual budget of Y9.2 billion (1989). It is the central surveying and mapping organisation in Japan.

The Meteorological Research Institute, which belongs to the Ministry of Transportation, has a total staff of 179 (142 researchers) and an annual budget of Y2.5 billion (1989). It performs research on atmospheric, hydrological and geophysical phenomena. Further, it actively participates in international co-operative research projects initiated by organisations such as the World Meteorological Organisation. The institute is organised in nine research divisions which include climate research.

Chapter 18

Regional policy and science and technology

There is an inherent conflict between regional or localised development on one hand and the rapid concentration of industrial and technological activities on the other. About 50 per cent of Japan's population has amassed in the Tokyo-Osaka corridor and even more of the country's economic activity is concentrated here. The outcome is that villages, small towns and even regions have been almost depleted of their population and economic activities. This process has caused serious concern since the early 1960s, although counter-measures have come too late and half-heartedly to have any impact. Even more significant is the prevailing attitude among power holders who in the main appear to favour a status quo situation. This is well illustrated by the location of the new Maglev test track in the northern part of the Tokyo-Osaka corridor with the aim of providing parallel services to the present Shinkansen trains.

The dilemma is evident in the MITI Vision for the 1990s which focuses not only on the need to internationalise Japan's research and development but also regional vitalisation. MITI argues that it is mandatory to correct the existing disparity between regions, and points to industrial technology as a possible means of changing the situation. MITI envisages that private industry, the government and the universities will join forces in research centres – a concept which still has to be defined. The basic philosophy is that industrial and technological stimulation of a region cannot depend on local relatively small companies but requires more substantial and sustained efforts. MITI has in fact initiated a somewhat similar programme – Technopolis – which started in 1980, although to date with only moderate success.

Science cities

The government may have been much more successful in bringing together a major fraction of science and technology activities in a regional cluster – Tsukuba Science City (*Tsukuba Kenkyu Gakuen Toshi*). Although for many years it has been viewed as a failure, Tsukuba is now seen as a model, in spite of shortcomings, and has prompted the initiation of a similar structure – Kansai Science City – at the other end of the corridor. Another 600 kilometres to the west discussions are now under way to create a third Science City in Northern Kyushu.

The growing importance of Tsukuba and the Kansai Science City has so far only marginally changed the dominant character of Tokyo as the centre for most R&D endeavours. The changing regional character should be understood at three different level: the internationalisation of R&D which is discussed in the following chapter; programmes for regionalised development of science and technology; and the clustering of science and technology in major centres. The latter are discussed below.

The rapidly changing regional distribution of economic activities and the population became clear in the late 1950s and regional problems started to appear on the political agenda. In a First National Comprehensive Development Plan of 1962 different approaches were spelled out. The plan indicates a desire to avoid excessive concentration of the population in big cities. The plan policy is based on Growth Pole development strategy, which was in vogue at the time, and the Diet passed the New Industrial City Construction Promotion Law.

Tsukuba Science City

Tsukuba was included in an early plan (1958) for the development of the Metropolitan Tokyo Area, seen as a satellite city of Tokyo – with an orientation towards science activities. A couple of years later, in 1961, an attempt was made at looking into the possibilities of relocating government agencies away from Tokyo. The following year the Council of Science and Technology concluded a proposal for the relocation of national research agencies. The cabinet approved a plan for Tsukuba Science City in 1965 and the start of construction was later approved for a period of ten years, 1965-75. The construction of the National Research Centre for Disaster Prevention, the first new institute to be established in Tsukuba, was finished in 1968. Tsukuba University was opened in October 1973 and by 1979 all 43 institutes originally scheduled to be relocated were completed. The total construction costs for research institutes and facilities and housing amounted to Y1,500 billion (1988).

Today Tsukuba houses one third of the approximately 100 national research institutes and also several other semi-official research organisations such as the Japan Automobile Research Institute, Inc. (JARI) and the Institute of Ocean Environmental Technology of the Japan Foundation for Shipbuilding Advancement. There are two national universities – University of Tsukuba with its new organisation (Chapter 8) and the rather small University of Library and Information Science. Today a number of private companies have also set up research laboratories in Tsukuba and a number of foreign companies have small research teams or laboratories there.

The major part of MITI laboratories organised by the Agency for Industrial Science and Technology, with the major exception of regional laboratories, are located in Tsukuba. The same is true of the laboratories of the Science and Technology Agency. Many other laboratories, belonging to other agencies, were already located outside Tokyo and were not urged to make the move. In recent years there has been a tendency to locate new major research projects at Tsukuba, such as the Sortec Corporation and the Opto-Electronics Technology Research Corporation, which are both organised as R&D companies with investment funds from the Japan Key Technology Centre and private companies. In recent years Kansai Science City has emerged as the major alternative when deciding the location of new research activities – not only for the government but also among private companies.

The institutes were originally grouped in a zone from south to north within the city according to their specialisation. Starting from the south is the biological and agricultural group which contains some fifteen organisations. Further to the north is the science and engineering group, followed by the common facilities which are basically in the centre of the Tsukuba Science City. North of the centre is the University of Tsukuba, with a number of institutes for construction. The National Laboratory for High Energy Physics, which is open to all university researchers, is located in the northernmost part of the City.

The arrangement of the institutes reflects the major aim at the time of construction of achieving cross-fertilisation of ideas by putting related institutes in one place. The mutual exchange of research results and other information has always been the goal. The construction of large-scale facilities which could be used by researchers from different organisations and the promotion of inter-disciplinary research have also been major objectives. Several organisations exist which contribute towards reaching these objectives.

The holding of Research Exchange Promotion Liaison Conferences started as early as 1976. A Research Exchange Centre, supervised by STA, was established in 1978. The earlier Liaison Conference was replaced in 1980 by the Tsukuba Science City Research Institutes Liaison Conference. Another support organisation is the Tsukuba Centre for Institutes, established in 1978, which provides a place for mutual contact and interchange among scientists. This centre acts as a clearing house for information for domestic and foreign visitors and provides a researchers' club and conference rooms.

A more recent addition is the Tsukuba Research and Development Support Centre, which came into existence in February 1988 as a joint venture between Ibaraki prefecture, where Tsukuba is located, the Japan Development Bank (of MITI) and private enterprises. This organisation is considered to be important for a further strengthening of the research system, which involves research activities of the government, the universities and the private sector.

The Tsukuba Research Support Centre is one of eight research parks (or research cores, as is the name in Japanese) which have been approved under the Private Sector Resources Utilisation Law. The idea originated from the Mitsui Group, which wanted to establish an interdisciplinary research and exchange centre which would permit fruitful contacts and collaboration between researchers from different disciplines and from different organisations. Using the site in Tsukuba, the policy is to provide support for individuals and private enterprises to exploit more fully the extensive knowledge resources in Tsukuba.

The facilities include, in addition to common facilities, 93 rooms for use in research and testing (32), promotion of research and development (20), and private liaison offices (40). There are also premises which can be rented to academic, industrial and governmental researchers for conducting joint research. An experiment facility room for joint use has a floor space of approximately 1,000 square metres suitable for large-scale experiments, e.g. pilot plant/systems. Such use is exemplified by joint experiments of the Engineering Research Association for Super Heat Pump Energy Accumulation and the Engineering Research Association of Automated Sewing Systems, which have both been organised by the Agency for Industrial Science and Technology (AIST).

Another organisation is the Tsukuba Research Consortium (TRC) which includes a core group of eight companies: Akashi Seisakusho Ltd, Stanley Electric Co. Ltd, Teisan Ltd, Harima Chemicals Inc, Japan and Metals Co.,

Ulvac Corporation, Hamamatsu Photonics Co., and Yaskawa Electric Manufacturing Co.. The companies, which are research-oriented and leaders in their respective fields, have formed a club – TRC.

TRC was established to promote research and development on advanced and innovative technologies in various field in an environment where there would be a free exchange of ideas and co-operation among researchers from different backgrounds and disciplines. In addition to the core group of eight companies, TRC also includes a satellite group of companies engaged in various service activities or research, making use of TRC facilities. The consortium provides facilities for seminars and meetings and often sponsors such activities. In this and other ways TRC provides opportunities for researchers from government and academic circles to meet with counterparts in the private sector.

The creation of a new science city naturally caused a number of problems. Many researchers and other staff were unwilling to move with their families – partly motivated by concern for children's schooling – and remained commuters for several years. Second, the interdisciplinary contacts and contacts between institutes belonging to different organisations have been much weaker than expected. The reasons are to be found in the geographical character of the Tsukuba Science City and the rivalry between agencies.

Third, the university, with its new organisation and interdisciplinary character could have served as a focal point for the research community, but has basically remained a teaching university and the Ministry of Education has been unwilling to spare research funds from its scant resources for the University – needed for, among other things, their own institutes located in Tsukuba. Finally, the private industry was initially not very eager to establish research facilities in the area.

However, Tsukuba Science City is gradually evolving into an integrated research environment which is seen as more and more attractive both domestically and internationally. The International Science and Technology Exhibition held in Tsukuba in 1985 not only helped to improve the image of the Science City but also prompted decisions on improvements of the infrastructure, such as the construction of the Joban Highway which makes it possible to travel between Tokyo and Tsukuba in one hour. This is one contributing factor in the increased interest of private companies in seeking laboratories, and the number has risen to more than 160, although most of them are still on a modest scale. The number of researchers in government laboratories has now reached 6,700.

Before comparing it with other science cities it should be noted that Tsukuba Science City consists of the "Science City" itself. The research and education facilities have been constructed along with housing and public facilities – in an area of about 2,700 hectares. The surrounding area makes up the remainder of the City and covers about 26,000 hectares. According to plans the former area will eventually have a population of 100,000, with another 120,000 in the remainder making a total population of 220,000 on 28,560 hectares.

The closest resemblance to Tsukuba Science City is to be found in Novosibirsk City in the USSR and South Ile de France Science City in France. See Table 18.1. The Research Triangle Park in the USA has a certain resemblance, although it has a much more active private industry participation, which may also develop in Tsukuba.

Table 18.1 World's principal science cities

	Tsukuba Science City	Research Triangle Park (US)	Novosibirsk Science City (USSR)	South Ile de France Science City (France)	Sophia Antipolis Science City (France)	Louvain University Science City (Belgium)	Remarks
Area (ha)	2,700 ha approx.	2,300 ha approx.	1,300 ha approx.	3,500 ha approx.	2,400 ha approx.	900 ha approx.	1) The Louvain University Science City was cited as an example since cities of this type are common in the US, UK, West Germany, East Germany, Italy, Portugal, Holland, Denmark, Sweden and other countries. 2) Although they are not shown in this table, there are more than 150 research parks (such as Silicon Valley) in the US
Population (Designed Scale)	136,000 approx.		50,000 approx.	112,000 approx.		50,000 approx.	
Objectives	Alleviation of trend of overconcentration of population and industrial plants in Tokyo area, and construction of a so-called 'brain city' with an ideal environment through concentration of research institutions	Fostering of industries that demand higher levels of technology, creation of job opportunities and promotion of local industrialisation	Creating an environment for pursuing elementary to applied research in order to develop Siberian natural resources	Construction of science city through concentration of research institutions, private industries, etc	Construction of international city for promotion of education, science and technology (to be completed in 1990s)	Establishment of a new setup for promotion of education through respective languages to eliminate cultural disputes arising in the country because of language difficulties	

Source: Science and Technology in Japan 2(5):7. Three 'I' Publications Limited, Tokyo.

					Catholic University of Louvain IBM Research Centre
Core institutions	44 national or quasi-governmental research organisations and 2 universities	More than 35 governmental, academic and private research institutions	20 national research institutions and universities	26 organisations comprising research institutions, universities, etc	49 organisations comprising research institutions, universities, etc
Number of employees, etc	About 11,000 employees of research organisations. About 31,000 including family	Over 8,000 employees of research organisations	About 18,000 employees of research organisations. About 45,000 including family	About 13,000 employees of research organisations	About 2,800 employees of research organisations
Distance from capital to large city	About 60 km from heart of Tokyo	11 km from Raleigh (population about 130,000), 23 km from Chapel Hill (population about 35,000) and 24 km from Durham (population about 110,000)	About 25 km from Novosibirsk (population about 1,000,000)	About 15 km from Paris	Situated between Nice and Cannes, about 22 km from Nice

Kansai Science City

The concept of a Kansai Science City was first brought forward in 1970 by Professor Azuma Okuda, former president of Kyoto University, who organised a study committee. The members, who came from academic and industrial circles of the region, contemplated the character of a research environment in the coming century. The early conceptualisation was helped by two factors. First, there was a growing realisation, based on experience from Tsukuba, that the early and active involvement of private industry was essential. Second, the need for closer collaboration among researchers in universities, in government institutions and private laboratories was also clearly realised.

The concept received a strong political boost from the plan to build the new Kansai International Airport in Osaka prefecture – in itself a consequence of the impossibility of reaching agreement on a new international airport outside Tokyo. In order to get the necessary local political support, Osaka offered the Kyoto prefecture support for the already conceptualised Kansai Science City. Local agreement from the mid-1980s or even earlier was transformed into national government actions during the following years. Thus a Kansai Science City Construction Promotion Act was promulgated in June 1987 to be followed by all the necessary political and bureaucratic procedures.

The outcome was evidently clear much earlier, as the Advanced Telecommunications Research Institute International (ATR, see Chapter 9), formally established as a R&D company, never did contemplate any other location than the *Kei-Han-Na Gakuen Toshi* (a short name for Kansai Science City). A number of other government-directed or sponsored research organisations have also been located at the City, as exemplified by the Protein Engineering Research Institute (PERI). See Chapter 15.

The size of the area set aside for research, education and culture is approximately the same as in Tsukuba Science City (and in other major science cities): 3,300 hectares. The surrounding area covers another 11,000 hectares and the total population is expected to reach 380,000. An interesting feature of Kansai Science City is that research activities are not concentrated but spread out in twelve clusters throughout the Kansai City. However, through the inability to obtain land in one concentrated location, the cluster concept may actually have provided a bias for selection and interaction among related institutions.

The Kansai region boasts of top schools like Kyoto University and Osaka University, and the area contains a total of 98 universities and 111 junior colleges. This is 21 per cent and 20 per cent respectively of the national total. Kansai Science City will not only benefit from contacts with the universities in the area but will also get a boost from branch university campuses set up within the clusters. This is exemplified by Doshisha University and Doshisha Women's University which have established new campuses in the Tanabe district.

Japan's single national university offering solely graduate programmes will be established in one of the districts. The Kansai area universities – in particular Kyoto University – claim that they are in a better position to offer a creative research environment, because they are organised in a freer way and their professors spend less time on official committees, compared with colleagues in Tokyo.

Furthermore, the companies in the Kansai region consider themselves to have a leading edge in biotechnological and chemical research. Consequently the Osaka urban prefecture in 1988 decided to open a research centre for biotechnology industry in the northern part of the prefecture. This area of 850 hectares is eventually expect to house some some 60,000 people – mainly researchers and their families.

The Suntory company, in beer-making and other drinks, and Tanabe Seiyaku in pharmaceuticals are among the companies which have decided to set up research centres in the new area. The new Peptide Institute, an R&D company with investment from the Japan Key Technology Centre, will also be located here. Two other organisations, the Senri Life Science Centre and the Osaka Bioscience Institute (OBI), will also be important for the future development of biotechnology in the region.

OBI is being built to commemorate the anniversary of the City of Osaka and will be one of the institutes in the Osaka Business Park. The activities of OBI will centre around four main themes: enzymes and metabolism; neuro-science; cell biology; and molecular biology. OBI has also set out to nurture young researchers who will play leading roles in the future, and actively promote international research in biosciences. The Senri Life Science Centre, located in the vicinity of Osaka University, will foster interdepartmental contacts for researchers who are active in the Institute for Molecular and Cellular Biology and the Research Institute for Microbial Diseases at Osaka University, as well as the Protein Engineering Research Institute (PERI).

The concentration of research activities in the Kansai region does not depend only on national or local government initiatives. Leading electronic companies, based in Tokyo, have started to move research facilities to the Kansai region. This is true for Hitachi and NEC, Toshiba and OKI are also contemplating setting up research stations. One factor is that big companies are finding it difficult to recruit enough competent researchers in the Tokyo region and by relocating research are expected to have access to a broader pool of scientific talent.

Another attraction has been the location of new institutions such as the ATR, which has influenced the software company CSK, to decide on a new laboratory nearby. This may have been one contributing factor leading Canon to locate its new laboratory for long term exploratory research in the area. See Chapter 10. Both Fujitsu and Hitachi are contemplating the establishment of centres or laboratories for software in the Kansai region in order to tap the pool of computer science graduates, who are reluctant to move to Tokyo.

The belated efforts of the Kansai region to establish a strong foothold in science and technology is also supported by the character of the region. About 20 million people, some 17 per cent of Japan's total population, live in the Kansai area. Aside from the market and source of quality of the labour-force, the area also accounts for a corresponding amount of the Gross Domestic Product – which is approximately the same as that of Italy or Canada. The scientification of industry and the growing internationalisation of R&D have provided Kansai with a good opportunity to establish not only a concentration of R&D efforts but also excellence in research. Given the importance of Kansai Science City for the long-term future, the estimated costs of Y3,000 billion may seem quite reasonable.

In a third location, at Fukuoka in northern Kyushu, politicians and academics, have started to look into the feasibility of establishing a third Science City in Japan. The Fukuoka prefecture wants the central government, universities and private companies to set up research centres which could be linked into an integrated research system. Despite its less broad economic base northern Kyushu considers that it has an extra advantage in being closer to the rapidly developing Asian countries. If such expectations materialise, Japan would have a chain of three Science Cities spread out at intervals of some 600 kilometres.

The Technopolis Concept – plan and policy

A Technopolis Plan was proposed by MITI in its report on long-term development for the 1980s, with a suggestion to build two or three technopolises. The basic idea was to promote the economic development of a local area, basing this on high-technology industry, R&D activities (within a university or elsewhere) and residential areas – all organically integrated. Almost all the 47 prefectures immediately responded to the MITI idea and wanted to have technopolises established within their borders. In meeting the demand MITI decided that nineteen technopolises should be selected initially, with additions later on.

The technopolis should fulfil four conditions. First, all three components of industries, university or research basis, and living area should be in one location. Second, the technopolis should be built near a city which has a population of 200,000 or more. Third, it should be located near an airport or a major railway station so that contacts with the Tokyo or Kansai region can be easily maintained. Fourth, the main structure for the technopolises should be basically completed by 1990 – with further development and measures to follow. In 1990 MITI, in co-operation with other ministries, embarked on a mid-term evaluation of the Technopolis Programme which will receive new guidelines in 1991 for the remaining part of the decade.

It is possible to classify the experience in three groups. First, in a number of locations there was already a strong industrial base which naturally provided good conditions. This is exemplified by Oita prefecture which is strong in electronics although the value-added level is relatively low. In Oita, which lies at the north-eastern wing of Kyushu Island, the technopolis zone is spread over nineteen municipalities and townships, including two other cities – Oita and Beppu.

The vastness of the zone reflects the decision to develop a dispersed technopolis in which high-tech factories are scattered throughout a zone rather than clustered around a technopolis centre. Kumamoto, also on Kyushu, has had similar favourable conditions of a high level of industrial sophistication – also in electronics.

A second category comprises technopolises aimed at developing a frontier line of development. This may be true for the Ehime Technopolis where under the theme of "Man and Technology – Creating an Ehime Technopolis" the Technopolis Foundation has sponsored various projects in biotechnology, telecommunications and mechatronics. A third category is formed by those areas which have a weak industrial and technological base and have seen little progress.

Apart from certain exceptional cases, the technopolis has not really taken off. There are a number of reasons. The increasing value of the yen made it difficult for many small local companies to compete in a high technology market. The screening of investment proposals may not have been given sufficient attention with the consequence that many products from several Technopolis companies have been difficult to sell. Second, the Technopolis Programme has been strongly controlled by MITI, with few possibilities for the prefectural governments to control and co-ordinate – unless there is a strong governor, like Hiramatsu in Oita prefecture.

In sum, the Technopolis Programme runs counter to major trends in the ongoing restructuring of R&D activities and industrial activities. The former seem to accumulate in certain natural locations or in designated science cities while the latter are relocated – increasingly abroad – according to the strategic plans of large companies. This excludes the possibility of identifying suitable candidates for more than a limited number of technopolises – unless the concept is radically revised. However, changes are a likely outcome of the mid-term evaluation.

Administrative competition, or rivalry, is also evident in regional technological development. The Science and Technology Agency announced for the fiscal year 1990 that it plans to establish a number of Science Centres which in many ways are parallel to the Technopolis concept – although STA has a much weaker supporting network in the regions than MITI. An important factor, compared with similar attempts in other countries, is that the Ministry of Education does not participate. In this context it should also be noted that only a limited number of the institutions of higher learning are research universities and they are usually located in large urban centres.

Research cores in research parks

The term "research park" generally refers to a concentration of research and development activities which are carried out in the facilities of universities, public institutions and private company laboratories. In a certain sense Tsukuba Science City is a giant research park. The concept has recently attracted much attention from various regional bodies in Japan which are looking for new possibilities to promote local development.

In 1990 construction was in progress on more than 30 sites, with existing construction plans totalling nearly 50. These plans aim to establish centres which integrate governmental, public and corporate research institutions and enterprises. Several projects are of larger scale and have been approved under the Private Sector Resources Utilisation Law. This law is formally the Temporary Law for Promoting the Strengthening of Specific Facilities by Utilising Private Sector Business Capabilities and came into existence in May 1986.

The principal objective is to encourage and facilitate the use of private sector funds and resources in joint projects with the public sector. The law initially designated eight kinds of basic facilities for promotion which include basic facilities for research and development as well as commercialization, and facilities for telecommunications research and development promotion (telecom research parks). In 1990 eight research core projects had been approved in the first category – of which the earlier mentioned Tsukuba Research Support Centre is one.

The projects must be managed by public and private partnership enterprises and must include four types of facilities – research and experimental facilities, training facilities, display and conference facilities, and management facilities. An approved project will be given preferential treatment which includes tax reduction/exemption and low-interest loans. The projects include the Kanagawa Science Park, Tsukuba Research Support Centre, Senri Life Centre (near Osaka), Kurume Techno-Research Park (Northern Kyushu), Eniwa Research Business Park (Hokkaido), 21st Century Plaza (Sendai), Toyama

Figure 18.1 Location of research core projects

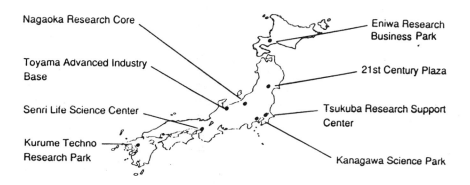

Source: "Introduction to Japanese Research Parks" in New Technology Japan (JETRO), vol. 18, no. 2, May 1990, p. 5

Advanced Industry Base and Nagaoka Research Core. The last two are in locations facing the Japan Sea – opposite to the Kanto region. See Figure 18.1.

The Kanagawa Science Park was the first research core project, authorised under the Private Sector Resources Utilisation Law, and opened in November 1989. The project, which saw its origin in a proposal in 1977 to establish an "intelligence centre", is a huge complex. It has two major buildings – R&D Business Park and Innovation Centre, with a total floor space of 146,000 square metres.

This reflects the fact that Kawasaki, where the project is located, has become the preferred location for many research and development institutes. The city has in fact been transformed into a centre for the nation's leading electronic and mechatronic industries.

Locational pattern for R&D and high-technology industries

The total number of research personnel in the private sector is 214,000. Almost 41,000 are working in Metropolitan Tokyo. Another 56,000 are employed in Kanagawa prefecture, which also includes Yokohama, immediately south of

Figure 18.2 Regional distribution of high-technology factories established during 1979-83 and 1984-88 respectively

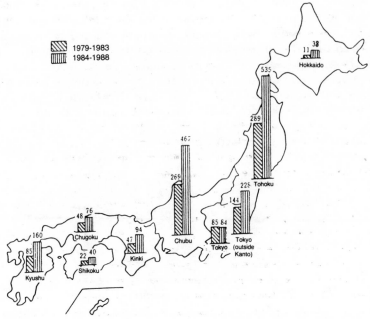

Source: Science and Technology White Paper (Kagaku Gijutsu Hakusho). Compiled by Science and Technology Agency, Tokyo 1989. Printing Bureau, Ministry of Finance, p. 72

Tokyo, where many of the major electronics and electrical machinery companies maintain large laboratories. Another 20,000 are in Osaka and 16,000 in Aichi prefecture, which also includes Nagoya.

The orientation of research differs very distinctly between the different regions. More than 30 per cent of the 128,000 research staff in the Kanto region are working in telecommunications and electronics and electrical machinery. Electrical machinery research occupies more than 40 per cent of the 44,000 research staff in the Kinki region.

The location of manufacturing plants for high-technology products shows a distinctly different pattern. Many more new plants have, since the late 1970s, been established in Tohoku and the northern part of central Honshu. This trend has been considerably accelerated during the latter half of the 1980s. See Figure 18.2.

The regions outside the Tokyo-Osaka corridor have traditionally had a large share of high-technology plants and factories and the role of those regions has continued to increase during the 1980s. See Table 18.2.

Table 18.2 indicates that research and development activities are increasingly located in a limited number of large urban centres while industrial plants are decentralised. This pattern is also confirmed by information on the establishment of new manufacturing plants and research institutes. In the interior of Kanto, which includes Saitama prefecture, there is an approximate balance between new establishment of factories and new research institutes. In the coastal areas, with Tokyo itself and Kanagawa prefecture, the

Table 18.1 Regional distribution of researchers in private industry – by prefecture

Prefecture	Researchers	Prefecture	Researchers	Prefecture	Researchers
Hokkaido	214	Ishikawa	670	Okayama	1,220
Aomori	21	Fukui	203	Hiroshi	4,188
Iwate	49	Yamanashi	209	Yamaguchi	1,598
Miyage	577	Nagano	921	Tokushima	257
Akita	n.a.	Gifu	1,713	Kagawi	230
Yamagata	51	Shizuoka	7,522	Ehimi	414
Fukushima	336	Aichi	16,041	Kochi	n.a.
Ibaraki	7,064	Mie	2,417	Fukuoka	1,878
Tochigi	4,967	Shiga	4,022	Saga	180
Gumma	4,148	Kyoto	5,342	Nagasaki	354
Saitama	8,375	Osaka	20,147	Kumamoto	197
Chiba	6,912	Hyogo	8,278	Oita	387
Tokyo	40,837	Nara	3,186	Miyazaki	314
Kanagawa	55,700	Wakayama	496	Kagoshima	n.a.
Nigata	897	Tottori	445	Okinawa	n.a.
Toyama	1,314	Shimane	274		
				TOTAL	214,656

Source: Science and Technology White Paper (Kagaku Gijutsu Hakusho). Compiled by Science and Technology Agency, Tokyo 1989. Printing Bureau, Ministry of Finance, p. 76

Figure 18.3 Number of new research institutes related to the share of industrial plants – by region (1985-88)

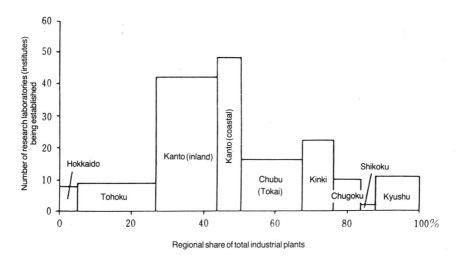

Source: Science and Technology White Paper (Kagaku Gijutsu Hakusho). Compiled by Science and Technology Agency, Tokyo 1989. Printing Bureau, Ministry of Finance, p. 70

establishment of research institutes predominates. In the rest of the country, with the exception of Kinki, the pattern of location shows a dominance of new industrial activities over new research activities. See Figure 18.3.

Thus, the regional distribution of research activities in Japan shows two different characteristics. One is the concentration of scientific research in two major science cities. The other is the heavy concentration of R&D in a small number of urban concentrations which are dominated by Tokyo-Kanagawa-Yokohama, Nagoya and Osaka. This is further accentuated by the concentration of research universities in the same locations. This location pattern is further supported by the attitudes of young people seeking university entrance and looking for job opportunities upon graduation. Until fundamental changes occur in structures and attitudes the present pattern for locating research is likely to prevail. The two science centres may grow in importance and the balance between Osaka and Tokyo may become more equal although the main structure will remain – only to be partially modified by the need to globalise R&D activities.

Chapter 19

Internationalising research and development in Japan

Japan is in marketing and sales, and recently also in finance, one of the most internationalised countries. Japan has in the past constantly been a net importer of technology. The country has been highly successful in importing technology and building an industrial and technological capability which has few if any parallels. This has led the USA and Europe to accuse Japan of being a free rider for technological development. In the following an attempt will be made to clarify the situation and indicate both the many ongoing changes and the shortcomings on both sides in the debate whether Japan should make a larger contribution to sustaining the global scientific basis.

Let us look first at the Japanese university system, which lacks the research tradition and initiative which are the hallmark of the top universities in the US – and to a lesser extent of universities in Europe. This is also true for the major national universities like the University of Tokyo, Kyoto University and Osaka University, to mention some of the universities in the Japanese top league.

A major and highly successful attempt to raise the standard of university research has been the establishment of research institutes for joint use by all universities. Since the Second World War research institutes have been established at national universities to carry out fundamental research and to be available to scientists outside the university to which they belong, with the objective of encouraging communication and co-operation among scientists. More recently a new kind of institute, the National Research Institutes for Joint Use by Universities, has been set up. These are not dependent on any particular university but have the same legal status as universities and are open to visiting researchers. They promise to go a long way towards improving basic research in Japan.

Still the Japanese research system is considered weak by its own scientists as revealed in a survey carried out by the Science and Technology Agency and directed towards scientists belonging to the Science Council of Japan. The respondents cited lack of financial resources and lack of opportunities for young scientists as a major hindrance to Japan in developing centres of excellence. The scientists were asked to rank the ten best research centres in the world and in Japan. None of the world centres chosen were located in Japan. See Table 19.1. Four of the special university institutes were among the top ten in Japan but only Kyoto University qualified, among the universities.

Table 19.1 Ten best research centres in Japan and the world

Japan	World
1 National Laboratory for High Energy Physics of Education Ministry	National Institutes of Health (US)
2 Institute of Physical and Chemical Research of Science and Technology Agency	Massachusetts Institute of Technology (US)
3 Electrical Communications Laboratories of Nippon Telegraph and Telephone Corp.	Max-Planck Gesellschaft for the Promotion of the Sciences (West Germany)
4 Institute for Molecular Science of Education Ministry	Harvard University (US)
5 Kyoto University	Stanford University (US)
6 National Cancer Centre of Health and Welfare Ministry	Princeton University (US)
7 Electrotechnical Laboratory of the Ministry of International Trade and Industry	University of California at Los Angeles (US)
8 Earthquake Research Institute of the University of Tokyo	California Institute of Technology (US)
9 Okazaki National Research Institute of Education Ministry	Bell Laboratory of American Telephone & Telegraph Co. (US)
10 Engineering Faculty of Kyoto University	University of California at Berkeley (US)

Source: Japan Times

Exchange of researchers

However, the Japanese universities are attracting more and more foreign students. The number has risen from a total of 6,000 in 1978 to more than 31,000 students in 1988. Students from Asian countries constitute approximately 90 per cent with 10,850 from China, 6,575 from South Korea and 6,063 students from Taiwan. See Figure 19.1. The government has set the goal of increasing foreign enrolment in the Japanese universities to 100,000 by the year 2000 – with some 10 per cent receiving scholarships from the Japanese government. A small number of universities and graduate programmes offer education in English. This is true for the International University of Japan in Niigata, where instruction in the Graduate School is conducted in English "with a view to educating talented men and women whose skills will be applicable throughout international society".

The exchange of researchers looks balanced when looking at the aggregate data, with about 25,000 Japanese going abroad and an equal number of foreigners coming to Japan in 1983. The Japanese number had increased to about 55,000 in 1986 while foreign researchers coming to Japan numbered about 43,000. However, the distribution between developing and industrialised countries is very unequal. See Figure 19.2.

Japan is sending most researchers to industrialised countries and receiving the majority of researchers from developing countries. The ratio between receiving and sending researchers is 2.90 for developing countries and 0.16 for industrialised countries. These statistics do not provide any details about the

Figure 19.1 Foreign students in Japan

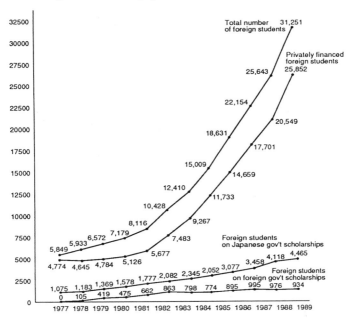

Source: Japan Times, June 28, 1990

length of stay. However, there can be little doubt that the figures indicate an imbalance; the USA and Europe want to redress the balance and urges Japan to embark on various initiatives, some of which are covered in the following.

The dominance of researchers from developing countries has two fundamental reasons. First, Japan has become the dominant aid donor in the world surpassing the USA in 1989 – even if the total amount is a low 0.32 per cent of Japan's gross national product. Second, many developing countries perceive Japan to be a first choice when shopping for technology, even if the country may not be willing to transfer its most advanced technologies.

Globalisation of company research

When viewing the location of company R&D facilities it is apparent that Japan is much less internationalised than other developed countries. An estimated 2 per cent of private company research is conducted outside Japan, while the corresponding figure for Sweden is 25, which reflects the small size of the country. However, more than 10 per cent of US private company research is conducted outside the USA, with the outstanding example of IBM which conducts 40 per cent of its research outside.

Most major Japanese companies having substantial sales abroad have indicated plans for relocating or rapidly expanding research and development overseas. Sony and Canon have indicated that they may have 10 per cent of total R&D outside Japan as early as 1992, while Sumitomo Electric and NEC may reach the same percentage in 1995. The major electronics makers and also other companies also forecast that a substantial part of their long-term and

Figure 19.2 Number of researchers entering and leaving Japan

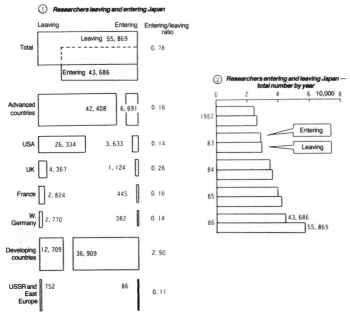

Source: Readings from *Nikkei Economic Reporters,* 1990 edition (*Nikkei Keizai Kiji no Yomikata* '90 Nenban), Tokyo 1990

exploratory research will be conducted outside Japan by the year 2000. The globalisation of company research could mean that by 1995 Japan would have 20,000 researchers outside Japan, which could increase to 30,000 some five years later. Naturally the foreign companies are likely to build up corresponding R&D facilities inside Japan. According to MITI statistics there were in 1987 5,192 researchers in 155 laboratories in Japan controlled by foreign companies with a total annual expenditure of Y68 billion.

Two years later there were 7,863 research staff in 144 foreign-controlled research facilities. The largest of them all is IBM Japan which has almost 2,000 staff in its three research laboratories in Japan.

Most of the large chemical companies in Europe and in the USA maintain laboratories in Japan, as do several electronics and computer makers as well as many other companies. Tsukuba has become an increasingly popular place, where more than 1,000 foreigners work (1990).

There are already many research facilities controlled by Japanese companies abroad although available MITI statistics are not very detailed. The information indicates that company R&D abroad in 1987 was about one fourth in Asian countries with the remainder equally divided between North America and Europe. The R&D expenditure given by MITI was Y44 billion in the fiscal year 1987, which is on the same level as foreign-controlled research in Japan. In the late 1980s many Japanese companies started more systematically building R&D structures abroad, which has occasionally includeed taking over foreign companies as exemplified by Fujitsu buying the computer company ICL in Great Britain in 1990.

Thus, there is at present a balance in the location of company R&D. Japanese universities are increasingly being utilised by foreigners. Japan receives almost as many researchers as it sends abroad. However, there is a more fundamental problem which has more and more a central theme in the international discussion on technology and Japan. Is Japan a free technology rider? It is the theme of many books and the issue will be mentioned only briefly below.

There is no doubt that Japan has in the past benefited from technology being freely available, although at a cost, at a time when free trade was prevalent and huge markets expanding, not only in the USA and Europe but also elsewhere. Japan, or rather its industrial companies, eliminated the technology gap vis-a-vis the developed countries and in fact in many sectors established a new gap – in its own favour.

There is also little doubt that Japan is underinvesting in its university system, compared with the USA and many European countries. As a corollary there is also a continuing underinvestment in basic research – given Japan's resources and level of economic development. Finally, the homogeneity of the country and its subsequent closed character of the society have preserved bureaucratic practices which have in the past hindered easy entry into the research community in Japan.

It has occasionally been argued by key people in the US administration that Japan should grant access to Fujitsu laboratories in exchange for access to the laboratories of the Massachusetts Institute of Technology. However, the causes for technological friction between Japan and developed countries have be understood in their special context and dealt with accordingly. The technological gap between companies in Japan and those of other countries has to be understood at company level, as the reasons for changes in a global dynamic economy are more likely to be found in company strategies and levels of markets and technological foresight, than in government actions.

Mutual access to research

The technology gap and the different character of the research system have bewildered policy makers in the USA, and they have tried to deal with both in a mixture. The two countries agreed on a second agreement for co-operation in research and development in science and technology in July 1988.

This agreement replaces an earlier one from 1980. The new one states, in the first article, that there should be comparable access to major government-sponsored or government-supported programmes and facilities for visiting researchers, and also comparable access to and exchange of information.

Assuming that various research consortia in Japan should be open for US researchers, one would assume that US projects on high definition television and semiconductor technology would be open to the Japanese – as would defence research projects. The consequences have obviously not been carefully thought through.

Then a related confusion added fuel to the fire of technology friction and almost led to the cancellation of a joint US-Japan development of the FSX fighter for the Defence Forces in Japan. Powerful political interests in the USA wanted to cancel the agreement, as they feared it would provide Japanese industry with the knowledge to challenge Boeing in the civilian aircraft market. However, such views neglect the fact that Japan has for decades been building aircraft fighters based on American technology, and has already become a supplier of aircraft components which are highly regarded both in the US and in Europe.

Furthermore, an important element is the control of market, in which leasing companies are important. The financial clout of Japan may mean that Japanese capital is, in principle, controlling a significant share of the market for civilian aircraft through its financial control of leasing companies.

Second, there is good reason for Japan to invest considerably more in long-term basic and exploratory research with only weak or no strings to industrial applications. Previous chapters in this book have provided many demonstrations that Japan is moving – at least slowly – in this direction.

There is little doubt that much research will in the future be carried out by international research consortia – not least for meteorological and environmental research – and Japan is more than likely to want to participate. However, it appears to be a poorly conceived thought for the US government to come begging for a major Japanese contribution to the Superconducting Super Collider (SSC).

Although international co-operation is a good idea, the US Administration should have started with an international project and asked the foreign research community to participate in all stages. Equally, ill-conceived ideas are raised to suggest that the Japanese government should pay for this or that research, or even make a major contribution to the university system, because so many Japanese are undertaking research at US universities. Similarly the Japanese approach in inviting foreign participation in large-scale research programmes has seldom been well conceived, as illustrated below.

Third, many procedures, regulating conditions for staff at national research laboratories and national universities, have in the past almost completely excluded foreign researchers. This has gradually changed during the 1980s and no longer poses a major hindrance. The Science and Technology Agency has, through its Special Co-Ordination Funds for the Promotion of Science and Technology, established a fellowship programme under which 100 young foreign researchers are accepted in various national research institutions. Similar changes are under way in many other parts of the system.

Another example, also from STA, is the International Core System for Basic Research (*Kokusai Ryudo Kiso Kenkyu*) which was announced in May 1988. This system is planned in particular to promote inter-agency, inter-sector and international co-operation for basic research in government laboratories in Japan. Researchers in the groups must come not only from several laboratories in Japan but also from foreign countries. Several companies, such as Hitachi, have created scholarship programmes – usually in the central research laboratories.

Japanese international projects

In October 1980 *Japan Economic Journal* reported that Japan, the US, West Germany, Britain and France were going to undertake joint research and development to make a practical fifth generation computer (FGC) available in the 1990s. An expert meeting was to be held in Tokyo the following year. The ten-year project, which was given a budget of Y65 billion, was started in early

1982 and immediately founded the Institute for New Generation Computer Technology (ICOT). The direct foreign participation never materialised but the project triggered intensive planning activity at the EC Commission in Brussels, and by government agencies in London and several other places. So the outcome was a number of competing projects rather than collaboration along the lines suggested by the Japanese.

In the ten-year FGC Project, computer scientists were expected to devote the first three years to basic research, the next four years to the development of sub-systems and the last three years to the completion of the total system. Today it has become clear that the project will not reach its final goal and this is seen as a failure in the West without any consideration of the benfits that have been gained. Dr Fuchi, the project leader, has also indicated that foreigners misunderstood the project in that its major aim was not to provide a practical application. He also argues that time perspectives are different in Europe compared with Japan.

However, the question may also be asked whether MITI and the major participating Japanese computer companies actually wanted foreign participation in the project. There can be little doubt that there was a desire on the Japanese side to establish good working relations in various technological fields. This may on the Japanese side have been compounded by a desire to learn in a field where Japan was not so advanced. The foreigners may have thought that they should guard their knowledge assets and that participation would be equal to giving them away.

It is also important to understand that FGC is not an isolated project. There are at least three directly related projects. One is the SIGMA Project which aims at the mundane task of increasing productivity when developing software. Another is TRON which is an attempt to develop a new operating system. See Chapter 9. The third project is an attempt to develop inter-operable databases which will facilitate networking. There is also the Electronic Dictionary Research Institute, which is a direct spin-off from ICOT where the activities started.

The International Superconducting Technology Centre (ISTEC) was established in January 1988 with the purpose of co-ordinating inter-industry research in the area of superconducting materials. The centre was established with support from MITI, academic researchers and private industry. It is basically supported by 150 industrial companies, of which some 50 are special supporting members.

The latter cover the major part of operating costs and also have a direct influence over operations. The others are mainly the observers. A handful of foreign companies have decided to join as observers, including British Telecom, DuPont Japan, IBM Japan, Kernforschungszentrum Karlsruhe, Rhone-Poulenc Japan, and Rockwell International Corporation.

The centre has two research laboratories, a major one in Tokyo and a small research centre in Nagoya. ISTEC has four major functions: surveys and studies; basic research and development; education and dissemination: and an international exchange programme. Professor Tanaka Shoji, Vice-President of ISTEC and Director of the research laboratory, argues that the centre provides a unique opportunity for international co-operation. For the first time the researchers in Japan, USA, Europe and developing countries start at the same time.

This may be only partly correct as the countries have different conditions and different perspectives. The overall approach towards superconductivity research in Japan is characterised by an attempt to integrate research and industrial technology development. Consequently, there has been a simultaneous revival of many industrial technology projects, based on superconductivity – once the implication of high temperature superconductivity was understood. Such an integration is less evident in the USA and Europe. Finally, it appears that researchers in developing countries can participate, but there are far fewer opportunities for them to reap the benefits from industrial exploitation.

The experience gained from launching ISTEC as an international project may be more positive than was the case for FGC. However, it appears difficult to persuade foreign companies to become full members. When asked, several have responded that it is too costly and will not pay them to become a full member.

The Joint International Research Programmes into an Intelligent Manufacturing System (IMS) is another proposal to provide a platform for a broad international programme to research some of the technologies for the factories of tomorrow. The project is planned for ten years, like the earlier two examples, and the planned budget is in the region of Y150 billion to be borne by the public and private sectors in Japan, North America and Europe. An International Institute for the Promotion of IMS will be established in one or two locations outside Japan.

Within the institute there will be a joint international research centre to manage specific research projects which are expected to have members from universities, research institutes and private industry. The research will be oriented towards five areas: configuration of production systems; information and telecommunications technology for IMS; production and control equipment; new materials for upgrading production equipment; and human factors in production.

The overall aim of IMS is to integrate and systematise production technology for common use around the world. The specific Japanese concern may be a desire to provide manufacturing environments which are attractive to the young, are extremely flexible and require little manpower, which is in short supply. The latter point may alarm the foreign partners as they are afraid that the project will give Japanese manufacturers a leading edge in robotics equipment and other automated production systems. Another related aspect is the fact that new standards in manufacturing technology are being established, at least on a de facto basis.

The International Human Frontier Science Programme Organisation (HFSPO) was legally established in Strasbourg, France, in October 1989. This organisation will implement the Human Frontier Science Programme, which was officially presented for the first time at the Economic Summit Meeting in Venice in June 1987. In the preceding year MITI and STA had proposed similar programmes. The original MITI proposal was geared to bio-sciences with the expectation that technologies for the next century would follow.

MITI at this stage assumed a budget in the region of Y800 billion – most of it coming from Japan – and a time span for the project of 20 years. It was, in the early stage, often referred to as Japan's initiative to rival the US Strategic Defence Initiative (SDI) but in the civilian area. The feasibility study for the

Human Frontier Science Programme, carried by the Science and Technology Agency became very prolonged.

The momentum was partly lost and basic research rather than potential technologies came into focus. Subsequently the budget visions became much more modest. Foreign participation, by scientists and high level science managers, was very prominent throughout this preparatory stage which saw the creation of both the International Feasibility Study Committee and the Scientific Committee, preceded by London Wise Men' Conference for the Human Frontier Science Programme. Throughout the lengthy preparatory stage the members of the original Venice Summit Meeting were consulted.

The activities will focus on basic research on the complex mechanisms of living organisms. Initially the two priority areas are the higher order functions of the brain and molecular recognition and response functions. The funds will be given as research grants, fellowships and support for workshops. The majority of applications in the first round came from the seven countries which make up the Summit Club.

It would have been possible to include other projects which also have an international orientation, like ERATO, which is generally considered as a basically very successful programme. The four examples above all have common characteristics in that they aim at being international and dispel the notion of Japan being a free-rider. Let us start with the Human Science Frontier Programme which has definitely become international with headquarters outside Japan. However, its technology orientation, its original boldness and scope have almost completely disappeared. A major reason for the lack of interest in maintaining more of the original objective is a belief that Japan can, for the time being, make only limited contributions in life sciences.

The same attitude was prevalent when assessing the the Fifth Generation Computer Project. In both FGC and ISTEC foreigners may not been able to appreciate the objective which may have appeared too fuzzy. For all the projects the time perspective which has generally been ten years, with suggested 20 years for HFS, may have increased this problem. In sum, Japan's efforts to internationalise research during the 1980s have met with only limited success.

The conclusion is that the agencies and ministries which seriously want to promote international projects in science and technology have to find new procedures. The parties courted for participation in specific research must be asked to participate from the very stage of conceptualisation.

Chapter 20

Sources of scientific and technical information

Libraries have traditionally been the important source and repository of knowledge, and the history of libraries in Japan can be traced back even before the Nara period, 710-794. Various daimyo during the Edo period built their own collections for the use of their educated retainers.

After 1868 Japan came under strong Western influences which affected its library system. The largest library in Japan is the National Diet Library, modelled on the Library of Congress which in turn was modelled on the British Museum Library. It is open to the public and has 90,000 periodical titles of which 40,000 are current. The Science and Technology Materials Division looks after reference books, indexes and abstract journals, etc. This section produces the *Directory of Japanese Scientific Periodicals* which is now on a database and accessible by a variety of methods. The current number of periodicals is 12,000 and the Directory was published in 1989 in two parts – Journals and Indexes.

Libraries in Japan are generally classified both by the source of major support, such as national, prefectural, or municipal, and by the nature of the customers they are designed to serve such as public school, academic and so on. All 47 prefectures in Japan sponsor public library services. Academic institutions control more than 800 libraries over half of which are privately sponsored. The national government supports some 300 libraries in its national universities.

Public libraries in Japan compete with various weighty traditions in society. One is the high regard for private book ownership and the relatively low cost of books which at least until recently has fostered indifference toward public libraries. Another is the large number of generally well-stocked bookstores. A third factor is the rotation management system which means that the head librarian often stays for only a couple of years. Given such a system it is not surprising that government and corporate special libraries have assumed the major burden of meeting the information needs of a technological Japan.

Structure for scientific and technical information

Scientific and technical information is generated in two separate sectors of the Japanese society – the government sector and the private industry. However, the patenting activity of industrial companies, and science and technology articles published in journals and magazines, naturally appear in the public domain. The following will provide some basic information about the government structure and focus on STA, MITI and the Ministry of Education.

STA has, as explained earlier, the double function of attempting science and technology co-ordination and implementing big science projects, partly in their own research institutes. The Japan Information Centre of Science and Technology (JICST) is part of STA and produces indexes and abstracts from Japanese and foreign scientific and technical journals. This information is organised in a number of databases which are distributed directly through JICST On-Line Information System (JOIS) or through various database vendors. JOIS is, together with NIKKEI Telecom (NEEDS), one of the most heavily used databases in Japan. JICST, which primarily serves the scientific community in Japan, has in recent years also established an English language database by translating entries and abstracts from the main database.

However, a limited number of scientists in Japan contribute papers in English to domestic journals. Such articles will naturally be included in the coverage of JICST and their share has increased from 8.0 per cent in 1985 to 9.8 per cent in 1988. The English-language papers originating in Japan are heavily concentrated in basic sciences and nuclear engineering. See Figure 20.1.

JICST is part of the STA National Information System for Science and Technology (NIST) which will support a number of activities: expand Japan's databases; construct a comprehensive on-line network; construct a chemical compound information system, and so on. JICST already has several numerical databases such as a chemical dictionary, thermophysical properties and mass spectrometry and will develop DNA and metal fatigue databases.

The next important ministry is the Ministry of International Trade and Industry (MITI) which has its laboratories organised in the Agency for Industrial Science and Technology (AIST), with a number of the supported projects, large-scale or otherwise, supervised by the increasingly independent New Energy and Industrial Technology Development Organisation (NEDO). This expanding and changing role, with a considerable direct influence from the private sector, may mean that that the information flow will be constrained.

Other important information-gathering and distribution organisations belonging to MITI are the Japan External Trade Organisation (JETRO) and Japan Standards Association (JSA). The former provides information about Japanese industries to promote co-operation abroad while the latter approves and publishes Japan Industrial Standards (JIS). The Japan Patent Information Organisation (JAPIO) is directly related to the Patent Office under MITI and runs a database called PATOLIS. This database contains all Japanese industrial property – examined/unexamined patents and utility models. The database is available abroad, although in Japanese, with the possibility of obtaining the information on CD-ROM.

The third important organisation is Monbusho, which is developing a nation-wide information system. The University of Tokyo used to operate a documentation centre which has now become the National Centre for Science Information System (NACSIS). The reorganisation took place in 1986 when NACSIS became one of the national inter-university research institutes. NACSIS collects, organises and provides science information. It supports the databases existing within the university system.

The main purpose of NACSIS is to share information for university researchers both from within the universities and from the outside. So it provides electronic mail facilities, shared cataloguing and information. It also generates a *Union Catalogue* for the libraries of the approximately 100

254   SCIENCE AND TECHNOLOGY IN JAPAN

Figure 20.1 Ratio by field of English-language articles to all articles in the JICST-E file (1988)

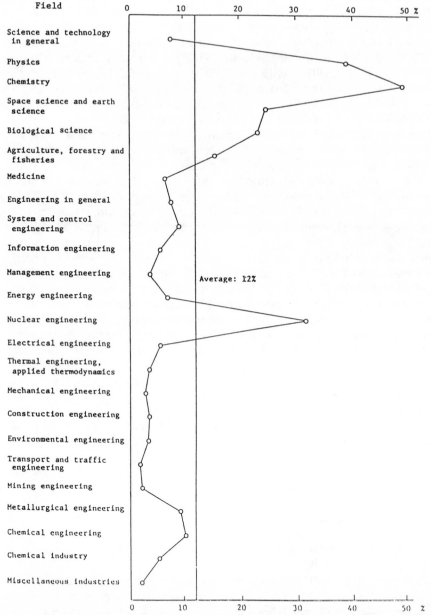

Source: Obara, Michio "Effort for Internationalisation of Scientific and Technological Information in Japan" in *Japanese Information in Science, Technology and Commerce,* 1990. Proceedings of the 2nd International Conference held by Gesellschaft fur Mathematik und Datenverarbeitung in co-operation with Japanese Deutsches Zentrum Berlin, Staatsbibliothek Preussischer Kulturbesitz on 23-25 October, 1989, in Berlin. Edited by D. Mönch, U. Wattenberg (GMD), T. Graf Brockdorff (JDZB), R. Kempien and H. Walravens (SPK). Amsterdam, IOS Press, p. 213

participating universities. This includes a *Japanese Periodicals Union Catalogue*, which has 40,000 titles for 88 university libraries, and a *Foreign Periodicals Union Catalogue*, which has 92,000 titles for 926 university libraries.

The other ministries and agencies with their research institutes are also important sources of scientific and technical information, although they have not yet set up special information structures to meet an external demand. However, MITI has taken an active interest in promoting the development of databases and easing the restrictions on government-held information so that it can be electronically transferred to commercial databases. To meet this and other objectives it created the Database Promotion Centre which has a parallel organisation in the private sector – Database Industry Association (DINA).

One of the interesting newcomers, among information providers, is the Electronic Library (ELNET) which came into existence in 1988. The most inspiring thing is that ELNET stores full text images, including pictures on optical disk. Thus retrieval can be achieved automatically online by fax machines and in fact operates as an automated newspaper clipping service for 32 newspapers and more than 200 magazines. However, ELNET has great financial difficulties (1990) as the cost of inputting is high and the number of subscribers is still very low.

Another interesting phenomenon is that new technologies such as optical filing system, referred to above, CD-ROM and high quality telefax equipment have made it possible to generate a new type of database – the image databases. Many such databases are at present being developed in Japan. They cover tables, diagrams and photographs and offer a valuable supplement to ordinary databases. In 1987 JAPIO started to distribute the entire contents of patents applications on CD-ROM which provides customers with easily-accessed high-quality images of detailed illustrations and photographs, when included in the patents. Another example comes from the Construction Information Centre in Tokyo which has created a number of databases related to construction and architecture in Japan. An additional service, available online through vendors, also provides architectural drawings and photos.

Information industry and databases in Japan

The information industry in Japan will account for 20 per cent of the country's gross national product in the year 2000, according to a report prepared by the Industrial Structure Council and published in the middle of June 1987. The report, prepared under the guidance of the Ministry of International Trade and Industry, notes that the corresponding figure was only 6.4 per cent in 1984. The council argues that the information industry must be developed in order to make the export-oriented Japanese economy more dependent on domestic demand. Thus, the government must view information industry as a "kind of infrastructure" which will require the easing of regulations on forms and fees related to electric communication services.

The information society has since the early 1980s been a common catchphrase when discussing the future in Japan and the country is in that sense no different from other industrialised countries. The indicated restructuring of the economy is based on the assumption that the economy will grow at a nominal average of 5 per cent per year while the annual increase of the information sector may be close to 20 per cent. As a consequence the information industry may in terms of production value exceed the automobile industry as early as 1993.

Naturally, the employment structure will change as the information industry develops. The Economic Planning Agency (EPA) earlier in 1987 reported that job opportunities in Japan's high value-added service areas, notably those of the information industry, will expand by 6 million by the year 2000. The agency expects the economy to shift from a heavy emphasis on production to service industries such as software writing, leisure activities and those related to health. EPA says that such new business will develop into a major industrial sector and should be differentiated from other traditional service industries such as transportation, finance and standard types of telecommunications.

Where does Japan stand today and what are the Japanese information

Figure 20.2 Comparison between Japanese and US databases (1987)

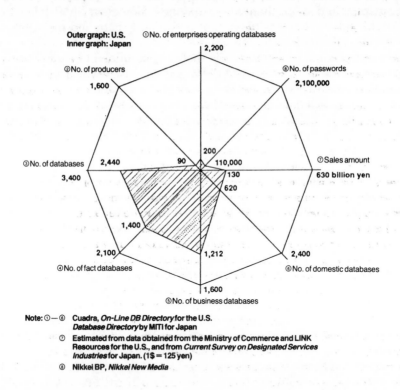

Source: Setoya, Hideo "Trends in Japanese Database Industry" in *Japanese Information in Science, Technology and Commerce*, 1990. Proceedings of the 2nd International Conference held by Gesellschaft fur Mathmatik und Datanverarbeitung in co-operation with Japanisch Deutsches Centrum Berlin, Staatsbibliothek Preussischer Kulturbesitz on 23-25 October 1989, in Berlin. Edited by D. Mönch, U. Wattenberg (GMD), T. Graf Brockdorff (JDZB), R. Krempien and H. Waltravens (SPK). Amsterdam, IOS Press, p. 24

companies doing in order to reach the rosy goals of the future? I will not try to cover the full spectrum of activities but only indicate the present role of electronic databases, present limitations and some recent developments. It is generally argued in Japan that the country is about ten years behind the US and maybe five years behind Europe in database services and usage. The total number of databases in Japan is quite impressive compared with the USA, although most are foreign. See Figure 20.2. However, when it comes to actual usage and production of databases Japan is still far far behind.

An important explanation is the fact that, until recently, there has been only limited government support for the database industry compared with early support in the US and many countries in Western Europe. Another factor may be the unfamiliarity among businessmen with computer keyboards and the often cumbersome search procedures in many of the databases.

There were in 1987 more than 4 million personal computers in Japan, including 8-bit machines and those with MSX specifications. However, a minuscule total of 70,000 personal computers were being used for communication with other users or to retrieve information over the telephone lines. There may be a rapid increase in the number of personal computers used for retrieving information, reaching almost a million in 1990 according to an article in Japan Times in early 1987.

The present shortcomings lie both in the relatively high costs for communications and computers, and in unfamiliarity with searches in databases. Today there are two major groups of users of database services – section managers and college and graduate school graduates. Information from a recent survey by Nikkei Industry Research Institute is used to illustrate present views on the database services in Japan (Table 20.1).

Table 20.1 Frequency of use

Location	Response (%)
Daily at both office and home	0.4
Daily at office	12.2
Daily at home	-
Occasionally at both office and home	3.8
Occasionally at office	81.5
Occasionally at home	1.3

The survey report also notes that databases service pioneers – Nihon Keizai Shimbun and the Japan Information Centre for Science and Technology (JICST) – are those which are most widely used. The respondents voiced a number of complaints which do not necessarily relate to the database companies mentioned. Table 20.2 clearly shows that most users consider the costs too high. This may indicate a price structure which is still too high or a lack of appreciation of the value of information retrieved from electronic databases.

However, the survey revealed that there may be high demand for market-related databases and for those that provide information on finance and investment securities. Today the most important commercial databases in Japan are those listed below, ranked in accordance to use by respondents of the survey by Nikkei Industry Research Institute.

Table 20.2 Shortcomings in database services

Complaint	Age group (%)		
	all	30s	60s
Information charges too high	33.7	38.2	32.0
Necessary database non-existent	26.6	27.6	24.0
Terminal costs too high	20.0	17.1	22.7
Complicated search procedures	19.8	19.5	25.3
Communication charges too high	17.8	21.5	18.7
Online terminals complicated	16.4	16.3	21.3
Expensive PC modems/software	16.2	16.7	9.3
Complicated subscription rules	9.7	10.2	8.0
No need for database services	21.0	17.5	29.3

NIKKEI TELECOM
Services: Business and industry data, current news abstracts, financial market data
Distributor: Nihon Keizai Shimbun, Inc.

NEEDS (Nikkei Economic Electronic Databank System)
Services: Business and industry data, newspaper articles
Distributor: Nihon Keizai Shimbun, Inc.

JOIS (JICST ON-LINE INFORMATION SYSTEM)
Services: Files on scientific/technical, medical and chemical reference literature, and public documents
Distributor: Japan Information Centre for Science and Technology (JICST) (government affiliated, comprehensive information centre)

PATOLIS (Patent On-Line Information System)
Services: Japanese patent information
Distributor: Japan Patent Information Organisation (JAPIO) (government affiliated patent information service organisation)

COSMOS
Services: Corporate credit research files
Distributor: Teikoku Databank, Ltd. (private corporate research company)

QUICK
Services: Financial and securities market data and general news
Distributor: Quick Corp. (formerly known as Quotation Information Centre K.K.; affiliated with Nihon Keizai Shimbun, Inc.)

TSR-BIGS
Services: Corporate credit research files
Distributor: Tokyo Shoko Research, Ltd. (private corporate credit research company)

LEX/DB
Services: Legal data (laws and cases)
Distributor: TKC Co., Ltd (information service company)

ORBIT
Services: Patent literature from over 30 countries
Distributor: System Development Corporation of Japan Ltd. (software development and database service company)

Technical developments are likely to make searches in databases much more attractive than has previously been the case. One such development is the use of artificial intelligence or expert systems in order to enhance user friendliness and improve the searching for information. Advances have already been made in the practical application in the domestic construction industry. CSK which is Japan's largest independent software company, reports that an expert system has been applied for making sense of the intricate sets of government building-code regulations. Another recent development is the introduction of compact-disk read-only memories (CD ROMs) for storing vast amounts of information.

However, it is essential for users to be able to recognise the value of quick access to information provided by a particular database service. Furthermore, the costs of building and improving databases are so huge that risk money and entrepeneurial spirit are necessary requirements. There appears to be a consensus that Japanese financial information is a likely area for growth and similarly good prospects exist for services related to Japan's scientific and technological developments. It is also possible to cover access to all essential information through the use of databases – but only if Japanese-language databases are included. See Figure 20.3.

Machine translation – an approaching possibility

Japan has in the past couple of years experienced a boom in machine translation systems. As early as the mid-1980s there were more than ten companies marketing such systems – most of them needing a mainframe computer. Major research projects on machine translation had started in the the US and Europe in the early 1950s, but most of them were perceived as blind alleys when it came to practical applications.

There are three major reasons for the sudden increase of activity in Japan. First, the rapid internationalisation of trade and financial transactions has dramatically increased the amount of information to be translated without undue delay. Second, there are now government-sponsored projects to develop technical and scientific dictionaries and practical systems which are able to handle relatively simple texts rather than literature. Third, the intense competition between major mainframe computers and between software companies speeded up the process.

None of the systems are perfect, which will become obvious from the following discussion. There are three major problems to be overcome when using a Japanese-English machine translation system. First, it is necessary to input the source text to be translated. This is a relatively costly procedure, even in Japan. Consequently, it is a major attraction that data files downloaded from

Figure 20.3 Image of needs structure for information in Japan

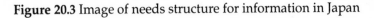
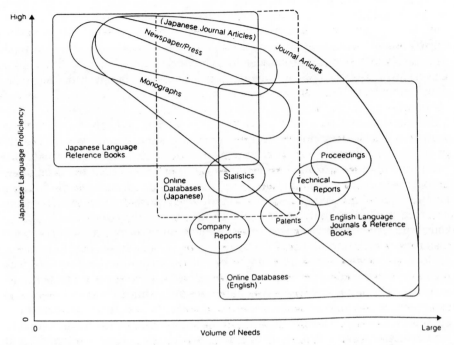

Source: Miwa, Makiko "Globalisation of Japanese Database Services: Possibilities and Limitations" in *Japanese Information in Science, Technology and Commerce*, 1990. Proceedings of the 2nd International Conference held by Gesellschaft fur Mathematik und Datenverarbeitung in co-operation with Japanisch Deutsches Zentrum Berlin, Staatsbibliothek Preussischer Kulturbesitz on 23-25 October 1989, in Berlin. Edited by D. Mönch, U. Wattenberg (GMD), T. Graf Brockdorff (JDZB), R. Kempien and H. Walravens (SPK). Amsterdam, IOS Press, p. 31

online electronic databases in Japan can be used as source text in machine translation systems. There is little doubt that optical character recognition (OCR) systems will in the future be able to transfer printed Japanese into electronic source texts. For the time being, available systems are still far from perfect and still very costly.

Second, the quality of translation depends on the availability of dictionaries to match the vocabulary of the source text. It is hardly to be expected that general dictionaries will provide all the necessary words and expressions which occur in specialised technical, scientific or economic texts. Thus it is necessary to compile or build up dictionaries which not only meet the needs of groups of specialist users but also those of individual members of such groups.

Third, most machine translation systems require not only post-editing of translated texts but also pre-editing of the source text in order to provide readable texts. Experience shows that substantial editing is generally needed in order to weed out ambiguities and render the translated text in a form which is recognisable as English.

When creating new source texts, which will be the case for Japanese companies writing manuals or other documents to be used for export promotion abroad, this may be less of of problem. Original texts from databases or other sources have to be modified in order to yield acceptable translations.

However, the need for editing may be drastically reduced for certain types of source texts. This appears to be the case for titles of scientific and technical articles as well as patents. Certain abstracts also yield themselves to machine translation (MT) without substantial editing. Furthermore, there are several developments which in the future may considerably reduce the need for editing.

First, much of the source texts originating in electronic databases may in the near future be edited in such a way as to yield easily to MT without further editing, a major reason being that the database companies will themselves introduce machine translation services. Second, editing programs for specialised technical and scientific texts may be developed and marketed on the assumption that there is a sufficiently strong demand for a such a development to take place.

National governments and international organisations are obviously very keen to obtain efficient machine translation systems in order to have early access to Japanese information sources in areas such as biotechnology, factory automation, office automation, the fifth-generation computer project and other high-tech developments.

However, the major potential demand for Japanese-English machine translation originates with private Japanese companies which need to translate huge amounts of manuals, catalogues and other literature to support their marketing efforts abroad. The total amount of translation work amounted to US$5.5 billion in 1986 according to an estimate made by Japan Electronics Industry Promotion Association, of which a very substantial share was translation from Japanese to English.

Today, only a minute part is being processed on machine translation systems. However, the potential market is huge and the market possibilities were early on identified by Bravice International which launched a mini computer system in mid-1984 to be followed by a micro-computer system a year later. Two years later more than ten companies had announced commercial machine translation systems or declared their readiness to deliver such systems.

However, a hectic race is going on among the various companies and ministries. All electronic makers are active and employ some 500 researchers and engineers in the field. MITI and MPT are jointly sponsoring the Electronic Dictionary Project and sub-project within ATR. MITI has its own project the Fifth Generation Computer Project with its research laboratory ICOT. Several universities are also involved with Kyoto University's Department of Electrical Engineering playing a leading role. This has also been a major point of contact and support for the JICST project on machine translation. Finally there are the software companies like CSK and private database vendors like Nikkei.

Obviously, practical machine translation from Japanese to English still has a number of hurdles to overcome if it is to be efficiently utilised by major government organisations abroad or by private companies in Japan. What then are the prospects for introducing an MT system in a major international company in Sweden or elsewhere in Europe or the US in order to facilitate

Figure 20.4 Research and development on machine translation in Japan

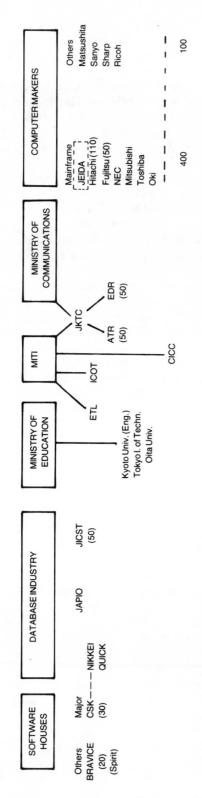

(Note: Number of researchers within brackets)

R&D in MT in Japan 1987 800-900 people (Y20 billion)
ATR = Advanced Telecommunications Research Institute
CICC = (ASEAN)
EDR = Japan Electronic Dictionary Research Institute
ETL = Electrotechnical Laboratory
ICOT = Institute of the Fifth Generation Computer Project

JAPIO = Japan Patent Information Organisation
JEIDA = Japan Electronic Industries Development Association
JICST = Japan Information Centre for Science and Technology
JKTC = Japan Key Technology Centre

Source: Sigurdson, Jon and Greatrex, Roger *Machine Translation of On-line Searches in Japanese Databases. A Way to Facilitate Access to Japanese Techno-economic Information?* 1987, Lund, Research Policy Institute, p. 27

timely and selective access of Japanese information? First, it is recognised by more and more international companies that they have not only neglected the Japanese market but also neglected to watch closely the Japanese scene for new developments in science and technology. Second, many companies are still lagging behind in collecting information from Japan, and few of them have efficient means of transforming data and information from Japanese into English or other national languages.

Machine translation in itself would not bridge the information or intelligence gap which many companies now perceive. However, much vital data is available in Japanese-language electronic databases which in principle can be reached on-line in any industrialised country. The databases in principle provide an efficient tool to select and quickly transfer data. Furthermore this is immediately available in machine-readable form and can be used as a source text in MT systems. What then are the limitations?

Any user of Japanese-language databases must have a working knowledge of Japanese even if search procedures are simplified by the use of codes or the use of romaji – the latin alphabet transcription of Japanese. Downloaded texts do not immediately render themselves for machine translation. Such text must be laundered and new symbols inserted. The MT system must have specialised dictionaries in order to cope with diverse scientific disciplines, technological fields or economic specialties. When such conditions are met, the required pre-editing and postediting of many types of texts may be minimal – on the assumption that understandability rather than quality is the objective. Such findings are however based on translation of texts in a limited number of technological and scientific fields and a sprinkling of economic source texts.

Chapter 21

Technology and society

The 1989 White Paper on Science and Technology was published in early 1990. A commentator in *Mainichi Daily News* gave a critical review. He noted that Japan may have entered into the world league of top spenders on research and development. However, the public sector's share is only 20 per cent, of which a substantial proportion goes to big science in nuclear energy and space. Japan has concentrated its efforts primarily on closing the nuclear fuel cycle for a visionary plutonium-based economy using fast-breeder reactors.

The commentator criticises the fact that the Japanese approach is given full public support while similar efforts are fading all over the world because of technical difficulties, the high costs of operation and risk of proliferation. The power utilities expect to double the number of reactors to about 40 and suggest that another 60 are needed to drastically reduce the CO_2 problem in Japan – and at the same time to reduce Japan's dependence on oil. The commentator laments the lack of attention to energy savings and alternative energy sources and notes that the TV public is treated with programmes which have been designed to make people, especially the young, more scientifically-minded and "to widen public acceptance of science, in many cases to rid them of their nuclear allergy".

He also notes that large government funds go into space research, which draws its major justification from national prestige but also from a need to be prepared for new economic exploitation. The Maglev Project with the 70 kilometre test track for linear motor cars is also criticised. Although the prospects for technical and commercial success are bright the results will not ease the burden of commuters moving in and out of Tokyo.

Japan may continue to be successful in its continuing exploitation of new technologies – also in the areas indicated above. However, the country still lacks the creative support system for future science and technology and the commentator sees too little exertion to remedy the situation. Finally he refers to an opinion poll to determine the effects of technological progress on human life, which is also included in the White Paper. According to this more than 70 per cent of the respondents answered that technological progress had improved their living standards although more than 40 per cent said that it had undermined the morals of the society.

The poll figures indicate the favourable attitudes towards science and technology which still prevail in Japan. In the following sections brief descriptions will be offered to indicate some of the forecasting, screening and evaluation methods which are practised in Japan.

Forecasting

It has been noted by several observers – most notably by Martin and Irvine (Research Foresight: Priority-Setting in Science, London 1989) – that Japan has the most developed research foresight capability. A contributing reason is that government and industry share a common interest in long-term planning. The number of participants in the process may have increased since the early 1980s as Japan realised that the catch-up phase of technological development was basically completed. The new epoch has seen a proliferation of policy instruments, often involving participants in various types of networks, as government funding has constantly decreased in relative terms.

Martin and Irvine note that the process of formulating science and technology policy in Japan has three main characteristics: integration of discussions on broad priorities and budget requirements; emphasis on consensus-seeking advisory councils with such a breadth and seniority that suggested policies are also implemented; and hierarchical process with guidelines at the higher level to be framed by intermediate bodies and implemented by research institutes and scientists.

These views indicate a situation in which conflicts and competition are kept at bay. Although partially correct it overlooks the possibilities of ministries and agencies pursuing alternative goals, and the role of the Science and Technology Agency in co-ordinating national R&D efforts is exaggerated. However, there can be little doubt that the intensive and far-reaching exploration of future technological possibilities have a profound effect in setting the priorities. It is the process rather than the results of specific studies which provides the beneficial effect.

The Science and Technology Agency has in the past conducted four surveys on the direction of Japan's technological development – each at an interval of five years. The last one, carried out by the Institute for Future Technology, was completed in 1987. The survey was conducted in two stages using a Delphi technique, in which a large number of respondents were posed with a set of identical questions with a convergence of the various opinions.

The respondents were asked to make forecasts over the 30 year period – until 2015. The following six categories were used in the survey: degrees of importance; time of realisation; limits to realisation; methods for promoting research and development; agents for research and development; and national policies and measures. The surveyed fields covered almost the complete spectrum of science and technology and participants included not only those engaged in the fields of natural science in industry, academia and government but also experts from the social sciences and humanities.

In degree of importance of various items the 1985 forecast clearly indicated life sciences, health and medical care, and aerospace. On specific topics those related to cancer came out on top followed by atomic energy (fast breeder reactor) and information processing (high speed microchips).

The STA Delphi study indicated that early realisation of research subjects was widely expected of information technologies including electronics and software. However, many subjects in life sciences and energy could only expect late realisation. The respondents indicated only limited social limitations while economic and technical hindrances were seen as more significant. The social limitations were seen as most severe in public safety and environment.

The study also indicated that more than 70 per cent of the subjects could be promoted through indigenous research and development. The percentage was considerably higher for three categories: urbanisation and construction; substances, materials and processing; and communications. On the other hand the respondents indicated that international joint efforts were important in life sciences, with aerospace falling between the two extremes.

Generally the respondents felt that national/local public corporations, together with the private sector, are most suitable for promoting most research subjects which was particularly pronounced for life sciences, substances, materials and processing, and information electronics and software. The private sector will for the time being remain secondary agents for carrying out research in aerospace and environment fields while the private sectors should dominate in fields like transportation and communication.

A majority of the respondents agreed that national policies and measures were required for about 70 per cent of the subjects surveyed in the Delphi study. The study indicated that national funds were very important in three areas: aerospace; substances, materials and processing; and mineral and water resources. Development of human resources – by the nation – was considered important for life sciences and information technologies, while new research structures were seen as essential for the environment sciences.

When comparing the latest figures with earlier ones it is obvious that both life sciences and aerospace have been gaining more and more recognition by the research community. STA has, since the second study in 1977, included questions on the methods to promote research and development. All the three studies have since recorded a growing number of subjects which could be promoted through indigenous technological development. At the same time there have also been an increasing number of subjects for which joint international development should be sought. Finally, when looking into the old forecasts it is obvious that predictions for energy and transportation have been widely off the mark. The reason is that technological developments in these fields were adversely affected by changes in supply/demand structure for various energy sources and also by changes in the economy and society.

Understanding the future – and shaping consensus

When viewing the R&D landscape in Japan in 1990 it is not difficult to find direct linkages between the findings of the STA Delphi study and various initiatives which have been promoted by STA and other agencies. However, it is more important to view the expressed opinions and policy measures as an outflow of activities in which the same group of influential and knowledgeable people participate, as indicated by Martin and Irvine. It is argued that the strength of the STA surveys is that they meet a need to identify basic technological trends – in a national context – and how the various agents should respond to the new challenges.

All government ministries and major agencies involved in research and development have their own advisory councils which organise study committees of various sizes and duration in order to seek the direction and achieve the desired consensus. Some of these mechanisms have been described in the preceding chapters. The reader who wants to understand the system in more detail should consult the Martin-Irvine volume on forecast which has a comprehensive chapter on Japan.

The forecasting system of Japan, although working well, has a number of limitations. First, it cannot anticipate major scientific and technological breakthroughs and provide the necessary preparatory structures for such events. Second, the system, which is basically an ex-ante evaluation, does not include any good approach for ex-post evaluation. Third, the social or societal dimension (outside the industrial-technological-economic circles) has in the past been able to influence the process only marginally. Let us look at these weaknesses.

Tanaka, in an article in *Research Policy* (No 18, 1989) argues that evaluation in Japan has the following three characteristics: it is performed at the micro-level; it is made from the standpoint of technological objectives; and it is dependent on in-house self-assessment. Although he is basing his work on the large-scale projects promoted by MITI and a rather scanty database, his analysis has wider relevance for understanding the evaluation mechanisms in Japan.

The large-scale projects include manganese module mining, automated sewing, advanced robot technology etc. See Appendix IV for a complete list. When selecting projects the following criteria should be met. First, the project should be urgently needed to upgrade national industrial standards, promote efficient utilisation of natural resources, prevent industrial pollution, etc. Second, it should make its greatest impact on the progress of mining and manufacturing industries. Third, it cannot be undertaken by private firms because of huge investments, long-term nature, absence of immediate profit possibilities, high risks, etc. Fourth, it has clearly specified targets and well-examined attainment prospects. Fifth, it can be carried out in co-operation with universities and industry.

Tanaka notes that the large-scale projects, and also the overall organisation, have been evaluated – although hardly in a consistent and systematic way. The evaluations include pre-, mid-term, and post-assessment and also in-house review of the research itself. Tanaka comments that the two advisory bodies, the Council of Science and Technology and the Extraordinary Council on Administrative Reform, in their 1984 and 1985 reports highlighted the need for adaptability of government policies and organisation. In essence they were concerned with the evaluation and reconstruction of the R&D system itself and less with scientific and technological matters.

Another force changing the system comes from the shifting relations between government and private industry, the latter having become strong, independent and with diversified interests which overlap only partially with those of the government. Furthermore, the expanding technological base and the increasing scientification of many areas have pushed new government actors on to the R&D policy stage, which has intensified the competition for funds. Tanaka remarks that the budget constraints may in fact require a wider consensus in order to reach acceptance. Furthermore, a changing emphasis from applied to more basic research may also require more specialised knowledge for the responsible officials in order to play a key role.

Generally there are few professional appraisers who contribute to the evaluation through independent and objective analysis. The evaluation of a specific large-scale project is undertaken in committees where members share their knowledge to handle problems and issues, which partly compensates for the lack of qualified expertise. Such a system may work well for projects which aim at incremental improvements and possibly for the creation of a new research programme.

However, there is little doubt that the consensus-seeking system is losing some of its dominance, although it is still difficult to find a new system to replace the old one. Two major reasons are to be found in the lack of professional evaluators who can contribute to an objective analysis and the reluctance to voice open criticism in the context of Japanese culture.

The Science Council of Japan was brought into being in 1949 after a series of discussions and deliberations in the wake of the country's defeat in the Second World War, "with all the scientists in Japan firmly determined to reflect upon their studies and conducts in time of war, to strive for reconstruction and rehabilitation of their fatherland and thereby to accomplish their responsibilities".The Science Council of Japan is a government agency, although operating autonomously, and its main functions are to act as a deliberative body and as a communications or liaison arm for matters pertaining to science. As well as answering the government's inquiries on scientific matters, the Council also has the right to offer advice on such matters.

The foreword of the "First Five Years" states: that "frankly speaking, the Science Council of Japan was founded under unprecedentedly specific social conditions. It has thus suffered, and will suffer, from various intrinsic contradictions and un-necessary disputes and, still worse, it has not seldom failed to realise what was expected of it at the the time of inauguration." There can be no doubt that the government for a long time wanted to establish a stronger control over the Council.

The members of the governing council were formerly elected directly by scientists, which provided a strong counter-force against any plans to restructure the university system. The governing council was summarily dismissed in 1983 and the organisation is now under tighter government control, as the Prime Minister's Office has to approve the nominations for members suggested by the academic societies. Altogether there are 739 affiliated societies with a total membership of close to half a million.

The following reorganisation of the Science Council of Japan has created a more systematic approach in suggesting guidelines for the future development of science in Japan. General plan activities are prepared every three years – the latest in 1988. The plan, which could be called an un-official White Paper on Science and Technology, draws on the very considerable scientific insights of the members of the scientific societies. In a first step the Council obtained views on the following key issues:

1. the relative international strength of science in Japan;

2. scientific fields of particular promise;

3. research areas of great potential for industry and the society; and

4. consequences for funding, including international collaboration.

The findings were summarised, covering 71 scientific fields, and appended to the overall plan.

The plan, no doubt, envisages that fundamental science in Japan will become stronger and stronger, although certain shortcomings have to be addressed. One is the need for a considerabe increase in the level of funding for research and training in priority fields by special budget allocations. Another is the need for a reducion in the funding for big science. Finally, the Science Council of Japan also considers that is is essential to improve the system for planning and evaluation in the academic system.

Regulations on biotechnology research and development

Life sciences are progressing rapidly through the recent development of molecular biology, molecular genetics, recombinant DNA and cell fusion technologies. The Ministry of Agriculture, Forestry and Fisheries in 1982 promoted large-scale projects in life sciences which included, among other things, gene manifestation mechanisms and cell fusion and nucleus transplantation. MITI at approximately the same time initiated a number of projects which include bio-reactors, cell cultivation technology and recombinant DNA technology. Related activities were also started by the Ministry of Health and Welfare. Simultaneously research on recombinant DNA also grew remarkably in the private industries.

So far, government guidelines for recombinant DNA studies have been issued by four agencies: Prime Minister's Office; Ministry of International Trade and Industry (MITI); Ministry of Health and Welfare (MHW); and Ministry of Education, Science and Culture (Monbusho). The guidelines from the Prime Minister's Office are intended for basic research – for laboratories not belonging to the university system. These guidelines, which are similar to those issued by the National Institutes of Health (NIH) in the USA, are intended for closed systems, while MITI guidelines have been prepared for industrial applications of recombinant technology in open systems.

Monbusho was the first agency to issue guidelines for recombinant DNA research in 1979: these were substantially revised in 1982 and again amended in 1983 and 1985. The main guidance is provided in "Guidelines on experiments of recombinant DNA at university institutes" (Monbusho Notice No 131, 1982) which is based on the recommendations of the Monbusho Science Council.

The Monbusho rules cover experiments in departments and institutes which are under the direct control of Monbusho. Under these guidelines each university is required to establish a committee for recombinant DNA studies which reviews all relevant research proposals. If a proposal meets Monbusho guidelines the Committee recommends the university president to authorise the research. If there is any doubt the proposal is submitted to the ministry's Subcommittee on Recombinant DNA Research – with final approval coming from the minister.

In early 1989 there were still guidelines for recombinant DNA experiments in the field and approval was given in response to specific requests. The Ministry of Agriculture, Forestry and Fisheries in the same way prepared a new set of guidelines for recombinant DNA and cell fusion experiments to be conducted both in closed and open systems.

International relations

Japan's per-capita GDP has become one of the highest in the world and the country has become the world's largest creditor nation. The frictions in trade and technology are spreading beyond the realm of economics to encompass social and cultural frictions. Thus the national system and heritage are being questioned while the the attitude of the Japanese people toward the world remains basically passive and non-assertive – with little readiness to make an active contribution to a global society.

In many circles there is a growing realism that it is essential for Japan actively to formulate concepts and proposals directed at seeking solutions to the problems that confront all mankind. Such solutions should offer new modes of industrial activity, daily living and culture that are attractive to the global society. This would require the Japanese people to foster a broad global perspective. Two research institutes may be of particular interest in carrying out research on the indicated issues.

One is the Global, Industrial and Social Progress Research Institute, which has been founded with an aim of contributing to the prosperity of the international community. The Institute will conduct research into a wide range of problems affecting the world's industry and culture, and in particular the problem of determining the most desirable relationship between industrial and economic factors on the one hand and resources, the environment, daily living and culture on the other. Subsequently, the Institute will formulate comprehensive policy proposals.

The second is the National Institute for Research Advancement (NIRA), a joint-public organisation established in 1974 with substantial funding from the national government, local government and private industry, which is tackling similar issues. NIRA notes that Japan is witnessing rapid change in the development of a new industrial society, new sciences and technologies, new styles of local communities and new life-styles among individual citizens. The Institute says that an urgent need exists for various systemic reforms to deal with such changes and cope with the new economy and society. To seek viable solutions to the complex, interrelated issues confronting society, interdisciplinary studies bringing together a comprehensive range of experts are necessary – which is the function of NIRA.

There are naturally many more institutes, apart from the two mentioned, which tackle the many emerging and important societal issues which cannot be solved by science and technology. Many of these are big private "think tanks" like Nomura Research Institute, Mitsubishi Research Institute and Hitachi Research Institute, generally focused on research topics which are narrowly defined by clients.

References

The following is only a sample of the very rich information resources which exist in Japan. Each ministry publishes a yearly White Paper (*hakusho*) which gives very detailed information about all major activities including those in science and technology. Various publications provide detailed information on companies and structural relation such as *Industrial Groupings in Japan* and *Japan Company Handbook*, the latter one published quarterly. Several directories in Japanese provide detailed information about the research laboratories (and their activities and structure) belonging to private companies, universities or directly controlled by ministries or government agencies.

All Japan Directory of Test and Research Organisations 1989-1990 (*Zenkoku Shiken Kenkyu Kikan Meikan*) (1989). Vol I and II. Tokyo: Rateisu.
All Japan Research Institute Planning Directory (*Zenkoku Kenkyujo Keikaku Soran*) (1988). Tokyo: Sangyo Times.
Annual Report of Transport Economy, Summary. (Annual). Compiled by Ministry of Transport. Tokyo: Printing Bureau, Ministry of Finance.
Atomic Power White Paper (*Genshiryoku Hakusho*) (Annual). Compiled by Atomic Energy Commission. Tokyo: Printing Bureau, Ministry of Finance.
Communications White Paper (*Tsushin Hakusho*) (Annual). Compiled by Ministry of Posts and Telecommunications. Tokyo: Printing Bureau, Ministry of Finance.
Construction White Paper (*Kensetsu Hakusho*) (Annual). Compiled by Ministry of Construction. Tokyo: Printing Bureau, Ministry of Finance.
Defense of Japan (Annual). Compiled by Defense Agency. Tokyo: The Japan Times.
Defence White Paper (*Boei Hakusho*) (Annual). Compiled by Defense Agency. Tokyo: Printing Bureau, Ministry of Finance.
Diamond's Japan Business Directory 1990 (1990). Tokyo: Diamond Lead.
Directory of Japanese Scientific Periodicals 1988 (*Nihon Kagaku Gijutsu Chikuji Kankobutsu Soran*) (2 Vols) (1989). Tokyo: Kokuritsu Kokkai Toshokan.
A standard list of periodicals in the field of pure and applied sciences, agriculture, city planning, landscape achitecture, architecture, photography and geography.
Directory of Japan's Private Technological Research Institutes (*Moeru zuno shudan Nihon no minkan gijutsu kenkyujo soran*) (1987). Tokyo: Nihon Kogyo Shimbun Sha.
Directory of Research Projects in National Laboratories and Research Public Corporations – Science and Technology (*Kokyo Shiken Kenkyu Kikan Kadai Annai – Kagaku Gijutsu Tema-hen*) (1989). Tokyo: The Japan Information Center for Science and Technology.
Directory of Scientific Research Institutes of Universities in Japan (*Daigaku Kenkyujo*

Yoran) (1990). Tokyo: Japan Society for the Promotion of Science (Nihon Gakujutsu Shinkokai) and Maruzen.

Directory of University Professors and Researchers in Japan 1990 – Natural Sciences (Kenkyusha, Kenkyu Kadai Soran 1990 – Shizen Kagaku-hen) (5 vol.) (1990). Tokyo: Japan Society for the Promotion of Science (comp.).

Economic Survey of Japan (Annual). Compiled by Economic Planning Agency. Tokyo: The Japan Times.

Education in Japan: A graphic presentation (1988). Tokyo: Ministry of Education.

Environment White Paper (Kankyo Hakusho) (Annual). Compiled by Environment Agency. Tokyo: Printing Bureau, Ministry of Finance.

Future Technology in Japan – Forecast to the year 2015 (Nihon no Gijutsu, 1987-2015) 1988, Tokyo, Institute for Future Technology.

Government Policies in Education, Science and Culture, 1989 (1990). Tokyo: Ministry of Education (comp.).

A Guide to Reference Books for Japanese Studies (1989). Tokyo: The International House of Japan Library.

Historical Review of Japan's Science and Technology Policies. (1989) Tokyo: The Society of Non-Traditional Technology, National Institute of Science and Technology Policy (NISTEP), Science and Technology Agency.

Indicators of Science and Technology (Kagaku Gijutsu Yoran) (Annual). Compiled by Science and Technology Agency. Tokyo: Printing Bureau, Ministry of Finance.

Industrial Groupings in Japan (1988). The 8th edition 1988/89. Tokyo: Dodwell Marketing Consultants.

International Conference on Japanese Information in Science, Technology and Commerce. University of Warwick, 1-4 September 1987 (1987). Reprints. London: British Library Japanese Information Service.

Irvine, John and Martin, Ben R.; *Creating the Future. Research Foresight* (1989). Netherlands: Ministry of Education and Science.

Japan Company Handbook (1990). First Section. Tokyo: Toyo Keizai Inc.

Japan Company Handbook (1990). Second Section. Tokyo: Toyo Keizai Inc.

Japan Periodicals. A Guide to Business and Economic Periodicals in English Published in Japan (1989). Tokyo: Keizai Koho Centre, Japan Institute for Social and Economic Affairs.

Japanese Colleges and Universities 1987 (1987). Tokyo: Maruzen Co.Ltd.

Japanese Companies: Consolidated Data 1989/1990 (1989). Tokyo: Nihon Keizai Shimbun.

Japanese Information in Science, Technology and Commerce. (1990) Proceedings of the 2nd International Conference held by Gesellschaft fur Mathematik und Datenverarbeitung in cooperation with Japanisch Deutsches Zentrum Berlin, Staatsbibliothek Preussischer Kulturbesitz on 23-25 October 1989, in Berlin. Edited by D. Monch, U. Wattenberg (GMD), T. Graf Brockdorff (JDZB), R. Krempien and H. Walravens (SPK). Amsterdam: IOS Press.

Japanese Who's Who in Science and Technology 1986 (Gendai Nihon Kagaku Gijutsusha Daijiten) (5 Vols) (1986-87). Tokyo: Nichigai Associates.

Includes 13,000 people with 180,000 publications. Each entry provides name, a brief biography, activities, publications, and literature about him/her. A CD-ROM edition is available from the same publisher.

Japan's Private Colleges and Universities. Yesterday, Today, and Tomorrow (1987). Translated by SIMUL INTERNATIONAL, Inc. Tokyo. Tokyo: The Japan

Association of Private Colleges and Universities.

JTECH Panel Report on The Japanese Exploratory Research for Advancement Technology (ERATO) Program (1988). Coordinated by Science Applications International Corporation, Virginia, USA. Washington, DC: Japanese Technology Evaluation Program, NSF.

National Laboratories and Research Public Corporations in Japan. Tokyo: Science and Technology Agency. (2 parts)

Nomura Search (monthly, 1980-) Tokyo: Nomura Sogo Kenkyujo. A publication of the Nomura Research Institute, a major think tank in Japan. It provides a one-page summary of selected reports published by various research institutions, such as think tanks and the research sections of banks. It also includes brief summaries of other reports either published independently or in periodicals.

Okimoto, Daniel I; *Between MITI and the Market. Japanese Industrial Policy for High Technology* (1989). Stanford, CA: Stanford University Press.

Our Country's Educational Measures (Waga Kuni no Bunkyo Shisaku) (1990). Tokyo: Ministry of Education (comp.).

Pacific Research Centres: A Directory of Scientific, Industrial, Agricultural, and Biomedical Laboratories (1990). Harlow, Essex: Longman Group UK Ltd.

Quality of the Environment in Japan 1988 (Annual). Tokyo: Environment Agency (comp.).

A Reference Guide to Science and Technology Prize in Japan (Kagakusho Jiten) (2 vols) (1986). Tokyo: Nichigai Associates. A total of 456 prizes and awards in science and technology, industry, architecture, an invention are described.

Report on the Survey of Research and Development (Kagaku Gijutsu Kenkyu Chosa Hokoku) (1955-). Tokyo: Statistics Bureau, Management and Coordincation Agency (Somucho Tokeikyoku). A statistical report on research and development activities in research institutions, universities and corporations.

Research Institute Management – Realized Examples. (Kenkyujo Unei Katsuseika Jitsurei Shu). Tokyo: 1987 Japan Management Organisation (Nihon Noritsu Kyokai).

Science and Technology Agency Annual Report No 33 (Kagaku Gijutsu Cho Nempo) (1990). Tokyo: Science and Technology Agency (ed.).

Science and Technology White Paper (Kagaku Gijutsu Hakusho) (Annual). Compiled by Science and Technology Agency. Tokyo: Printing Bureau, Ministry of Finance.

Sigurdson, Jon and Greatrex, Roger: *Machine Translation of On-line Searches in Japanese Databases. A Way to Facilitate Access to Japanese Techno-economic Information?* (1987). Lund: Research Policy Institute.

Statistical Abstract of Education, Science and Culture (1988). Tokyo: Research and Statistics Division, Minister's Secretariat, Ministry of Education, Science and Culture.

Survey of Japan's Research Institutes (Nihon no Kenkyujo Yoran) (1986). Tokyo: Nikkan Kogyo Shimbun.

Technical Expert Education – Sample Collection (Gijutsusha Kyoiku Jitsurei Shu) (1987). Tokyo: Japan Management Organisation (Nihon Noritsu Kyokai).

Think Tank Almanac (Shinku Tanku Nenpo) (1986) Tokyo: Sogo Kenkyu Kaihatsu Kiko.

Published by the semi-governmental National Institute for Research Advancement (NIRA). It provides abstracts of reports and publications of think tanks in Japan. A one-page introduction to each institution is also provided in the latter half. The think tank guide, will be succeeded by *Kenkyu Kikan no Gaiyo*, scheduled to be published in 1990.

Trade White Paper (*Tsusho Hakusho*) (Annual). Compiled by MITI. Tokyo: Printing Bureau, Ministry of Finance.

Transportation White Paper (*Unyu Hakusho*) (Annual). Compiled by Ministry of Transport. Tokyo: Printing Bureau, Ministry of Finance.

Trends and Future Tasks in Industrial Technology – Developing Innovative Technologies to Support the 21st Century and Contributing to the International Community – Summary of the White Paper on Industrial Technology. (1988). Tokyo: Ministry of International Trade and Industry (MITI).

Trends and Tasks in Industrial Technology (*Sangyo Gijjutsu no Doko to Kadai*) (1988). Tokyo: Ministry of International Trade and Industry (MITI).

The University Research System in Japan (1988). Tokyo: Ministry of Education.

White Paper on International Trade Japan (Annual). Tokyo: Japan External Trade Organization (comp.).

General guideline for science and technology policy (1986)

Basic principles

Highly creative science and technology should be the core of the nation's science and technology policy if we are to respond correctly to the various needs to make our society and national life richer in the coming 21st century as well as to open up new possibilities in the future.

Especially, we should concentrate on encouraging basic research to pave the way for technological progress in the next generation. Steps should be taken to create technological seeds brought up from further studies and reviews of theories, principles and phenomena, which will lead to promotion of more creative and imaginative science and technology capable of exceeding the bounds of mere modifications and improvements by combining such seeds with the emerging social needs.

In doing so, we should be aware that developments in science and technology are greatly dependent on a wide range of domains related to national life, dignity of man, ethics etc. While maintaining the basic recognition that science and technology should serve man and society, and deepening our understanding of man itself, we should develop science and technology in harmony with man and society. We should also realize that Japan's contributions to science and technology should be appropriate for its increasingly significant role in the world community of nations. On this recognition, we should seek to internationalize our science and technology personnel, organizations and activities and to promote international exchanges and cooperation while giving sufficient consideration to the importance of cooperation with developing countries and to the latest international trends in high technology areas. Due attention should be paid to this global aspect in our science and technology promotion programme.

Emphasizing priority programmes

In encouraging creative science and technology, it is important to develop and strengthen favourable systems and conditions for R&D activities. Therefore, we should carry out the following programmes in a comprehensive and flexible manner, while continuing to formulate timely and improve basic guidelines for implementing priority programmes for this purpose.

1. Developing and strengthening systems
Universities, which are endowed to make academic research for continued progress in basic research, should further improve and upgrade their research

activities to keep up with and exceed the international level while taking into account the social requirements and acting on their initiative based on their missions and objectives.

National research institutes and similar bodies should expand and strengthen their basic, leading research and development programmes while properly reviewing their internal systems in accordance with changing social and economic needs.

From the viewpoint of activating national research institutes, the basic principles for their intermediate and long-range operations should be established on the basis of our Council's finding.

Considering that private enterprises are stepping up basic research as a basis for expanding into new areas of activity, resulting in increased opportunities for industrial-academic-government cooperation in all stages of R&D ranging from basic research to applications and product development, the government should endeavour to promote industrial-academic-government research exchanges by improving pertinent systems, operating them more flexibly, encouraging practical applications of research findings, and taking other appropriate steps. The government should also improve cooperative research projects, comprehensive research projects, flexible research systems and other systems and encourage contacts among researchers through research meetings and so forth.

2. Developing and improving conditions

1) Increasing R&D investment
Continued investment in research and development should be ensured since the capacity of R&D depends largely on the accumulation of knowledge and skill generated by R&D investment. For this purpose, the government should provide more R&D funds, use them more effectively, and improve environmental conditions favourable for vitalizing private R&D activities while taking steps to increase the national total of R&D investment.

2) Securing and training R&D personnel
Since people are a key factor in promoting science and technology, it is essential to secure and train young researchers and other R&D personnel at universities, national research institutes and other facilities that constitute the core of the nation's basic research sector while paying attention to the needs for such personnel in these new growth areas of activity.

Special efforts should be made to improve the quality of undergraduate-level training and graduate-level training, research guidance, etc., to secure necessary personnel mainly in the public sector where private initiatives cannot be continued on, and to improve conditions for more successful performance on the part of the researchers.

3) Consolidating the basis for science and technology promotion
Considering the markedly increasing importance of the intellectual basis on which the promotion of science and technology rests, efforts should be made to expedite the production and distribution of science and technology information by facilitating transfers of literature and encouraging the

construction and utilization of factual databases, to upgrade facilities for developing, maintaining and making available such equipment, materials, genetic resources, etc., as the private sector cannot be counted on to provide, and to improve environmental conditions to give vitality to the supporting activities, thus helping to consolidate the basis for further promotion of science and technology.

4) Expanding international exchanges and cooperation in science and technology
Under the basic principles outlined in 1, we should endeavour to promote mutual understanding between nations and positively expand international exchanges and cooperation activities. For this purpose, the government should take steps to develop an internationally open research system, by increasing the number of foreign researchers employed and admitted to universities and national research institutes. Also, efforts should be made to improve and upgrade various international cooperative research projects, to expedite exchanges of researchers and information, and to develop necessary conditions to deal with such problems as protection of rights involved in research cooperation.

5) Promoting public understanding and securing cooperation
Now that science and technology have reached every corner of the economy and society as well as national life, it is important to develop a climate in which the people can not only take advantage of science and technology effectively but also cooperate in promoting science and technology. Therefore, the government should endeavour to stimulate the interest of the younger generation in science and technology, and to take other steps for the fulfilment of this purpose.

Encouraging important areas of research and development

To promote highly creative sciences and technologies, we should, while taking the various steps mentioned above, emphasize research and development not only in the areas mentioned in 1 below but also basic, leading sciences and technologies in the areas indicated in 2 and 3 properly evaluating research projects and carrying out R&D activities energetically and effectively. For this purpose the prime minister should formulate a series of basic research and development plans each intended for a specific area to be encouraged with priority.

1. Encouraging basic, leading sciences and technologies in which new progress can be expected
Efforts should be made in a much more energetic manner to encourage basic, leading areas of science and technology with emphasis on developing new scientific findings, looking for seeds of revolutionary technological developments and helping them grow while being aware of the importance of basic scientific research and taking care to promote growth in that area.

Special emphasis should be laid on the following objectives:

(1) Investigating the limitations of the existing technology in dealing with matter, energy, information and other basic factors involved in science and technology, looking for and unveiling new principles and phenomena and exploring new possibilities in science and technology, exceeding the bounds of the existing technology;

(2) Investigating life phenomena by taking advantage of latest developments in molecular biology and related areas in recent years and looking for possible applications of new knowledge resulting therefrom:

and

(3) Acquiring better insight into man, the earth, outer space, the ocean, and other macroscopic entities in the environment around us, and looking for possible applications of new knowledge resulting therefrom.

For this purpose, the following areas of research should be more energetically encouraged:

a) Matter/materials sciences and technologies

b) Information/electronics sciences and technologies

c) Life sciences

d) Soft series of sciences and technologies

e) Space sciences and technologies

f) Ocean sciences and technologies

g) Earth sciences and technologies

2. Encouraging sciences and technologies for activating the economy

Now that it is important for the nation to revitalize its economy in relation to the rest of the world as well as to maintain and increase economic growth at home, thus further strengthening the basis for our survival, we should endeavour to encourage the following areas of research as sciences and technologies for activating the economy:

a) Development and management of natural resources

b) Development and utilization of energy

c) Upgrading of production technologies and distribution systems

d) Recycling and effective utilization of resources

e) Improvement of service to society and life

3. Encouraging sciences and technologies for improving the quality of society and life

At a time when the nation is becoming more mature socially and more advanced in average age while it is increasingly required to operate in harmony with the rest of the world community, it is important for us to promote sciences and technologies characterised by still greater respect for man, better adapted to people and society, and contributing to their sound growth. In particular, the following areas of research should be encouraged:

a) Maintaining and improving the mental and physical health of the people

b) Formulation of individual and cultural life

c) Formulation of comfortable and safe society

d) Improving the human environment based on a global viewpoint.

Source: Indicators of Science and Technology (Kagaku Gijutsu Yoran). Compiled by Science and Technology Agency, Tokyo 1990: Printing Bureau, Ministry of Finance, p.99, 101 and 103.

Directory of major research establishments

Government research institutes

The following is an almost complete listing of Government research institutes in Japan.

Each entry gives name, address and fax number, where available. The following three lines give information on:
- year of establishment
- total staff (researchers only)
- total budget

This list is compiled from information contained in *National Laboratories and Research Public Corporations in Japan*, Tokyo: Science and Technology Agency (2 parts); and *Indicators of Science and Technology*, Tokyo: Science and Technology Agency, 1990.

Building Research Institute (BR); Ministry of Construction
1-Tatehara, Tsukuba-shi, Ibaraki Pref. 305
fax (0298) 642989
1987
173 (118)
2154 million yen
Central Customs Laboratory; Ministry of Finance
531, Iwase, Matsudo-shi, Chiba Pref. 271
fax (0473) 610531
1963
18 (13)
Chugoku National Agricultural Experimental Station; Ministry of Agriculture, Forestry and Fisheries (MAFF)
6-12-1, Nishifukazu-cho, Fukuyama-shi, Hiroshima Pref. 721
fax (0849) 247893
1987
222 (107)
1611 million yen
Chuo Regional Fisheries Research Laboratory; MAFF
5-5-1, Kachidoki, Chuo-ku, Tokyo 104
fax (03) 35335693
1949
170 (92)
1600 million yen

Civil Engineering Research Institute; Hokkaido Development Bureau, Hokkaido Development Agency
Hiragishi 1-jo 3-chome, Toyohira-ku, Sapporo-shi, Hokkaido 062
fax (011) 8241226
1937
213 (105)
1306 million yen
Economic Research Institute; Economic Planning Agency
3-1-1 Kasumigaseki, Chiyoda-ku, Tokyo 100
78 (19)
Electronic Navigation Research Institute; Ministry of Transport
6-38-1, Shinkawa, Mitaka, Tokyo 181
fax (0422) 481618
1967
36 (29)
1746 million yen
Electrotechnical Laboratory; AIST, MITI
1-1-4, Umezono, Tsukuba-shi, Ibaraki Pref. 305
fax (0298) 551729
1891
686 (552)
9447 million yen
Far Seas Fisheries Research Laboratory; MAFF
7-1, Orido, Shimizu-shi, Shizuoka-ken 424
fax (0543) 359642
1967
102 (55)
275 million yen
Fermentation Research Institute; AIST, MITI
1-1-3, Higashi, Tsukuba-shi, Ibaraki Pref. 305
fax (0298) 546009
1940
89 (71)
1200 million yen
Fire Research Institute (FRI); Fire Prevention Agency, Ministry of Home Affairs
14-1, Nakahara 3-chome, Mitaka, Tokyo 181
fax (0422) 427719
1948
53 (35)
536 million yen
Forestry and Forest Products Research Institute; MAFF
1 Matsuno Sato, Kukizaki-machi, Inashiki-gun, Ibaraki Pref. 305
fax (0298) 743720
1905
757 (503)
6800 million yen
Fruit Tree Research Station; MAFF
2-1, Fujimoto Tsukuba-shi, Ibaraki Pref. 305
fax (02975) 66437

1902
222 (116)
1625 million yen
Geographical Survey Institute (GSI); Ministry of Construction
Kitasato-1, Tsukuba-shi, Ibaraki Pref. 305
fax (0298) 642654
1869
884 (46)
9219 million yen
Geological Survey of Japan; AIST, MITI
1-1-3, Higashi, Tsukuba-shi, Ibaraki Pref. 305
fax (0298) 543571
1882
353 (235)
2225 million yen
Government Industrial Development Laboratory, Hokkaido; AIST, MITI
17-2-1, Higashi 2-jo, Tsukisamu, Toyohira-ku, Sapporo, Hokkaido 004
fax (011) 8544676
1960
96 (72)
1194 million yen
Government Industrial Research Institute, Chugoku; AIST, MITI
2-2-2, Hiro-Suehiro, Kure-shi, Hiroshima Pref. 737-01
fax (0823) 733284
1971
52 (39)
696 million yen
Government Industrial Research Institute, Kyushu; AIST, MITI
807-1, Shuku-machi, Tosu-shi, Saga Pref. 841
fax (0942) 830850
1964
91 (70)
1200 million yen
Government Industrial Research Institute, Nagoya; AIST, MITI
1, Hirate-cho, Kita-ku, Nagoya 462
fax (052) 9162802
1952
241 (185)
885 million yen
Government Industrial Research Institute, Osaka; AIST, MITI
1-8-31, Midorigaoka, Ikeda-shi, Osaka-fu 563
fax (0727) 512156
1918
219 (167)
3115 million yen
Government Industrial Research Institute, Shikoku; AIST, MITI
2-3-3 Hananomiya-cho, Takamatsu-shi, Kagawa Pref. 761
fax (0878) 678234
1967
45 (35)

460 million yen
Government Industrial Research Institute, Tohoku; AIST, MITI
4-2-1 Nigatake, Miyagino-ku, Sendai-shi, Miyagi Pref. 983
fax (022) 2366839
1967
53 (38)
561 million yen
Hokkaido National Agricultural Experiment Station; MAFF
1, Hitsujigaoka, Toyohira-ku, Sapporo-shi, Hokkaido 004
fax (011) 8535916
1901
385 (186)
3205 million yen
Hokkaido Regional Fisheries Research Laboratory; MAFF
116, Katsurakoi, Kushiro-shi, Hokkaido 085
fax (0154) 919355
1950
87 (26)
989 million yen
Hokuriku National Agricultural Experiment Station; MAFF
1-2-1, Inada, Joetsu-shi, Niigata Pref. 943-01
fax (0255) 248578
1950
145 (74)
924 million yen
Hydrographic Department; Maritime Safety Agency
5-3-1 Tsukiji, Chuo-ku, Tokyo 104
1871
374 (35)
1974 million yen
Industrial Products Research Institute; AIST, MITI
1-1-4, Higashi, Tsukuba-shi, Ibaraki Pref. 305
fax (0298) 546601
1928
125 (101)
1447 million yen
Institute of Population Problems; Ministry of Health and Welfare
2-2, Kasumigaseki, 1-chome, Chiyoda-ku, Tokyo 100-45
1939
36 (26)
288 million yen
Institute of Public Health (IPH); Ministry of Health and Welfare
6-1, Shirokanedai 4-chome, Minato-ku, Tokyo 108
fax (03) 34464314
1938
166 (114)
1596 million yen
Japan Sea Regional Fisheries Research Laboratory; MAFF
5939-22, 1 Suido-cho, Niigata-shi, Niigata Pref. 951
fax (025) 2240950

1987
64 (24)
240 million yen
Kyushu National Agricultural Experiment Station; MAFF
496, Izumi, Chikugo City, Fukuoka Pref. 833
fax (0942) 537776
1950
323 (158)
2650 million yen
Mechanical Engineering Laboratory; AIST, MITI
1-2, Namiki, Tsukuba-shi, Ibaraki Pref. 305
fax (0298) 542549
1937
276 (215)
3221 million yen
Meteorological Research Institute (MRI); Meteorological Agency
1-1, Nagamine, Tsukuba-shi, Ibaraki Pref. 305
fax (0298) 511449
1946
179 (142)
2500 million yen
Nansei Regional Fisheries Research Laboratory; MAFF
7782-9, Maruishi Ohno-cho, Saiki-gun, Hiroshima Pref. 739-04
fax (0829) 541216
1967
78 (48)
752 million yen
National Aerospace Laboratory (NAL); STA
7-44-1, Jindaiji-machi Chofu, Tokyo 182
fax (0422) 485888
1955
442 (331)
10266 million yen
National Agriculture Research Centre; MAFF
3-1-1, Kannondai, Tsukuba-shi, Ibaraki Pref. 305
fax (02975) 68484
1981
330 (210)
3404 million yen
National Cancer Centre Research Institute; Ministry of Health and Welfare
1-1, Tsukiji, 5-chome, Chuo-ku, Tokyo 104
fax (03) 35453567
1962
131 (130)
National Cardiovascular Centre Research Institute; Ministry of Health and Welfare
7-1, Fujishiro-dai, 5-chome, Suita-shi, Osaka 565
fax (06) 8339865
1979
109 (109)

National Chemical Laboratory for Industry; AIST, MITI
1-1, Higashi, Tsukuba-shi, Ibaraki Pref. 305
fax (0298) 544488
1900
350 (274)
4092 million yen
National Food Research Institute; MAFF
2-1-2, Kannondai, Tsukuba-shi, Ibaraki Pref. 305
fax (02975) 67996
1934
138 (110)
1489 million yen
National Grassland Research Institute; MAFF
768, Nishinasuno-machi, Nasu-gun, Tochigi Pref. 329-27
fax (02873) 66629
1970
214 (115)
1678 million yen
National Institute for Environmental Studies (NIES); Environment Agency
16-2 Onogawa, Tsukuba-shi, Ibaraki Pref. 305
fax (0298) 514732
1974
273 (182)
4099 million yen
National Institute for Minamata Disease (NIMD); Environment Agency
PO Minamata, Kumamoto 867, 4058-18 Hama, Minamata-shi, Kumamoto Pref.
867
fax (0966) 636844
1978
28 (12)
415 million yen
National Institute for Research in Inorganic Materials (NIRIM); STA
1-1, Namiki, Tsukuba-shi, Ibaraki Pref. 305
fax (0298) 527449
1966
166 (119)
2078 million yen
National Institute of Agro-Environmental Sciences; MAFF
3-1-1 Konnondai, Tsukuba-shi, Ibaraki Pref. 305
fax (02975) 68199
1983
221 (121)
3195 million yen
National Institute of Agrobiological Resources; MAFF
2-1-2, Kannondai, Tsukuba-shi, Ibaraki Pref. 305
fax (02975) 67408
1983
253 (151)
378 million yen
National Institute of Animal Health (NIAH); MAFF

3-1-1, Kannondai, Tsukuba-shi, Ibaraki Pref. 305
fax (02975) 67880
1891
313 (152)
2451 million yen
National Institute of Animal Industry; MAFF
2, Ikenodai, Kukizaki-machi, Inashiki-gun, Ibaraki Pref. 305
fax (02975) 68606
1916
221 (121)
2355 million yen
National Institute of Educational Research of Japan (NIER); Ministry of Education
5-22, Shimomerugo 6-chome, Meguro-ku, Tokyo 153
93 (72)
National Institute of Health; Ministry of Health and Welfare
10-35, Kamiosaki 2-chome, Shinagawa-ku, Tokyo 141
fax (03) 34466286
1947
415 (319)
4463 million yen
National Institute of Hospital Administration; Ministry of Health and Welfare
1-21-3 Toyama, Shinjuku-ku, Tokyo 162
fax (03) 32026853
1949
16 (10)
157 million yen
National Institute of Hygienic Sciences (NIHS); Ministry of Health and Welfare
1-18-1, Kamiyoga, Setagaya-ku, Tokyo 158
fax (03) 37076950
1874
277 (205)
2940 million yen
National Institute of Industrial Health; Ministry of Labour
21-1, Nagao 6-chome, Tama-ku, Kawasaki-shi, Kanagawa 214
fax (044) 8656116
1976
36 (28)
888 million yen
National Institute of Leprosy Research; Ministry of Health and Welfare
2-1, Aobacho 4-chome, Higashimurayama-shi, Tokyo 189
1955
28 (19)
734 million yen
National Institute of Mental Health; Ministry of Health and Welfare
1-7-3, Konodai, Ichikawa-shi, Chiba 272
fax (0473) 712900
1952

427 million yen
National Institute of Neuroscience; Ministry of Health and Welfare
4-1-1, Ogawahigashi, Kodaira-shi, Tokyo 187
fax (0423) 446745
1978
1071 million yen
National Institute of Nutrition; Ministry of Health and Welfare
1-23-1 Toyama-cho, Shinjuku-ku, Tokyo 162
fax (03) 32023278
1920
48 (34)
451 million yen
National Institute of Radiological Sciences (NIRS); STA
4-9-1, Anagawa, Chiba-shi, Chiba Pref. 260
fax (0472) 569616
1957
394 (208)
7085 million yen
National Institute of Science and Technology Policy (formerly National Institute of Resources); STA
1-11-39 Nagata-cho, Chiyoda-ku, Tokyo 100
fax (03) 35033996
1968
46 (9)
280 million yen
National Institute of Special Education; Ministry of Education
2360 Nobi, Yokosuka-shi, Kanagawa Pref. 239
86 (52)
National Research Centre for Disaster Prevention; STA
3-1 Tenno, Tsukuba-shi, Ibaraki Pref. 305
1963
118 (77)
2550 million yen
National Research Institute for Metals; STA
2-3-12, Nakameguro, Meguro-ku, Tokyo 153
fax (03) 37923337
1956
431 (331)
4514 million yen
National Research Institute for Pollution and Resources; AIST, MITI
16-3, Onogawa, Tsukuba-shi, Ibaraki Pref. 305
fax (0298) 543049
1920
319 (243)
4560 million yen
National Research Institute of Agricultural Economics; MAFF
2-2-1, Nishigahara, Kita-ku, Tokyo 114
fax (03) 39400232
1946
88 (52)

632 million yen
National Research Institute of Agricultural Engineering; MAFF
2-1-2, Kannondai, Tsukuba-shi, Ibaraki Pref. 305
fax (0297) 567609
1961
112 (73)
1328 million yen
National Research Institute of Aquaculture; MAFF
422-1, Nakatsuhama Nansei-cho, Watarai-gun, Mie Pref. 516-01
fax (05996) 61962
1979
93 (59)
669 million yen
National Research Institute of Brewing; Tax Administration Agency
2-6-30, Takinogawa, Kita-ku, Tokyo 114
fax (03) 9106239
1904
37 (23)
335 million yen
National Research Institute of Fisheries Engineering; MAFF
Ebidai, Hasaki-machi, Kashima-gun, Ibaraki Pref. 314-03
fax (0479) 441875
1979
63 (43)
713 mllion yen
National Research Institute of Police Science (NIPS); National Police Agency
6 Sanban-cho, Chiyoda-ku, Tokyo 102
fax (03) 32619986 ext 309
1948
109 (92)
925 million yen
National Research Institute of Vegetables, Ornamental Plants and Tea; MAFF
360, Kusawa, Ano-cho, Aki-gun, Mie Pref. 514-23
fax (0592) 681339
1986
293 (164)
2659 million yen
National Research Laboratory of Metrology; AIST, MITI
1-4, Umezono, 1-chome, Tsukuba-shi, Ibaraki Pref. 305
fax (0298) 544135
1903
218 (127)
2057 million yen
National Science Museum; Ministry of Education
7-20, Ueno Park, Taito-ku, Tokyo 110
151 (79)
Port and Harbour Research Institute; Ministry of Transport
1-1, Nagase, 3-chome, Yokosuka-shi, Kanagawa Pref. 239

fax (0468) 429265
1962
184 (140)
1994 million yen
Public Works Research Institute; Ministry of Construction
1-Asahi, Tsukuba-shi, Ibaraki Pref. 305
fax (0298) 642840
1922
286 (192)
5183 million yen
Radio Research Laboratory; MPT
4-2-1, Nukui, Kita-machi, Koganei-shi, Tokyo 184
fax (0423) 249062
1952
423 (270)
404 million yen
Research Institute for Polymers and Textiles; AIST, MITI
1-1-4, Higashi, Tsukuba-shi, Ibaraki Pref. 305
fax (0298) 546233
1918
125 (101)
2838 million yen
Research Institute of Industrial Safety; Ministry of Labour
5-35-1, Shiba, Minato-ku, Tokyo 108
fax (03) 34526565
1942
80 (65)
600 million yen
Seikai Regional Fisheries Research Laboratory; MAFF
49, Kokubu-cho, Nagasaki-shi, Nagasaki Pref. 850
fax (0958) 214494
1949
83 (40)
774 million yen
Sericulture Experiment Station; MAFF
1-2, Owashi, Tsukuba-shi, Ibaraki Pref. 305
fax (02975) 66028
1911
213 (126)
2586 million yen
Shikoku National Agricultural Experiment Station; MAFF
1-3-1, Senyu-cho, Zentsuji-shi, Kagawa Pref. 765
fax (0877) 631683
1946
129 (68)
1013 million yen
Ship Research Institute; Ministry of Transport
38-1, Shinkawa, 6-chome, Mitaka, Tokyo 181
fax (0422) 424533
1963

263 (193)
3306 million yen
Technical Research Institute; Defence Agency
1-2-24 Ikejiri, Setagaya-ku, Tokyo 154
919 (548)
Tohoku National Agricultural Experimental Station; MAFF
4 Akahara, Shimo-Kuriyagawa, Morioka-shi, Iwate Pref. 020-01
fax (0196) 417794
1950
362 (170)
2688 million yen
Tohoku Regional Fisheries Research Laboratory; MAFF
3-27-5, Shinhama-cho, Shiogama-shi, Miyagi Pref. 985
fax (022) 3671250
1949
69 (39)
649 million yen
Traffic Safety and Nuisance Research Institute; Ministry of Transport
38-1, Shinkawa 6-chome, Mitaka-shi, Tokyo 181
fax (0422) 483866
1970
57 (49)
1800 million yen
Tropical Agricultural Research Centre (TARC)
1-2, Owashi, Tsukuba-shi, Ibaraki Pref. 305
fax (02975) 66316
1970
141 (103)
1533 million yen

University research institutes

The following is an almost complete list of research institutes at the national universities.

Each entry gives name, address and telephone number, if available. The list is compiled from information contained in *Indicators for Science and Technology*, Tokyo: Science and Technology Agency, 1990.

The following three lines give information on:
– year of establishment
– total staff
– total budget (in million yen)

The information on year of establishment, staff and budget has been extracted from Directory of Scientific Research Institutes of Universities in Japan (Daigaku Kenkyujo Yoran) (1990). Tokyo: Japan Society for the Promotion of Science (Nihon Gakujutsu Shinkokai) and Maruzen.

Gunma University
  Institute of Endocrinology
  3-39-15, Showa-machi, Maebashi-shi, Gunma Pref. 371

tel. 0272-31-7221
1951
42
Y 340 million
Hiroshima University
Research Institute for Nuclear Medicine and Biology (RINMB)
1-2-3, Kasumi, Minami-ku, Hiroshima-shi, Hiroshima Pref. 734
tel. 082-251-1111
1958
92
Y 785 Million
Research Institute for Theoretical Physics
1294, Takehara-cho, Takehara-shi, Hiroshima Pref. 725
tel. 08462-2-2362
1944
13
Y 134 million
Hokkaido University
Institute of Low-Temperature Science
Kita-19, Nish-8, Kita-ku, Sapporo Hokkaido 060
tel. 011-716-2111
1935
84
Y 790 million
Research Institute of Applied Electricity
Kita-12, Nishi-6, Kita-ku, Sapporo Hokkaido 060
tel. 011-716-21111
1941
84
Y 650 million
Research Institute of Immunological Science
Kita-15, Nishi-7, Kita-ku, Sapporo Hokkaido 060
tel. 011-716-2111
1942
28
Y 317 million
Kanazawa University
Cancer Research Institute
13-1, Takara-machi, Kanazawa-shi, Ishikawa Pref. 920
tel. 0762-62-8151
1940
62
Y 509 million
Kyoto University
Chest Disease Research Institute
53, Kawara-cho, Shogoin, Sakyo-ku, Kyoto 606
tel. 075-751-3111
1941
49
Y 627 million

Disaster Prevention Research Institute
Gokasho, Uji-shi, Kyoto 611
tel. 0774-32-3111
1951
156
Y 1517 million
Institute for Chemical Research
Gokasho, Uji-shi, Kyoto 611
tel. 0774-32-3111
1916
172
Y 2102 million
Institute for Virus Research
53 Kawara-cho, Shogoin, Sakyo-ku, Kyoto 606
tel. 075-751-3111
1956
69
Y 623 million
Institute of Atomic Energy
Gokasho, Uji-shi, Kyoto 611
tel. 0774-32-3111
1915
47
Y 497 million
Research Institute for Food Science
Gokasho, Uji-shi, Kyoto 611
tel. 0774-32-3111
1946
37
Y 409 million
Wood Research Institute
Gokasho, Uji-shi, Kyoto 611
tel. 0774-32-3111
1944
35
Y 307 million
Kyushu University
  Department of Molecular Biology, Graduate School of Medical Science
  6-1, Kasuga Koen, Kasuga-shi, Fukuoka Pref. 816
  Medical Institute of Bioregulation
  3-1-1, Maedashi Higashi-ku, Hukuoka-shi, Hukuoka Pref. 812
  tel. 092-641-1151
  1931
  60
  Y 680 million
  Research Institute for Applied Mechanics
  6-1, Kasuga-Koen, Kasuga-shi, Fukuoka Pref. 816
  tel. 092-573-9611
  1942
  77

Y 1680 million
Nagasaki University
Institute of Tropical Medicine
12-4, Sakamoto-machi, Nagasaki-shi, Nagasaki 852
tel. 0958-47-2111
1942
44
Y 492 million
Nagoya University
Research Institute of Atmospherics
3-13, Honohara, Toyokawa-shi, Aichi 442
tel. 05338-63154
1949
45
Y 486 million
Research Institute of Environmental Medicine
Furo-cho, Chikusa-ku, Nagoya 464-01
tel. 052-781-5111
1943
41
Y 385 million
Water Research Institute
Furo-cho, Chikusa-ku, Nagoya 464-01
tel. 052-781-5111
1957
32
Y 377 million
Niigata University
Brain Research Institute
1-757, Asahimachi, Niigata 951
tel. 025-223-6161
1957
47
Y 456 million
Okayama University
Institute for Bio-resources Sciences
2-20-1, Chuo, Kurashiki-shi, Okayama 710
tel. 0864-24-1661
1915
61
Y 504 million
Osaka University
Institute of Scientific and Technical Research (ISTR)
8-1, Mittogaoka, Suita-shi, Osaka 567
tel. 06-877-5111
1939
168
Y 1614 million
Research Institute for Microbial Diseases
3-1, Yamada-kami, Suita-shi, Osaka 565

tel. 06-877-5121
1934
91
Y 890 million
Shizuoka University
Research Institute of Electronics
3-5-1, Jyohoku, Hamamatsu-shi, Shizuoka 432
tel. 0534-71-1171
1950
54
Y 433 million
Tohoku University
Chemical Resarch Institute of Non-Aqueous Solutions
2-1-1, Katahira, Aoba-ku, Sendai-shi, Miyagi Pref. 980
tel. 022-227-6200
1944
87
Y 831 million
Institute of Fluid Science
2-1-1, Katahira, Aoba-ku, Sendai-shi, Miyagi Pref. 980
tel. 022-227-6200
1943
85
Research Institute for Scientific Measurements
2-1-1, Katahira, Aoba-ku, Sendai-shi, Miyagi Pref. 980
tel. 022-227-6200
1943
112
Y 932 million
Research Institute for Tuberculosis and Cancer
4-1, Seiryo-machi, Sendai 980
tel. 022-274-1111
1941
78
Y 951 million
Research Institute of Electrical Communication
2-1-1, Katahira, Aoba-ku, Sendai-shi, Miyagi Pref. 980
tel. 022-227-6200
1935
133
Y 1413 million
Research Institute of Mineral Dressing and Metallurgy
2-1-1, Katahira, Aoba-ku, Sendai-shi, Miyagi Pref. 980
tel. 022-227-6200
1941
83
Y 932 million
Tokyo Institute of Technology
Research Laboratory for Nuclear Reactors
2-10-2, Ookayama, Meguro-ku, Tokyo 152

tel. 03-3726-1111
1956
69
Y 635 million
Research Laboratory of Engineering Materials
4259, Nagatsuta-cho, Midori-ku,
Yokohama-shi, Kanagawa Pref. 227
tel. 045-922-1111
1934
45
Y 593 million
Research Laboratory of Precision Machinery and Electronics
4259, Nagatsuta-cho, Midori-ku
Yokohama-shi, Kanagawa Pref. 227
tel. 045-922-1111
1939
71
Y 744 million
Research Laboratory of Resources Utilization
4259, Nagatsuta-cho, Midori-ku
Yokohama-shi, Kanagawa Pref. 227
tel. 045-922-1111
1939
63
Y 727 million
Tokyo Medical And Dental University
Institute for Medical and Dental Engineering
2-3-10, Kanda-Surugadai, Chiyoda-ku, Tokyo 101
tel. 03-3291-3721
1951
55
Y 569 million
Medical Research Institute
2-3-10, Kanda-Surugadai, Chiyoda-ku, Tokyo 101
tel. 03-3294-7311
1953
102
Y 845 million
University of Tokyo
Earthquake Research Institute
1-1-1, Yayoi, Bunkyo-ku, Tokyo 113
tel. 03-3812-2111
1883
151
Y 2193 million
Institute of Applied Microbiology (IAM)
1-1-1, Yayoi, Bunkyo-ku, Tokyo 113
tel. 03-3812-2111
1943
90

Y 743 million
Institute of Industrial Science
7-22-1, Roppongi, Minato-ku, Tokyo 106
tel. 03-3402-6231
1942
402
Y 2999 million
Institute of Medical Science
4-6-1, Shirokanedai, Minato-ku, Tokyo 108
tel. 03-3443-8111
1883
242
Y 1992 million
Toyama Medical and Pharmaceutical University
Research Institute for Wakan-Yaku (Oriental Medicines)
2630, Sugitani, Toyama-shi, Toyama Pref. 930-01
tel. 0764-34-2281
1952
23
Y 262 million

Public (research) corporations (Tokushuhojin)

The following is an almost complete listing of public (research) corporations in Japan.

Each entry gives name, address and fax number. The following three lines give information on:
– year of establishment
– total staff (researchers only)
– total budget

This list is compiled from information contained in *National Laboratories and Research Public Corporations in Japan*, Tokyo: Science and Technology Agency (2 parts); and *Indicators of Science and Technology*, Tokyo: Science and Technology Agency, 1990.

Agricultural Policy Research Committee Inc.
26-3, Nishigahara 1-chome, Kita-ku, Tokyo 114
fax (03) 39107267
1961
16(4)
Bio-oriented Technology Research Advancement Institution (BRAIN)
1-40-2, Nisshin-cho, Omiya-shi, Saitama Pref. 331
Hokkaido River Disaster Prevention Research Centre
2nd Yuraku Building, West 1 South 1, Chuo-ku, Sapporo-chi, Hok –
kaido 060
fax (011) 2313380
1986
16 (4)
543 million yen

Institute of Agricultural Machinery (IAM) (Bio-oriented Technology Research Advancement Institution, BRAIN)
1-40-2 Nisshin, Omiya-shi, Saitama Pref. 331
fax (0486) 519655
1962
99 (58)
4328 million yen
Institute of Physical and Chemical Research (RIKEN); Prime Minister's Office
2-1 Hirosawa, Wako-shi, Saitama Pref. 351-01
fax (0484) 621554
1958
612 (435)
15823 million yen
International Association of Traffic and Safety Science
20-6, 2-chome, Yaesu, Chuo-ku, Tokyo 04
fax (03) 32727054
1974
74
700 million yen
International Development Centre of Japan
Shuwa Daini Toranomon Building, 21-19, Toranomon 1-chome, Minato-ku, Tokyo 105
fax (03) 35921614
1971
54 (26)
1176 million yen
Japan Atomic Energy Research Institute; Prime Minister's Office
2-2-2, Uchisaiwaicho, Chiyoda-ku, Tokyo 100
fax (03) 35806107
1956
2524 (992)
108527 million yen
Japan Chemical Analysis Centre
295-3 Sanno-cho, Chiba-shi, Chiba Pref. 281
fax (0434) 235372
1974
72
996 million yen
Japan Information Centre of Science and Technology (JICST); Prime Minister's Office
2-5-2 Nagata-cho, Chiyoda-ku, Tokyo 100
fax (03) 35933375
1957
12 million yen
Japan Key Technology Centre (JKTC)
Ark Mori Building 16F, 1-12-32 Akasaka, Minato-ku, Tokyo 107
fax (03) 35056830, (03) 35056831
Japan Marine Science and Technology Centre; Prime Minister's Office
2-15 Natsujima-cho, Yokosuka-shi, Kanagawa Pref. 237

fax (0468) 662119
1971
145 (75)
8615 million yen
Japan Sewage Works Agency
Simosasame 5141, Toda-shi, Saitama Pref. 335
fax (0484) 217542
1972
28
402 million yen
Japan Society for Promotion of Science (JSPS)
Yamato Building, 5-3-1, Koji-machi, Chiyoda-ku, Tokyo 102
Japan Weather Association
5, Kojimachi 4-chome, Chiyoda-ku, Tokyo 102
fax (03) 32349667
1950
734 (18)
10770 million yen
Japanese Environmental Sanitation Centre
10-6, Yotsuyakami-cho, Kawasaki-ku, Kawasaki-shi, Kanagawa Pref. 210
fax (044) 299-2294
1954
161 (16)
1910 million yen
Japanese Foundation for Cancer Research
Kami-Ikebukuro 1-37-1, Toshima-ku, Tokyo 170
fax (03) 39180167
1908
854
13700 million yen
National Space Development Agency of Japan; Prime Minister's Office
World Trade Centre Building, 4-1, Hamamatsu-cho 2-chome, Minato-ku,
Tokyo 105
fax (03) 4330796
1969
933 (647)
114940 million yen
New Energy and Industrial Technology Development Organization (NEDO)
Sunshine 60 Building, 3-1-1 Higashi Ikebukuro, Toshima-ku, Tokyo 170
NHK Science and Technical Research Laboratories
1-10-11, Kinuta, Setagaya-ku, Tokyo 157
fax (03) 34175536
1930
327 (252)
5840 million yen
Nippon Institute for Biological Science
222-1, Shinmachi, Ome-shi, Tokyo 198
fax (0428) 316166
1947
59

678 million yen
Osaka Bioscience Institute
6-2-4, Furuedai, Suita-shi, Osaka-fu 565
1987
34 (12)
921 million yen
Overseas Coastal Area Development Institute of Japan
Kazan Building, 3-2-4 Kasumigaseki, Chiyoda-ku, Tokyo 100
fax (03) 35803657
1976
49
1005 million yen
Power Reactor and Nuclear Fuel Development Corporation (PNC) Prime
Minister's Office
9-13, Akasaka 1-chome, Minato-ku, Tokyo 107
fax (03) 35867726; (03) 35867427
1967
2823 (2465)
218575 million yen
Railway Technical Research Institute
2-8-38 Hikari-cho, Kokubunji-shi, Tokyo 185
fax (0425) 737356
1986
550 (440)
11400 million yen
Remote Sensing Technology Centre of Japan
Uni-Roppongi Building, 7-15-17 Roppongi, Minato-ku, Tokyo 106
fax (03) 34031766
1975
83 (32)
1183 million yen
**Research and Development Programme on Medical and Welfare Equipment
Technology**
Sunshine 60 Building, 3-1-1 Higashi Ikebukuro, Toshima-ku 170
Research Development Corporation of Japan (JRDC); Prime Minister's Office
2-5-2 Nagata-cho, Chiyoda-ku, Tokyo 100
fax (03) 35811486
1961
18914 million yen
Research Institute of Tuberculosis; Japan Anti-Tuberculosis Association
3-1-24 Matsuyama, Kiyose-shi, Tokyo 204
fax (0424) 924600
1939
55 (40)
513 million yen
Telecommunications Satellite Corporation of Japan
Banzai Building, 2-31-19, Shiba, Minato-ku, Tokyo 105
Tottori Mycological Institute
Kokoge-211, Tottori-shi, Tottori Pref. 689-11
fax (0857) 531986

1959
51 (18)
304 million yen

National inter-university research institutes

The following is an indication of national inter-university research institutes in Japan, which have the same legal status as universities.
Each entry gives name, address and telephone number, where available.
This list is compiled from information contained in *Indicators of Science and Technology*, Tokyo: Science and Technology Agency, 1990. Institutes in Social Sciences and Humanities have not been included.
The following three lines give information on:
– year of establishment
– total staff
– total budget (in million yen)
The information on year of establishment, staff and total budget has been extracted from *Directory of Scientific Research Institutes of Universities in Japan* (Daigaku Kenkyujo Yoran) (1980). Tokyo: Japan Society for the Promotion of Science (Nihon Gakujutsu Shinkikai) and Maruzen.

Okazaki National Research Institutes:
  Institute for Basic Biology
  38, Nishigonaka, Myodaiji, Okazaki-shi, Aichi 444
  tel. 0564-54-1111
  1981 (1976)
  86
  Y 1048 million
  Institute for Molecular Science
  38, Nishigonaka, Myodaiji, Okazaki-shi, Aichi 444
  tel. 0564-54-1111
  1981 (1974)
  137
  Y 2971 million
  Institute for Physiological Sciences
  38, Nishigonaka, Myodaiji, Okazaki-shi, Aichi 444
  tel. 0564-54-1111
  1981 (1976)
  87
  Y 1080 million
Institute of Space and Astronautical Science (ISAS)
3-1-1 Yoshinodai, Sagamihara-shi, Kanagawa Pref. 229
tel. 0427-51-3911
(1959)
289
Y 23069 million
National Institute of Polar Research (NIPR)
1-9-10, Kaga, Itabashi-ku, Tokyo 173
tel. 03-3962-4711

1973 (1962)
111
Y 2725 million
National Laboratory for High Energy Physics (KEK)
1-1, Oho-machi, Tsukuba-shi, Ibaraki Pref. 305
tel. 0298-64-1171
1971 (1964)
662
Y 28210 million
National Institute for Fusion Science
(formerly Institute of Plasma Physics)
Furo-cho, Chigusa-ku, Nagoya-shi, Aichi Pref. 464-01
tel. 052-781-5111
1988
Y 161 million
Institute of Statistical Mathematics
4-6-7 Minamiazabu, Minato-ku, Tokyo 106
tel. 03-3446-1501
1985 (1934)
76
Y 1017 million
National Centre for Science Information System (NACSIS)
3-29-1 Otsuka, Bunkyo-ku, Tokyo 112
tel. 03-3942-2351
1989 (1976)
76
Y 2218 million
National Institute of Genetics (NIG)
1111 Yata, Mishima-shi, Shizuoka Pref. 411
tel. 0559-75-0771
1984 (1947)
103
Y 1319 million

University attached institutes for joint use

The following is a complete list of research institutes which are attached to specific universities but open to researchers from all universities.

Each entry gives name, address and fax number, if available, as well as year of establishment.

The list is compiled from *Indicators of Science and Technology*, Tokyo: Science and Technology Agency, 1990.

Institute for Cosmic Ray Research
Tokyo University
3-2-1 Midori-cho, Tanashi-shi, Tokyo 188
1953
Institute for Materials Research
Tohoku University

2-1-1 Katahira, Aboa-ku, Sendai-shi, Miyagi Pref. 980
1987
Institute for Nuclear Studies
Tokyo University
3-2-1 Midori-cho, Tanashi-shi, Tokyo 188
1955
Institute for Solid State Physics
Tokyo University
7-22-1 Roppongi, Minato-ku, Tokyo 106
1957
Institute of Plasma Physics
Nagoya University
Institute for Protein Research
Osaka University
3-2 Yamada oka, Suita-shi, Osaka-fu 565
1958
Ocean Research Institute
Tokyo University
1-15-1 Minamidai, Nakano-ku, Tokyo 164
1962
Primate Research Institute
Kyoto University
Kanrin, Inuyama-shi, Aichi Pref. 484
1967
Research Institute for Fundamental Physics
Kyoto University
Oiwake-cho, Kitashirakawa, Sakyo-ku, Kyoto-fu 606
1953
Research Institute for Mathematical Sciences
Kyoto University
Oiwake-cho, Kitashirakawa, Sakyo-ku, Kyoto-fu 606
1963
Research Reactor Institute
Kyoto University
Noda, Kumatori-cho, Sennan-gun, Osaka-fu 590-04
1963
Welding Research Institute
Osaka University
11-1 Mihoga oka, Ibaraki-shi, Osaka-fu 567
1972

Private companies and corporations

The following list provides names of the research laboratories of major
Japanese private companies. The information is extracted from *All Japan
Directory of Test and Research Organisations* (*Zenkoku Shiken Kenkyu Kikan Meikan*)
Vol 1 and 2. This directory lists the laboratories or research institutes of more
than 1000 companies. Among these some 100 companies were selected based
on a listing of "major private companies – strategy for research investments"

which appears in *All Japan Research Institute Planning Directory* (*Zenkoku Kenkyujo Keikaku Soran*) (1988), Tokyo, Sangyo Times. In addition, a number of major company-directed research institutes, organised as stock companies, have also been included. However, the reader is warned that this is in no way a complete list of all private company research institutes.

The readers should be also aware of the fact that the organisation of industrial research in Japan is undergoing rapid changes and names of research laboratories as well as their location may in several cases be changing.

Each specific company entry provides the company name, location of headquarters, telephone and fax numbers and research budget for 1990 – if reported in Japan Company Handbook (Toyo Keizai, Autumn 1990). Furthermore, the name and location of individual research laboratories – each with address and telephone number, and number of research staff (researchers), if available are provided, although not a comprehensive listing.

"Kenkyujo", which has a wide meaning of organisation or place for product development, as well as long term exploratory research, has been translated as "Research Institute" throughout. "Honbu" has been translated as "Headquarters". The English translations may not always correspond with those used by the respective companies in their English language publications. However, the transcription from Japanese (in romaji) corresponds with the actual names unless the company R&D organisation has changed the Japanese names, after publication of the directories.

Construction and engineering
Kajima Corporation
1-2-7, Moto-Akasaka
Minato-ku, Tokyo 107
tel. 03-3404-3311
fax 03-3470-1444
Y 15 billion
    Construction Technology Research Institute
    (Kajima Kensetsu Gijutsu Kenkyujo)
    2-19-1 Tobitakyu
    Chofu-shi, Tokyo 182
    tel. 0424-85-1111
    staff: 370
Taisei Corporation
1-25-1 Nishishinjuku
Shinjuku-ku, Tokyo 163
tel. 03-3348-1111
fax 03-3345-0481
Y 11 billion
    Technology Research Institute
    (Gijutsu Kenkyujo)
    344-1 Naze-cho
    Totsuka-ku, Yokohama-shi, Kanagawa Pref. 245
    tel. 045-812-1211
    staff: 352
Shimizu Construction Co. Ltd

2-16-1 Kyobashi
Chuo-ku, Tokyo 104
tel. 03-3535-4111
fax 03-3564-0467
Y 13 billion
Technology Research Institute
(Gijutsu kenkyujo)
3-4-17 Echujima
Koto-ku, Tokyo 135
tel. 03-3643-4311
staff: 240

Food industry
Ajinomoto Co. Inc.
1-5-8 Kyobashi
Chuo-ku, Toyo 104
tel. 03-3272-1111
fax 03-3297-8720
Y 18 billion
Central Research Institute
(Chuo Kenkyujo)
1-1 Suzuki-cho
Kawasaki-ku, Kawasaki-shi, Kanagawa Pref. 210
tel. 044-244-7111
staff: 600
Meiji Seika Kaisha Ltd.
2-4-16 Kyobashi
Chuo-ku, Tokyo 104
tel. 03-3272-6511
fax 03-3281-4058
Y 12 billion
Central Research Institute
(Chuo Kenkyujo)
760 Shioka-cho
Kohoku-ku, Yokohama-shi, Kanagawa Pref. 222
tel. 045-541-2521
Medicine Research Institute
(Yakuhin Kenkyujo)
760 Shioka-cho
Kohoku-ku, Yokohama-shi, Kanagawa Pref. 222
tel. 045-541-2521
Pharmacology Safety Research Institute
(Yakuri Anzensei Kenkyujo)
760 Shioka-cho
Kohoku-ku, Yokohama-shi, Kanagawa Pref. 222
tel. 045-541-2521
Bioscience Research Institute
(Seibutsu Kagaku Kenkyujo)
580 Harikawa-cho

Saiwai-ku, Kawasaki-ku, Kanagawa Pref. 210
tel. 044-548-6567
Food Development Research Institute
(Shokuryo Kaihatsu Kenkyujo)
580 Harikawa-cho
Saiwai-ku, Kawasaki-ku, Kanagawa Pref. 210
tel. 044-548-6591
Medicine Development Research Institute
(Yakuhin Kaihatsu Kenkyujo)
580 Harikawa-cho
Saiwai-ku, Kawasaki-ku, Kanagawa Pref. 210
tel. 044-548-6595
Fermentation Technology Research Institute
(Hakko Gijutsu Kenkyujo)
788 Kashiyama
Odawara, Kanagawa Pref. 250-01
tel. 0465-36-3111
Kirin Brewery Co. Ltd.
6-26-1 Jingumae
Shibuya-ku, Tokyo 150
tel. 03-3499-6111
fax 03-3499-6151
Y 15 billion
Beer Science Research Institute
(Beer Kagaku Kenkyujo)
3 Miyahara-cho
Takasaki-shi, Gumma Pref. 370-12
tel. 0273-46-1561
staff: 90
Medical Development Research Institute
(Iyaku Kaihatsu Kenkyujo)
1-2-2 Sojamachi
Maebashi-shi, Gumma Pref. 371
tel. 0272-52-7001
staff: 170
Plant Development Research Institute
(Shokubutsu Kaihatsu Kenkyujo)
3377 Saotome, Kizuregawa-machi
Shioya-gun, Tochigi Pref. 329-14
tel. 0286-86-4511
staff: 70
Japan Tobacco Inc.
2-2-1 Toranomon
Minato-ku, Tokyo 105
tel. 03-3582-3111
Central Research Institute
6-2 Umegaoka, Midori-ku
Yokohama-shi, Kanagawa Pref. 227
tel. 045-973-5611
Hiratsuka Research Institute of Engineering

1-31 Kurobegaoka
Hiratsuka-shi, Kanagawa Pref. 254
tel. 0463-31-2815

Textile and fibre industry
Asahi Chemical Industry Co. Ltd.
1-1-2 Yuraku-cho
Chiyoda-ku, Tokyo 100
tel. 03-3507-2730
fax 03-3507-2005
Y 40 billion
  Development Technology Headquarters
  1-1-2 Yuraku-cho
  Chiyoda-ku, Tokyo 100
  tel. 03-3507-2462
Toray Industries Inc.
2-2-1 Nihonbashi-Muromachi
Chuo-ku, Tokyo 103
tel. 03-3245-5111
fax 03-3245-5555
Y 26 billion
  Basic Research Institute
  (Kiso Kenkyujo)
  1111 Tehiro
  Kamakura-shi, Kanagawa Pref. 248
  tel. 0467-32-2111
  Polymer Research Institute
  (Kobunshi Kenkyujo)
  3 Sonoyama
  Ohtsu-shi, Shiga Pref. 520
  tel. 0775-37-0700
  Fibre Research Institute
  (Kobunshi Kenkyujo)
  3 Sonoyama
  Ohtsu-shi, Shiga Pref. 520
  tel. 0775-37-0700
  Engineering Research Institute
  (Enjiniyaringu Kenkyujo)
  3 Sonoyama
  Ohtsu-shi, Shiga Pref. 520
  tel. 0775-37-0700
  Film Research Institute
  (Fuirumu Kenkyujo)
  3 Sonoyama
  Ohtsu-shi, Shiga Pref. 520
  tel. 0775-37-0700
Toyobo Co. Ltd.
2-2-8 Dojimahama
Kita-ku, Osaka-shi 530

tel. 06-348-3374
fax 06-344-0444
Y 10 billion
General Research Institute
(Sogo Kenkyujo)
2-1-1 Katada
Ohtsu-shi, Shiga Pref. 520-02
tel. 0775-73-2111
staff: 700
Mitsubishi Rayon Co. Ltd.
2-3-19 Kyobashi
Chuo-ku, Tokyo 104
tel. 03-3272-4321
fax 03-3245-8790
Y 12 billion
Central Research Institute
(Chuo Kenkyujo)
20-1 Miyuki-cho
Ohtake-shi, Hiroshima Pref. 739-06
tel. 08275-2-4151
Product Development Research Institute
(Shohin Kaihatsu Kenkyujo)
4-1-60 Sunadabashi, Higashi-ku
Nagoya-shi, Aichi Pref. 461
tel. 052-721-6111
Tokyo Research Institute
(Tokyo Kenkyujo)
3816 Noborito, Tamaku
Kawasaki-shi, Kanagawa Pref. 214
tel. 044-933-9111

Printing industry
Toppan Printing Co. Ltd.
1 Kanda-Izumicho
Chiyoda-ku, Tokyo 101
tel. 03-3835-5111
fax 03-3835-0674
Y 10 billion
General Research Institute
(Sogo Kenkyujo)
1580 Shimotakano, Sugito-machi
Kitakatsushikagun, Saitama Pref. 345
tel. 0480-34-1011
Dai Nippon Printing Co. Ltd.
1-1-1 Ichigaya-Kagacho
Shinjuku-ku, Tokyo 162
tel. 03-3266-2111
fax 03-3266-2119
Y 10 billion

Central Research Institute
(Chuo Kenkyujo)
1-1-1 Ichigaya-Kagacho
Shinjuku-ku, Tokyo 162
tel. 03-266-2342

Chemical industry
Sumitomo Chemical Co. Ltd.
4-5-33 Kitahama
Chuo-ku, Osaka 541
tel. 06-220-3272
fax 06-220-3345
Y 36 billion
    Takarazuka General Research Institute
    (Takarazuka Sogo Kenkyujo)
    Ehime Research Institute
    (Ehime Kenkyujo)
    Chiba Research Institute
    (Chiba Kenkyujo)
    Resin Development Research Institute
    (Jushi Kaihatsu Kenkyujo)
    Osaka Research Institute
    (Osaka Kenkyujo)
    Takatsuki Research Institute
    (Takatsuki Kenkyujo)
Mitsubishi Kasei Corp.
2-5-2 Marunouchi
Chiyoda-ku, Tokyo 100
tel. 03-3283-6254
fax 03-3283-6287
Y 41 billion
    General Research Institute
    (Sogo Kenkyujo)
    1000 Kamoshida-cho
    Midori-ku, Yokohama 227
    tel. 045-962-1211
    staff: 1100
Showa Denko K. K.
1-13-9 Shiba-Daimon
Minato-ku, Tokyo 105
tel. 03-3432-5111
fax 03-3436-2625
Y 19 billion
    General Technology Research Institute
    (Sogo Kenkyujo)
    2-24-25 Tamagawa
    Ota-ku, Tokyo 146
    tel. 03-3733-0151
    Kawasaki Resin Research Institute

(Kawasaki Jushi Kenkyujo)
3-2 Chidori-cho
Kawasaki-ku, Kawasaki 210
tel. 044-277-7140
Ohta Research Institute
(Ohita Kenkyujo)
2 Nakanosu
Ohita-shi 870-01
tel. 0975-21-5111
Chemical Products Research Institute
(Kagakuhin Kenkyujo)
5-1 Ohgaimachi
Kawasaki-ku, Kawasaki 210
tel. 044-333-3541
Organic Chemistry Research Institute
(Seikagaku Kenkyujo)
2-24-25 Tamagawa
Ohta-ku, Tokyo 1463
tel. 03-3733-0151
Ohmachi Research Institute
(Ohmachi Kenkyujo)
6850 Ohmachi
Ohmachi-shi 398
tel. 0261-22-0400
Shiojiri Research Institute
(Shiojiri Kenkyujo)
1 Soga
Shiojiri-shi 399-64
tel. 0263-52-3194
Powder Research Institute
(Bifun Kenkyu Center)
1 Soga
Shiojiri-shi 399-64
tel. 0263-52-3194
Chichibu Research Institute
(Chichibu Kenkyujo)
1505 Shimokagemori
Chichibu-shi
tel. 0494-23-6117
Ube Industries Ltd.
1-12-32 Nishihonmachi
Ube-shi, Yamaguchi Pref. 755
tel. 03-3505-9212
fax 03-3505-9218
Y 15 billion
Ube Research Institute
(Ube Kenkyujo)
1978-5 Ogushi
Ube-shi, Yamaguchi Pref. 755
tel. 0836-31-1111

staff: 400
Chiba Research Institute
(Chiba Kenkyujo)
8-1 Goi-minami-Kaigan
Ichiharashi, Chiba 290
tel. 0436-23-5151
staff: 100
Hirakata Research Institute
Hirakata Kenkyujo
3-10 Nakamiya-Kitamachi
Hirakata-shi, Osaka 573
tel. 0720-48-0331
staff: 95
Mitsui Toatsu Chemicals Inc.
3-2-5 Kasumigaseki
Chiyoda-ku, Tokyo 100
tel. 03-3593-7111
fax 03-3592-4267
Y 20 billion
General Research Institute
(Sogo Kenkyujo)
1190 Kasama-cho
Sakai-ku, Yokohama, Kanagawa Pref. 247
tel. 045-891-1111
staff: 740
Kanegafuchi Chemical Industry Co. Ltd.
3-2-4 Nakanoshima
Kita-ku, Osaka 530
tel. 06-226-5095
fax 06-226-5037
Y 10 billion
Central Research Institute
Chuo Kenkyujo
1-2-80 Yoshidacho
Hyogo-ku, Kobe-shi 652
tel. 078-681-6551
staff: 150
Organic Chemistry Research Institute
(Seibutsu Kagaku Kenkyujo)
1-8 Miyamae-cho, Takasago-cho
Takasago-shi, Hyogo Pref. 676
tel. 07944-2-3181
staff: 130
Production Technology Research Institute
(Seisan Gijutsu Kenkyujo)
1-8 Miyamae-cho, Takasago-cho
Takasago-shi, Hyogo Pref. 676
tel. 07944-5-2430
staff: 45
Electronic Material Development Research Institute

(Denshi Zairyo-Kaihatsu Kenkyujo)
2-1-1 Hieitsuji
Ohtsu-shi, Shiga 520-01
tel. 0775-79-3884
staff: 55
Synthetic Resin Research Institute
(Goseijushi Kenkyujo)
1-8 Miyamae-cho, Takasago-cho
Takasago-shi, Hyogo Pref. 676
tel. 07944-5-2084
staff: 75
Mitsubishi Petrochemical Co. Ltd.
2-5-2 Marunouchi
Chiyoda-ku, Tokyo 100
tel. 03-3283-5700
fax 03-3283-5805
Y 19 billion
Central Research Institute
(Chuo Kenkyujo)
8-3-1 Chuo, Ami-machi
Inashiki-gun, Ibaraki Pref. 300-03
tel. 0298-87-1010
staff: 170
Synthetic Product Research Institute
(Kaseihin Kenkyujo)
1 Tohocho
Yokkaichi-shi, Mie Pref. 510
tel. 0593-45-1111
staff: 80
Resin Research Institute
(Jushi Kenkyujo)
1 Tohocho
Yokkaichi-shi, Mie Pref. 510
tel. 0593-45-1111
staff: 290
New Material Research Institute
(Shinsozai Kenkyujo)
1 Tohocho
Yokkaichi-shi, Mie Pref. 510
tel. 0593-45-1111
staff: 85
Mitsui Petrochemical Industries Ltd.
3-2-5 Kasumigaseki
Chiyoda-ku, Tokyo 100
tel. 03-3580-2012
fax 03-3593-0027
Y 29 billion
General Research Institute
(Sogo Kenkyujo)
6-1-2 Wagi

Wagi-machi 740
tel. 0827-22-4111
Polymer Application Research Institute
(Porima Oyo Kenkyujo)
6-1-2 Wagi
Wagi-machi 740
tel. 0827-22-4111
Functional Material Research Institute
(Kinozai Kenkyujo)
6-1-2 Wagi
Wagi-machi 740
tel. 0827-22-4111
Organic Industry Research Institute
(Seibutsu Kogaku Kenkyujo)
6-1-2 Wagi
Wagi-machi 740
tel. 0827-22-4111
total staff: 920
Kyowa Hakko Kogyo Co. Ltd.
1-6-1 Ohtemachi
Chiyoda-ku, Tokyo 100
tel. 03-3282-0007
fax 03-3284-1968
Y 15 billion
Tokyo Research Institute
(Tokyo Kenkyujo)
3-6-6 Asahicho
Machida-shi, Tokyo 194
tel. 0427-25-5555
Technology Research Institute
(Gijutsu Kenkyujo)
Hofu Factory
1-1 Kyowamachi
Hofu-shi 747
tel. 0835-22-2511
Medicine Research Institute
(Iyaku Kenkyujo)
Fuji Factory
1188 Shimotokari, Nagaizumi-cho
Suntogun, Shizouka Pref. 411
tel. 0559-86-7600
Sakai Research Institute
(Sakai Kenkyujo)
1-1-53 Takasucho
Sakai-shi, Osaka 590
tel. 0722-29-0825
Food and Beverage Research Institute
(Shokuhin, Sakerui Kenkyujo)
4041 Ami, Amimachi
Inashikigun, Ibaraki Pref. 300-03

tel. 0298-87-1221
Organic Research Institute
(Seibutsu Kenkyujo)
4041 Ami, Amimachi
Inashikigun, Ibaraki Pref. 300-03
tel. 0298-87-1221
Safety Research Institute
(Anzensei Kenkyujo)
2548 Fujimagari
Ube-shi, Yamaguchi Pref. 755
tel. 0836-22-5514
Marine Product Research Institute
(Suisan Kenkyujo)
2548 Fujimagari
Ube-shi, Yamaguchi Pref. 755
tel. 0836-22-5514
Yokkaichi Research Institute
(Yokkaichi Kenkyujo)
2-3 Daikyocho
Yokkaichi-Shi, Mie Pref. 510
tel. 0593-31-5111
Kato Memorial Bio-Science Research Institute
(Kato Kinen Baiosaiensu Kenkyujo)
3-6-6 Asahicho
Machida-shi, Tokyo 194
tel. 0427-25-2555
Shin Etsu Chemical Co. Ltd.
2-6-1 Ohtemachi
Chiyoda-ku, Tokyo 100
tel. 03-3246-5011
fax 03-3243-1491
Y 15 billion
Synthesis Technology Research Institute
(Gosei Gijutsu Kenkyujo)
28-1 Nishihukushima, Kubikimura
Naka-kubikigun, Niigata Pref. 942
tel. 0255-43-3711
Magnetic Material Research Institute
(Gisei Zairyo Kenkyujo)
2-1-5 Kitago
Takefu-shi, Fukui Pref. 915
tel. 0778-24-3141
Silicon and Electronic Material Technology Research Institute
(Sirikon Denshizairyo Gijutsu Kenkyujo)
2-13-1 Isobe
Annaka-shi, Gumma Pref. 379-01
tel. 0273-85-7111
High Polymer Functional Material Research Institute
(Kobunshi Kino Zairyo Kenkyujo)
1 Higashiwada, Kamisu cho

Kashimagun, Ibaraki Pref. 314-02
tel. 02999-6-3411
Hitachi Chemical Co. Ltd.
2-1-1 Nishi-Shinjuku
Shinjuku-ku, Tokyo 163
tel. 03-3346-3111
fax 03-3343-8488
Y 12 billion
　Tsukuba Development Research Institute
　(Tsukuba Kaihatsu Kenkyujo)
　48 Wadai, Tsukubamachi
　Tsukubagun, Ibaraki Pref. 300-42
　staff: 51
　Ibaraki Research Institute
　(Ibaraki Kenkyujo)
　4-13-1 Higasicho
　Hitachi-shi, Ibaraki Pref. 317
　tel. 0294-22-5111
　staff: 116
　Shimodate Research Institute
　(Shimodate Kenkyujo)
　1500 Ogawa
　Shimodate-shi, Ibaraki Pref. 308
　tel. 0296-28-1111
　staff: 83
Sekisui Chemical Co. Ltd.
2-4-2 Nishi-Tenma
Kita-ku, Osaka 530
tel. 06-365-4122
fax 06-365-4370
Y 20 billion
　General Research Institute
　(Sogo Kenkyujo)
　2-1 Mimoyama, Shimamoto-cho
　Mishima-gun, Osaka 618
　tel. 075-962-8811
　staff: 270
Kao Corporation
1-14-10 Nihonbashi-Kayabacho
Chuo-ku, Tokyo 103
tel. 03-3660-7111
fax 03-3669-5168
Y 25 billion
　Research and Development Headquarters
　(Kenkyu Kaihatsu Honbu)
　1-14-10 Nihonbashi-Kayabacho
　Chuo-ku, Tokyo 103
　tel. 03-3660-7193
　staff: 1230
　Kao Basic Science Research Institute

(Kao Kisokagaku Kenkyujo)
2606 Akabane, Ichigaimachi
Haga-gun, Tochigi Pref. 321-34
tel. 02856-8-2131
Production Technology Research Institute
(Seisan Gijutsu Kenkyujo)
2606 Akabane, Ichigaimachi
Haga-gun, Tochigi Pref. 321-34
tel. 02856-8-2131
Knowledge and Information Science Research Institute
(Chishiki Joho Kagaku Kenkyujo)
2606 Akabane, Ichigaimachi
Haga-gun, Tochigi Pref. 321-34
tel. 02856-8-2131
Kao Living Conditions Science Research Institute
(Kao Seikatsukagaku Kenkyujo)
1-14-10 Nihonbashi-Kayabacho
Chuo-ku, Tokyo 103
tel. 03-3660-7365
Lion Corporation
1-3-7 Honjo
Sumida-ku, Tokyo 130
tel. 03-3621-6211
fax 03-3621-6328
Y 8 billion
Research and Development Headquarters
(Kenkyu Kaihatsubu)
7-13-12 Hirai
Edogawa-ku, Tokyo 132
tel. 03-3613-6071
staff: 760
Dainippon Ink and Chemicals Inc.
3-7-20 Nihonbashi
Chuo-ku, Tokyo 103
tel. 03-3272-4511
fax 03-3278-8558
Y 20 billion

Pharmaceutical industry
Takeda Chemical Industries Ltd.
2-3-6 Dosho-machi
Chuo-ku, Osaka 541
tel. 06-204-2111
fax 06-204-2880
Y 49 billion
Central Research Institute
(Chuo Kenkyujo)
2-17-85 Juso-honmachi
Yodogawa-ku, Osaka 532

tel. 06-300-6111
Production Technology Research Institute
(Seisan Gijutsu Kenkyujo)
2-17-85 Juso-honmachi
Yodogawa-ku, Osaka 532
tel. 06-300-6111
Food Research Institute
(Shokuhin Kenkyujo)
2-17-85 Juso-honmachi
Yodogawa-ku, Osaka 532
tel. 06-300-6111
Synthetic Products Research Institute
(Kaseihin Kenkyujo)
2-17-85 Juso-honmachi
Yodogawa-ku, Osaka 532
tel. 06-300-6111
Agricultural Chemicals Research Institute
(Noyaku Kenkyujo)
2-17-85 Juso-honmachi
Yodogawa-ku, Osaka 532
tel. 06-300-6111
Veterinary Chemicals Research Institute
(Dobutsuyaku Kenkyujo)
2-17-85 Juso-honmachi
Yodogawa-ku, Osaka 532
tel. 06-300-6111
total staff: 1550
Sankyo Company Ltd.
2-7-12 Ginza
Chuo-ku, Tokyo 104
tel. 03-3562-0411
fax 03-3561-5409
Y 25 billion
General Research Institute
(Sogo Kenkyujo)
1-2-58 Hiromachi
Shinagawa, Tokyo 140
tel. 03-3492-3131
Chemical Research Institute
(Kagaku Kenkyujo)
1-2-58 Hiromachi
Shinagawa, Tokyo 140
tel. 03-3492-3131
Organic Research Institute
(Seibutsu Kenkyujo)
1-2-58 Hiromachi
Shinagawa, Tokyo 140
tel. 03-3492-3131
Bio-science Research Institute
(Baiosaiensu Kenkyujo)

1-2-58 Hiromachi
Shinagawa, Tokyo 140
tel. 03-3492-3131
Fermentation Research Institute
(Hakko Kenyujo)
1-2-58 Hiromachi
Shinagawa, Tokyo 140
tel. 03-3492-3131
Analytical Metabolism Research Institute
(Bunseki Taisha Kenkyujo)
1-2-58 Hiromachi
Shinagawa, Tokyo 140
tel. 03-3492-3131
Safety Research Institute
(Anzensei Kenkyujo)
1-2-58 Hiromachi
Shinagawa, Tokyo 140
tel. 03-3492-3131
Production Technology Research Institute (I & II)
(Daiichi Sesangijutsu Kenkyujo)
1-2-58 Hiromachi
Shinagawa, Tokyo 140
tel. 03-3492-3131
Agricultural Chemicals Research Institute
(Noyaku Kenkyujo)
1-2-58 Hiromachi
Shinagawa, Tokyo 140
tel. 03-3492-3131
total staff: 959
Shionogi and Co. Ltd.
3-1-8 Dosho-machi
Chuo-ku, Osaka 541
tel. 06-202-2161
fax 06-229-8154
Y 23 billion
Shionogi Research Institute
(Shionogi Kenkyujo)
5-12-4 Sagisu
Fukushima-ku, Osaka 553
tel. 06-458-5861
staff: 635
Kamisakigawa Branch Research Institute
(Kamisakigawa-bunshitsu)
3-1-1 Futabacho
Toyonaka-shi, Osaka 561
tel. 06-331-8081
staff: 92
Yunichi Laboratories
1405 Gotanda, Kogacho
Kogagun, Shiga Pref. 520-34

tel. 074888-3281
staff: 250
Taisho Pharmaceutical Co. Ltd.
3-24-1 Takada
Toshima-ku, Tokyo 171
tel. 03-3985-1111
fax 03-3982-9702
Y 13 billion
  General Research Institute
  (Sogo Kenkyujo)
  1-403 Yoshinocho
  Omiya, Saitama Pref. 330
  tel. 0486-63-1111
Fujisawa Pharmaceutical Co. Ltd.
3-4-7 Dosho-machi
Chuo-ku, Osaka 541
tel. 06-202-1141
fax 06-222-4988
Y 24 billion
  Central Research Institute
  (Chuo Kenkyujo)
  2-1-6 Kashima
  Yodogawa-ku, Osaka 532
  tel. 06-301-1271
  Properties Research Institute
  (Bussei Kenkyujo)
  2-1-6 Kashima
  Yodogawa-ku, Osaka 532
  tel. 06-301-1271
  Industrification Research Institute
  (Kogyoka Kenkyujo)
  2-1-6 Kashima
  Yodogawa-ku, Osaka 532
  tel. 06-301-1271
  Investigation Research Institute
  (Tansaku Kenkyujo)
  5-2-3 Tokodai, Toyosato
  Tsukubagun, Ibaraki Pref. 300-26
  tel. 0297-47-8611
  total staff: 1400
Daiichi Pharmaceutical Co. Ltd.
3-14-10 Nihonbashi
Chuo-ku, Tokyo 103
tel. 03-3272-0611
fax 03-3274-5704
Y 18 billion
  Central Research Institute
  (Chuo Kenkyujo)
  1-16-13 Kitakasai
  Edogawa, Tokyo 134

tel. 03-3680-0150
Production Technology Research Institute
(Seisan-gijutsu Kenkyujo)
1-16-13 Kitakasai
Edogawa, Tokyo 134
tel. 03-3680-0150
total staff: 620
Yamanouchi Pharmaceutical Co. Ltd.
2-3-11 Nihonbashi-Honcho
Chuo-ku, Tokyo 103
tel. 03-3244-3000
fax 03-3244-3102
Y 22 billion
    Central Research Institute
    (Chuo Kenkyujo)
    1-1-8 Azusawa
    Itabashi, Tokyo 174
    tel. 03-960-5111
    Development Research Institute
    (Kaihatsu Kenkyujo)
    1-1-8 Azusawa
    Itabashi, Tokyo 174
    tel. 03-960-5111
    total staff: 522
Tanabe Seiyaku Co. Ltd.
3-2-10 Dosho-machi
Chuo-ku, Osaka 541
tel. 06-205-5555
fax 06-205-5262
Y 18 billion
    Research and Development Headquarters
    (Kenkyu Kaihatsu Honbu)
    3-16-89 Kashima
    Yodogawa, Osaka 532
    tel. 06-300-2525
    total staff: 800
Eisai Co. Ltd.
4-6-10 Koishikawa
Bunkyo-ku, Tokyo 112-88
tel. 03-3817-5286
fax 03-3811-3305
Y 27 billion
    Research and Development Headquarters
    (Kenkyu Kaihatsu Honbu)
    5-1-3 Tokodai, Toyosato
    Tsukubagun, Ibaraki Pref. 300-26
    tel. 029747-2211
    staff: 618
Chugai Pharmaceutical Co. Ltd.
2-1-9 Kyobashi

Chuo-ku, Tokyo 104
tel. 03-3281-6611
fax 03-3281-2828
Y 20 billion
New Drugs Research Institute
(Shinyaku Kenkyujo)
3-41-8 Takada
Toshima, Tokyo 171
tel. 03-3987-7111
Development Research Institute
(Kaihatsu Kenkyujo)
3-41-8 Takada
Toshima, Tokyo 171
tel. 03-3987-7111
Application Research Institute
(Oyo Kenkyujo)
3-41-8 Takada
Toshima, Tokyo 171
tel. 03-3987-7111
total staff: 390
Nippon Kayaku Co. Ltd.
1-11-2 Fujimi
Chiyoda-ku, Tokyo 102
tel. 03-3237-5111
fax 03-3324-8098
Y 10 billion
Drug Business Division
(Iyaku Jigyohonbu)
General Research Institute
(Sogo Kenkyujo)
3-31-12 Shimo
Kita-ku, Tokyo 115
tel. 03-3598-5204
Agricultural Chemicals Industry Division
(Noyaku Jigyobu)
Ageo Research Institute
(Ageo Kenkyujo)
225-1 Horikomi, Koshikiya
Ageo, Saitama 362
tel. 0487-25-2511
Gunpowder Industry Division
(Kayaku Jigyobu)
Gunpowder Research Institute
(Kayaku Kenkyujo)
2300 Kori, Sanyocho
Atsusagun, Yamaguchi Pref. 757
tel. 08367-2-1234
Chemical Products Research Institute
(Kagakuhin Kenkyujo)
3-26-8 Shimo

Kita-ku, Tokyo 115
tel. 03-3598-5076
Takasaki Research Institute
(Takasaki Kenkyujo)
219 Iwahanacho
Takasaki, Gumma Pref. 370-12
tel. 0273-46-2411
Shiseido Co. Ltd.
7-5-5 Ginza
Chuo-ku, Tokyo 104-10
tel. 03-3572-5111
fax 03-3574-8380
Y 11 billion
Shiseido Research Institute
(Shiseido Kenkyujo)
1050 Shinhanecho, Kohoku-ku
Yokohama, Kanagawa Pref. 223
tel. 045-542-1331
staff: 380

Petroleum industry
Nippon Oil Company Ltd.
1-3-12 Nishi-Shimbashi
Minato-ku, Tokyo 105
tel. 03-3502-1111
fax 03-3502-9352
Y 11 billion
Central Technology Research Institute
(Chuo Gijutsu Kenkyujo)
8 Chidoricho, Naka-ku
Yokohama, Kanagawa Pref. 231
tel. 045-212-7111
staff: 450
Idemitsu Kosan Co. Ltd.
3-1-1 Marunouchi
Chiyoda-ku, Tokyo 100
tel. 03-3213-3111
Central Research Institute
(Chuo Kenkyujo)
1280 Kamiizumi, Sodegaura
Kimitsugun, Chiba Pref. 299-02
tel. 0438-75-2312
staff: 450
Bridgestone Corporation
1-10-1 Kyobashi
Chuo-ku, Tokyo 104
tel. 03-3567-0111
fax 03-3535-2553
Y 36 billion

Development Headquarters
3-1-1 Ogawa Higashicho
Kodaira-shi, Tokyo 187
tel. 0423-41-1111
staff: 1380

Ceramics industry
Asahi Glass Co. Ltd.
2-1-2 Marunouchi
Chiyoda-ku, Tokyo 100
tel. 03-3218-5555 3
fax 03-3212-4026
Y 34 billion
   Research and Development Headquarters
   (Kenkyu Kaihatsubu)
   1150 Hazawa-cho
   Yokohama, Kanagawa Pref. 221
   tel. 045-381-1441
   staff: 577
   Asahi Glass Electronics Research Centre
   (Asahi Gurasu Denshi Shohin Kaihatsu Senta)
   1160 Hazawa-cho
   Yokohama, Kanagawa Pref. 221
   tel. 045-381-1441
   staff: 135
Ngk Insulators Ltd.
2-56 Suda-cho, Mizuho-ku
Nagoya, Aichi Pref. 467
tel. 052-872-7171
fax 052-872-7103
Y 10 billion
   Research Institute
   2-56 Suda-cho, Mizuho-ku
   Nagoya, Aichi Pref. 467
   tel. 052-872-7755
   staff: 230
   Very High Pressure Research Institute
   (Cho-Koatsu Kenkyujo)
   Tagami, Nijubori
   Komaki-shi, Aichi Pref. 485
   tel. 0568-72-3127
   staff: 23

Steel industry
Nippon Steel Corporation
2-6-3 Ohtemachi
Chiyoda-ku, Tokyo 100
tel. 03-3424-4111

fax 03-3275-5607
Electronics R&D Institutes (established in 1989)
Research and Engineering Centre (established in 1990 by merging R&D
Institutes I and II)
total staff around 1500
NKK (formerly Nippon Kokan K.K.)
1-1-2 Marunouchi
Chiyoda-ku, Tokyo 100
tel. 03-3212-7111
fax 03-3214-8417
Y 29 billion
Central Research Institute
(Chuo Kenkyujo)
1-1 Minami Wataridacho, Kawasaki-ku
Kawasaki, Kanagawa Pref. 210
tel. 044-355-1111
Heavy Industry Research Institute
(Jukogyo Kenkyujo)
1-1 Minami Wataridacho, Kawasaki-ku
Kawasaki, Kanagawa Pref. 210
tel. 044-355-1111
System Technology Research Institute
(Shisutemu Gijutsu Kenkyujo)
1-1 Minami Wataridacho, Kawasaki-ku
Kawasaki, Kanagawa Pref. 210
tel. 044-355-1111
total staff: 1700
Kawasaki Steel Corporation Ltd.
2-2-3 Uchi-Saiwaicho
Chiyoda-ku, Tokyo 100
tel. 03-3597-3111
fax 03-3597-4868
Y 35 billion
Technology Research Headquarters
(Gijutsu Kenkyubu)
1 Kawasaki-cho
Chiba 260
tel. 0472-62-2111
Steel Research Institute
(Tekko Kenkyujo)
1 Kawasaki-cho
Chiba 260
tel. 0472-62-2111
High Technology Research Institute
(Haiteku Kenkyujo)
1 Kawasaki-cho
Chiba 260
tel. 0472-62-2111
total staff: 1304

Sumitomo Metal Industries Ltd.
4-5-33 Kitahama
Chuo-ku, Osaka 541
tel. 06-220-5111
fax 06-223-0305
Y 33 billion
  General Technology Research Institute
  (Sogo Gijutsu Kenkyujo)
  1-3 Nishinagasu-Hondori
  Amagasaki, Hyogo 660
  tel. 06-401-6201
  staff: 1100
Kobe Steel Ltd.
1-3-18 Wakinohama-cho
Chuo-ku, Kobe 651
tel. 078-251-1551
fax 078-232-3459
Y 35 billion
  Material Research Institute
  (Zairyo Kenkyujo)
  1-3-18 Wakinoha-macho
  Chuo-ku, Kobe 651
  tel. 078-251-1551
  staff: 148
  Machinery Research Institute
  (Kikai Kenkyujo)
  1-3-18 Wakinoha-macho
  Chuo-ku, Kobe 651
  tel. 078-251-1551
  staff: 130
  Chemistry Research Institute
  (Kagaku Kenkyujo)
  1-3-18 Wakinoha-macho
  Chuo-ku, Kobe 651
  tel. 078-251-1551
  staff: 43
  Asada Research Institute
  (Asada Kenkyujo)
  53-3 Maruyama, Gomo
  Nada, Kobe 657
  tel. 078-801-5050
  staff: 71
  Organic Research Institute
  (Seibutsu Kenkyujo)
  1-3-18 Wakinoha-macho
  Chuo-ku, Kobe 651
  tel. 078-251-1551
  Prototype Experiment Center
  (Shisaku Jikken Senta)
  1-3-18 Wakinoha-macho

Chuo-ku, Kobe 651
tel. 078-251-1551
staff: 427
Nisshin Steel Co. Ltd.
3-4-1 Marunouchi
Chiyoda-ku, Tokyo 100
tel. 03-3216-5511
fax 03-3214-1895
Y 10 billion
Research Institute attached to production units
staff: 340

Metal industry
Hitachi Metals Ltd.
2-1-2 Marunouchi
Chiyoda-ku, Tokyo 100
tel. 03-3284-4511
Magnetic Material Research Institute
(Jisei Zairyo Kenkyujo)
5200 Mikajiri
Kumagaya, Saitama Pref. 360
tel. 0485-32-2211
Equipment Development Research Institute
(Setsubi Kaihatsu Kenkyujo)
5200 Mikajiri
Kumagaya, Saitama Pref. 360
tel. 0485-32-2211
Nippon Mining Co. Ltd.
2-10-1 Toranomon
Minato-ku, Tokyo 105
tel. 03-3505-8111
fax 03-3582-1813
Electronic Material and Component Research Institute
(Denshi Zairyo Buhin Kenkyujo)
3-17-35 Shinsominami
Toda, Saitama Pref. 335
tel. 0484-42-1811
General Research Institute
(Sogo Kenkyujo)
3-17-35 Shinsominami
Toda, Saitama Pref. 335
tel. 0484-42-1811
total staff: 430
Mitsubishi Metal Corporation
1-6-1 Ohtemachi
Chiyoda-ku, Tokyo 100
tel. 03-3231-2111
fax 03-3215-2435
Y 9 billion

Central Research Institute
(Chuo Kenkyujo)
1-297 Kitabukuro
Omiya, Saitama Pref. 330
tel. 0486-41-6721
Product Development Centre
(Shohin Kaihatsu Senta)
1-297 Kitabukuro
Omiya, Saitama Pref. 330
tel. 0486-45-7400
Compound Semiconductor Centre
(Kagobutsu Handotai Senta)
1-297 Kitabukuro
Omiya, Saitama Pref. 330
tel. 0486-45-7231
Naka Nuclear Energy Development Centre
(Naka Genshiryoku Kaihatsu Senta)
100-14 Nakamachi
Nakagun, Ibaraki Pref. 311-02
tel. 0292-95-2335
total staff: 460
Sumitomo Electric Industries Ltd.
5-15 Kitahama
Chuo-ku, Osaka 541
tel. 06-423-5711
fax 06-423-5093
Y 23 billion
  Basic Technology Research Institute
  (Kiban Gijutsu Kenkyujo)
  1-1-3 Shimaya
  Konohana-Ku, Osaka 55
  tel. 06-461-1031
  Osaka Research Institute
  (Osaka Kenkyujo)
  1-1-3 Shimaya
  Konohana-Ku, Osaka 55
  tel. 06-461-1031
  Itami Research Institute
  (Itami Kenkyujo)
  1-1-1 Konyokita
  Itami 664
  tel. 0727-81-5151
  Yokohama Research Institute
  (Yokohama Kenkyujo)
  1 Tanimachi
  Sakae-ku, Yokohama 244
  tel. 045-851-1281
The Furukawa Electric Co. Ltd.
2-6-1 Marunouchi
Chiyoda-ku, Tokyo 100

tel. 03-3286-3001
fax 03-3286-3747
Y 14 billion
Central Research Institute
(Chuo Kenkyujo)
2-9-15 Futaba
Shinagawa, Tokyo 142
tel. 03-3781-7121
staff: 200
Nikko Research Institute
(Nikko Kenkyujo)
500 Kiyotaki
Nikko, Tochigi Pref. 321-14
tel. 0288-54-0501
Hiratsuka Research Institute
(Hiratsuka Kenkyujo)
5-1-9 Higashihachiman
Hiratsuka, Kanagawa Pref. 254
tel. 0463-23-1211
staff: 63
Chiba Research Institute
(Chiba Kenkyujo)
6 Hachiman-Kaigandori
Ichihara, Chiba 290
tel. 0436-41-3111
staff: 85

Machinery industry
Kubota Ltd.
1-2-47 Higashi-Shikitsu
Naniwa-ku, Osaka 550
tel. 06-648-2111
fax 06-648-3862
Y 24 billion
Komatsu Ltd.
2-3-6 Akasaka
Minato-ku, Tokyo 107
tel. 03-35561-2609
fax 03-3587-2003
Y 34 billion
Technology Research Institute
(Gijutsu Kenkyujo)
1200 Manda
Hiratsuka, Kanagawa Pref. 254
tel. 0463-34-1111
Electrical Research Institute
(Denki Kenkyujo)
1200 Manda
Hiratsuka, Kanagawa Pref. 254

tel. 0463-34-1111
Production Technology Research Institute
(Seisan Gijutsu Kenkyujo)
3-1-1 Ueno
Hirakata, Osaka 573
tel. 0720-40-1101

Electrical and electronics industry
Hitachi Ltd. (Hitachi Seisakusho)
4-6 Kanda-Surugadai
Chiyoda-ku, Tokyo 101
tel. 03-3258-1111
fax 03-3253-2186
Y 340 billion
Central Research Institute
(Chuo Kenkyujo)
1-280 Kaigakubo
Kokubunji-shi, Tokyo 185
tel. 0423-23-1111
staff: 1300
Hitachi Research Institute
(Hitachi Kenkyujo)
4026 Kujicho
Hitachi, Ibaraki Pref. 319-12
tel. 0294-52-5111
staff: 1300
Machinery Research Institute
(Kikai Kenkyujo)
502 Kandatsu
Tsuchiura, Ibaraki Pref. 300
tel. 0298-31-5111
staff: 640
Energy Research Institute
(Energy Kenkyujo)
1168 Moriyama
Hitachi, Ibaraki Pref. 316
tel. 0294-53-3111
staff: 300
Production Technology Research Institute
(Seisan Gijutsu Kenkyujo)
292 Yoshida, Totsuka
Yokohama, Kanagawa Pref. 244
tel. 045-881-1241
staff: 500
System Development Research Institute
(Shisutemu Kaihatsu Kenkyujo)
1099 Ozenji, Tamaku
Kawasaki, Kanagawa Pref. 215
tel. 044-966-9111

staff: 370
Microelectronic Machinery Development Research Institute
(Maikuroerekutoronikusu Kiki Kaihatsu Kenkyujo)
292 Yoshida, Totsuka
Yokohama, Kanagawa Pref. 244
tel. 045-881-1241
staff: 110
Basic Research Institute
(Kiso Kenkyujo)
Saitama Pref.
staff: 70
Toshiba Corporation
1-1-1 Shibaura
Minato-ku, Tokyo 105-01
tel. 03-3457-4511
fax 03-3456-1631
Y 233 billion
  General Research Institute
  (Sogo Kenkyujo)
  1 Komukai-Toshibacho, Saiwaiku
  Kawasaki, Kanagawa Pref. 210
  tel. 044-511-2111
  ULSI Research Institute
  (Cho LSI Kenkyujo)
  1 Komukai-Toshibacho, Saiwaiku
  Kawasaki, Kanagawa Pref. 210
  tel. 044-511-2111
  Information Communications Research Institute
  (Joho-Tsushin Shisutemu Gijutsu Kenkyujo)
  1 Komukai-Toshibacho, Saiwaiku
  Kawasaki, Kanagawa Pref. 210
  tel. 044-511-2111
  Production Technology Research Institute
  (Seisan Gijutsu Kenkyujo)
  8 Shin-Sugitacho, Isogo
  Yokohama, Kanagawa Pref. 235
  tel. 045-756-2711
  Medical Equipment Technology Research Institute
  (Iyo-Kiki Gijutsu Kenkyujo)
  1385-1 Shimoishigami
  Ohtawara, Tochigi 329-26
  tel. 02872-9-6211
  Electronic Technology Research Institute
  (Denshi Gijutsu Kenkyujo)
  8 Shin-Sugitacho, Isogo
  Yokohama, Kanagawa Pref. 235
  tel. 045-756-2505
  Semiconductor Technology Research Institute
  (Handotai Gijutsu Kenkyujo)
  1 Komukai-Toshibacho, Saiwaiku

Kawasaki, Kanagawa Pref. 210
tel. 044-511-2111
AV Technology Research Institute
(AV Gijutsu Kenkyujo)
8 Shin-Sugitacho, Isogo
Yokohama, Kanagawa Pref. 235
tel. 045-756-3517
Household Electrical Machinery Technology Research Institute
(Kadenkiki Gijutsu Kenkyujo)
8 Shin-Sugitacho, Isogo
Yokohama, Kanagawa Pref. 235
tel. 045-756-3517
Atomic Energy Technology Research Institute
(Genshiryoku Gijutsu Kenkyujo)
4-1 Ukishimacho
Kawasaki, Kanagawa Pref. 210
tel. 044-277-3111
Heavy Electrical Technology Research Institute
(Juden Gijutsu Kenkyujo)
2-4 Suehirocho, Tsurumi
Yokohama, Kanagawa Pref. 230
tel. 045-511-1351
Mitsubishi Electric Corporation
2-2-3 Marunouchi
Chiyoda-ku, Tokyo 100
tel. 03-3218-2111
fax 03-3218-3686
Y 166 billion
Central Research Institute
(Chuo Kenkyujo)
8-1-1 Tsukaguchihoncho
Amagasaki, Hyogo 661
tel. 06-491-8021
Product Research Institute
(Shohin Kenkyujo)
2-14-40 Ohfuna
Kamakura, Kanagawa Pref. 247
tel. 0467-44-6111
Production Technology Research Institute
(Seisan Gijutsu Kenkyujo)
8-1-1 Tsukaguchihoncho
Amagasaki, Hyogo 661
tel. 06-491-8021
Application Machinery Research Institute
(Oyo Kiki Kenkyujo)
8-1-1 Tsukaguchihoncho
Amagasaki, Hyogo 661
tel. 06-491-8021
LSI Research Institute
(LSI Kenkyujo)

4-1 Mizuhara
Itami, Hyogo 664
tel. 0727-82-5131
Design Centre
(Dezain Senta)
5-1-1 Ohfuna
Kamakura, Kanagawa Pref. 247
tel. 0467-44-6111
Electronic Products Development Research Institute
(Denshi Shohin Kaihatsu Kenkyujo)
1 Babazusho,
Nagaoka Kyoshi, Kyoto 617
tel. 075-951-4111
Information Electronics Research Institute
(Joho-denshi Kenkyujo)
5-1-1 Ohfuna
Kamakura, Kanagawa Pref. 247
tel. 0467-44-1100
Material Research Institute
(Zairyo Kenkyujo)
8-1-1 Tsukaguchihoncho
Amagasaki, Hyogo 661
tel. 06-491-8021
Yasukawa Electric Mfg. Co. Ltd.
2346 Fujita Yahata-Nishi-ku
Aita-Kyushu-Shi 806
tel. 093-641-3111
fax 093-631-8837
Y 6 billion
Research Institute
(Kenkyujo)
2346 Fujita Yahata-Nishi-ku
Kita Kyushu 806
tel. 093-641-3111
staff: 140
Nippondenso Co. Ltd.
1-1 Showa-machi
Kariya, Aichi Pref. 448
tel. 0566-25-5511
fax 0566-25-4520
Y 83 billion (1989)
NEC Corporaton
5-7-1 Shiba
Minato-ku, Tokyo 108-01
tel. 03-3454-1111
fax 03-3457-7249
Y 280 billion
Research and Development Group
(Kenkyu Kaihatsu Gurupu)
4-1-1 Miyazaki, Miyamae-ku

Kawasaki, Kanagawa Pref. 213
tel. 044-855-1111
staff: 1000
Matsushita Electric Industrial Co. Ltd.
(Matsushita Denki Sangyo)
1006 Kadoma
Kadoma City, Osaka Pref. 571
tel. 06-908-1121
fax 06-906-1762
   Nakao Research Institute
   (Nakao Kenkyujo)
   3-15 Yagumo-nakacho
   Moriguchi, Osaka 570
   tel. 06-909-1121
   Central Research Institute
   (Chuo Kenkyujo)
   3-15 Yagumo-nakacho
   Moriguchi, Osaka 570
   tel. 06-909-1121
   Lighting Research Institute
   (Shomei Kenkyujo)
   3-15 Yagumo-nakacho
   Moriguchi, Osaka 570
   tel. 06-909-1121
   System Research Institute
   (Shisutemu Kenkyujo)
   3-15 Yagumo-nakacho
   Moriguchi, Osaka 570
   tel. 06-909-1121
   Wireless Research Institute
   (Musen Kenkyujo)
   1006 Kadoma
   Kadoma-shi, Osaka Pref. 571
   tel. 06-908-1291
   Sound Research Institute
   (Onkyo Kenkyujo)
   1006 Kadoma
   Kadoma-shi, Osaka Pref. 571
   tel. 06-908-1291
   Semiconductor Research Institute
   (Handotai Kenkyujo)
   3-15 Yagumo-nakacho
   Moriguchi, Osaka 570
   tel. 06-909-1121
   Device Develoment Research Institute
   (Debaisu Kaihatsu Kenkyujo)
   3-15 Yagumo-nakacho
   Moriguchi, Osaka 570
   tel. 06-909-1121
   Opto-Semiconductor Research Institute

(Hikari-Handotai Kenkyujo)
3-15 Yagumo-nakacho
Moriguchi, Osaka 570
tel. 06-909-1121
Production Technology Research Institute
(Seisan Gijutsu Kenkyujo)
2-7 Matsuba-cho
Kadoma-shi, Osaka Pref. 571
tel. 06-901-1171
Sanyo Electric Co. Ltd.
2-18 Keihan-Hondori
Moriguchi City, Osaka 570
tel. 06-991-1181
fax 06-992-0009
Y 62 billion
   Central Research Institute
   (Chuo Kenkyujo)
   1-18-13 Hashiridani
   Hirakata, Osaka 573
   tel. 0720-41-1161
   Development Research Institute
   (Kaihatsu Kenkyujo)
   180 Anpachi Omori
   Anpachi-kun, Gifu 503-01
   tel. 058464-3344
   Shioya Research Institute
   (Shioya Kenkyujo)
   809-332 Takamaru, Higashi-Tarumi
   Tarumiku, Kobe 655
   tel. 078-751-8811
   Applied Technology Research Institute
   (Ohyogijutsu Kenkyujo)
   100 Dainichi-higashi
   Moriguchi, Osaka 570
   tel. 06-901-1111
   Tsukuba Research Institute
   (Tsukuba Kenkyujo)
   2-1-1 Takanodai, Yatabe
   Tsukubagun, Ibaraki Pref. 305
   tel. 02975-5-1151
Sharp Corporation
22-22 Nagaike-cho
Abeno-ku, Osaka 545
tel. 06-621-1221
fax 06-628-1667
Y 78 billion
   Technology Headquarters
   (Gijutsu Honbu)
   2613-1 Ichinomoto
   Tenri-shi, Nara 632

tel. 07436-5-1321
staff: 770
Oki Electric Industry Co. Ltd.
1-7-12 Toranomon
Minato-ku, Tokyo 105
tel. 03-3501-3111
fax 03-3508-9465
Y 41 billion
  Basic Technology Research Institute
  (Kiban Gijutsu Kenkyujo)
  550-5 Higashi-Asakawa
  Hachioji, Tokyo 193
  tel. 0426-63-1111
  staff: 230
  General System Research Institute
  (Sogo Shisutemu Kenkyujo)
  4-10-12 Shibaura
  Minato-ku, Tokyo 108
  tel. 03-454-2111
  staff: 85
Matsushita Electric Works Ltd.
(Matsushita Denko)
1048 Kadoma
Kadoma City, Osaka Pref. 571
tel. 06-908-1131
fax 06-906-1860
Y 34 billion
  General Technology Research Institute
  (Sogo Gijutsu Kenkyujo)
  1048 Kadoma
  Kadoma City, Osaka Pref. 571
  tel. 06-908-1131
  staff: 436
Kokusai Electric Co. Ltd.
18 Mori, 2-3-13 Toranomon
Minato-ku, Tokyo 105
tel. 03-3591-7292
fax 03-3508-2419
Y 9 billion
Sony Corporation
6-7-35 Kita-shinagawa
Shinagawa-ku, Tokyo 141
tel. 03-3448-2111
fax 03-3448-2244
Y 165 billion
  Central Research Institute
  (Chuo Kenkyujo)
  174 Fujuzuka
  Hodogaya-ku, Yokohama 240
  tel. 045-351-1271

staff: 200
Develoment Research Institute
(Kaihatsu Kenkyujo)
6-7-35 Kita-Shinagawa
Shinagawa-ku, Tokyo 141
tel. 03-3448-2791
staff: 116
Technology Research Institute
(Gijutsu Kenkyujo)
1-7-4 Konan
Minato-ku, Tokyo 108
tel. 03-3458-7657
staff: 152
Information Management Research Institute
(Johoshori Kenkyujo)
4-14-1 Asahi-cho
Atsugi, Kanagawa Pref. 243
tel. 0462-30-5111
staff: 180
Victor Company of Japan Ltd.
4-8-14 Nihonbashi-Honcho
Chuo-ku, Tokyo 103
tel. 03-3279-4133
fax 03-3246-0780
Y 36 billion
Central Research Institute
(Chuo Kenkyujo)
3-12 Moriyacho, Kanagawa-ku
Yokohama, Kanagawa Pref. 221
tel. 045-453-1111
Sound Technology Research Institute
(Onkyo Gijutsu Kenkyujo)
1766 Otsu-ichi, Shimotsumura
Yamato-shi, Kanagawa Pref. 242
tel. 0462-74-2121
Television Research Institute
(Terebi Kenkyujo)
1106 Heta
Iwaishi, Ibaraki Pref. 306-06
tel. 02973-5-1111
IBM Japan Ltd.
3-2-12 Roppongi
Minato-ku, Tokyo 106
tel. 03-3586-1111
Yamato Research Institute
(Yamato Kenkyujo)
1623-14 Shimo Tsuruma
Yamato, Kanagawa Pref. 242
tel. 0462-76-1111
Tokyo Basic Research Institute

(Tokyo Kiso Kenkyujo)
36 Kowa, 5-19 Sanbancho
Chiyoda, Tokyo 102
tel. 03-3265-4232
Yokogawa Electric Corporation
2-9-32 Nakacho
Musashino-shi, Tokyo 180
tel. 0422-54-1111
fax 0422-55-0461
Omron Co.
10 Hanazono-Tsuchidocho
Ukyo-ku, Kyoto 616
tel. 075-463-1161
fax 075-464-2607
Y 26 billion
  Central Research Institute
  (Chuo Kenkyujo)
  20 Igadera, Shimo-Kaiinji
  Nagaoka-kyo, Kyoto 617
  tel. 075-951-5111
  Production Technology Research Institute
  (Seisan Gijutsu Kenkyujo)
  20 Igadera, Shimo-Kaiinji
  Nagaoka-kyo, Kyoto 617
  tel. 075-951-5111
  Software Technology Research Institute
  (Sofutouea Gijutsu Kenkyujo)
  20 Igadera, Shimo-Kaiinji
  Nagaoka-kyo, Kyoto 617
  tel. 075-951-5111
  Tokyo Communication Research Institute
  (Tokyo Tsushin Kenkyujo)
  2-5-48 Tadao
  Machida, Tokyo 194
  tel. 0427-92-8711
  Tsukuba Research Institute
  (Tsukuba Kenkyujo)
  45 Wadai, Tsukuba
  Tsukubagun, Ibaraki Pref. 300-42
  tel. 0298-64-4100
Alps Electric Co Ltd.
1-7 Yukigaya-Ohtsukacho
Ohta-ku, Tokyo 145
tel. 03-3726-1211
fax 03-3728-1812
Y 13 billion
  Central Research Institute
  (Chuo Kenkyujo)
  167 Hasuda, Nakazato
  Furukawa, Miyagi 989-61

tel. 0229-23-6611
staff: 100
TDK Corporation
1-13-1 Nihonbashi
Chuo-ku, Tokyo 103
tel. 03-3278-5111
fax 03-3278-5358
Y 23 billion
    Development Research Institute
    (Kaihatsu Kenkyujo)
    2-15-7 Higashi-Owada
    Ichikawa, Chiba 272
    tel. 0473-78-2121

Transportation industry
Nissan Motor Co. Ltd.
(Nissan Jidosha)
6-17-1 Ginza
Chuo-ku, Tokyo 104
tel. 03-35565-2148
fax 03-3546-2669
Y 220 billion
    Central Research Institute
    (Chuo Kenkyujo)
    1 Natsushimacho
    Yokosuka, Kanagawa Pref. 237
    tel. 0468-65-1123
Fuji Heavy Industries Ltd.
(Fuji Jukogyo)
Subaru Bldg.
1-7-2 Nishi-shinjuku
Shinjuku, Tokyo 160
tel. 03-3347-2024
fax 03-3347-2338
Y 26 billion
    Subaru Technology Headquarters
    (Subaru Gijutsu Honbu)
    10-1 Higashi-Honmachi
    Ota, Gunma Pref. 373
    tel. 0276-48-2400
    Omiya Production
    (Omiya Seisakujo)
    1-9 Miyahara-cho
    Omiya City, Saitama Pref. 330
    tel. 0486-52-5425
    Utsunomiya Production Plant (Car factory)
    (Utsunomiya Seisakujo – Sharyo Kojo)
    1-1-11 Yonan
    Utsunomiya-shi, Tochigi Pref. 320

tel. 0286-58-1111
Isezaki Production Plant
(Isezaki Seisakujo)
100 Suehiro-cho
Isezaki-shi, Gunma Pref. 372
tel. 0270-21-2013
Aircraft Technology Headquarters
(Koku Gijutsu Honbu)
1-1-11 Yonan
Utsunomiya-shi, Tochigi Pref. 320
tel. 0286-58-1111
Hino Motors Ltd.
3-1-1 Hinodai
Hino, Tokyo 191
tel. 0425-86-5011
fax 0425-86-5038
Y 32 billion
Research Development Headquarters
(Kenkyu Kaihatsubumon)
3-1-1 Hinodai
Hino, Tokyo 191
tel. 0425-86-5011
Mitsubishi Heavy Industries Ltd.
2-5-1 Marunouchi
Chiyoda-ku, Tokyo 100
tel. 03-3212-3111
fax 03-3284-1927
Y 92 billion
Basic Technology Research Institute
(Kiban Gijutsu Kenkyujo)
2-5-1 Marunouchi
Chiyoda-ku, Tokyo 100
tel. 03-3212-3111
Nagasaki Research Institute
(Nagasaki Kenkyujo)
1-1 Awabinouracho
Nagasaki 850-91
tel. 0958-61-2111
Takasago Research Institute
(Takasago Kenkyujo)
2-1-1 Niihama, Araicho
Tekasago-shi, Hyogo 676
tel. 07944-2-2121
Hiroshima Research Institute
(Hiroshima Kenkyujo)
4-6-22 Kannon-shinmachi
Nishi-ku, Hiroshima 733
tel. 082-291-2111
Yokohama Research Institute
(Yokohama Kenkyujo)

12 Nishikicho
Nakaku, Yokohama 231
tel. 045-621-1234
Nagoya Research Institute
(Nagoya Kenkyujo)
1 Takamichi, Iwazuka-cho
Nakamura, Nagoya 453
tel. 052-412-1111
Kawasaki Heavy Industries.
2-1-18 Nakamachidori
Chuo-ku, Kobe 650-91
tel. 078-341-7731
fax 078-371-9568
Y 20 billion
Technology Research Institute
(Gijutsu Kenkyujo)
1-1 Kawasaki-cho
Akashi-shi, Hyogo 673
tel. 078-923-1414
Ishikawajima-Harima Heavy Industries Co. Ltd.
2-2-1 Ohtemachi
Chiyoda-ku, Tokyo 100
tel. 03-3244-6496
fax 03-3244-5131
Y 28 billion
Technology Research Institute
(Gijutsu Kenkyujo)
3-1-15 Toyosu
Koto-ku, Tokyo 135
tel. 03-3534-3317
staff: 720

Precision machinery
Shimadzu Corporation
1 Nishinokyo-Kuwabaracho
Nakagyo-ku, Kyoto 604
tel. 075-823-1111
fax 075-811-3188
Technology Research Headquarters
(Gijutsu Kenkyu Honbu)
1, Nishinokyo-Kuwabaracho
Nakagyo-ku, Kyoto 604
tel. 075-823-1268
Canon Inc.
2-7-1 Nishi-Shinjuku
Shinjuku-ku, Tokyo 146
tel. 03-3348-2121
fax 03-3349-8957
Y 86 billion (1989)

Central Research Institute
(Chuo Kenkyujo)
5 Wakamiya, Morinosato
Atsugi, Kanagawa Pref 243-01
tel. 0462-47-2111
staff: 300
Fuji Xerox Co. Ltd.
3-3-5 Akasaka
Minato-ku, Tokyo 107
tel. 03-3585-3211
  General Research Institute
  (Sogo Kenkyujo)
  2274 Hongo
  Ebina, Kanagawa Pref. 243-04
  tel. 0462-38-3111
  staff: 540
Nippon Kogaku K.K.
Fuji Bldg.
3-2-3 Marunouchi
Chiyoda-ku, Tokyo 100
tel. 03-3214-5311
fax 03-3214-5320
Y 10 billion
  Development Headquarters Research Institute
  (Kaihatsu Honbu Kenkyujo)
  1-6-3 Nishi Oi
  Shinagawa-ku, Tokyo 140
  tel. 03-773-1111
  staff: 112
Minolta Camera Co. Ltd.
2-3-13 Azuchi-machi
Chuo-ku, Osaka 541
tel. 06-271-2251
fax 06-266-1010
Y 16 billion
  Takatsuki Research Institute
  (Takatsuki Kenkyujo)
  1-2 Sakura-cho
  Takatsuki, Osaka 569
  tel. 0726-85-6111
  staff: 200
Olympus Optical Company Ltd.
1-22-1 Nishi-Shinjuku
Shinjuku-ku, Tokyo 163-91
tel. 03-3340-2111
fax 03-3340-2201
Y 21 billion
  Technology Development Headquarters
  (Gijutsu Kaihatsu Honbu)
  2951 Ishikawa

Hachioji, Tokyo 192
tel. 0426-42-2111
Ricoh
1-15-5 Minami-Aoyama
Minato-ku, Tokyo 107
tel. 03-3479-3111
fax 03-3479-2900
Y 48 billion

Power industry
The Tokyo Electric Power Co. Ltd.
1-1-3 Uchi-Saiwaicho
Chiyoda-ku, Tokyo 100
tel. 03-3501-8111
fax 03-3591-4609
Y 65 billion

  Technology Research Institute
  (Gijutsu Kenkyujo)
  2-4-1 Tsutsujigaoka
  Chohu, Tokyo 182
  tel.03-3300-2241
  staff: 109
  Development Research Institute
  (Kaihatsu Kenkyujo)
  1-1-3 Uchisaiwaicho
  Chiyoda-ku, Tokyo 100
  tel. 03-3501-8111
  staff: 86
  Atomic Energy Research Institute
  (Genshiryoku Kenkyujo)
  1-1-3 Uchisaiwaicho
  Chiyoda-ku, Tokyo 100
  tel. 03-3501-8111
  staff: 38
The Kansai Electric Power Co. Inc.
3-3-22 Nakanoshima
Kita-ku, Osaka 530
tel. 06-441-8821
fax 06-443-0233
  General Technology Research Institute
  (Sogo Gijutsu Kenkyujo)
  3-11-20 Wakaoji
  Amagasaki, Hyogo 661
  tel. 06-491-0221
Tokyo Gas Co. Ltd.
1-5-20 Kaigan
Minato-ku, Tokyo 105
tel. 03-3433-2111
fax 03-3432-4574

Y 16 billion
Technology Research Institute
(Gijutsu Kenkyujo)
1-16-25 Shibaura
Minato-ku, Tokyo 105
tel. 03-3452-2211
staff: 133

Communication industry
Nippon Telegraph and Telephone Corporation (NTT)
1-1-6 Uchisaiwaicho
Chiyoda-ku, Tokyo 100
tel. 03-3509-5035
fax 03-3509-8188
Y 238 billion

Research and Development Headquarters
(Kenkyu Kaihatsu Honbu)
3-9-11 Midoricho
Musashino-shi, Tokyo 180
tel. 0422-59-2711
staff: 3072

Telecommunication Networks Laboratories
(Tsushinmo Daiichi Kenkyujo)
3-9-11 Midoricho
Musashino-shi, Tokyo 180
tel. 0422-59-3511

Radio Communication Networks Laboratories
(Tsushinmo Daini Kenkyujo)
1-2356 Take
Yokosuka, Kanagawa Pref. 238-03
tel. 0468-59-3208

Communications and Information Processing Laboratories
(Joho Tsushin Shori Kenkyujo)
1-2356 Take
Yokosuka, Kanagawa Pref. 238-03
tel. 0468-59-2398

Integrated Communications Laboratories
(Fukugo Tsushin Kenkyujo)
1-2356 Take
Yokosuka, Kanagawa Pref. 238-03
tel. 0468-59-2108

Basic Research Laboratories
(Kiso Kenkyujo)
3-9-11 Midoricho
Musashino, Tokyo 180
tel. 0422-59-2824

Electronics and Mechanics Technology Laboratories
(Denshi Kiko Gijutsu Kenkyujo)
3-9-11 Midoricho

Musashino, Tokyo 180
tel. 0422-59-2129
Software Production Technology Laboratories
(Sofutouea Seisan Gijutsu Kenkyujo)
1-2356 Take
Yokosuka, Kanagawa Pref. 238-03
tel. 0468-59-2175
Ibaraki Electrical Communications Laboratories
(Ibaraki Denki Tsushin Kenkyujo)
162 Shirane, Shirakata
Tokaimura, Nakagun, Ibaraki Pref. 319-11
tel. 0292-87-7111
Atsugi Electrical Communications Laboratories
(Atsugi Denki Tsushin Kenkyujo)
3-1 Wakamiya, Morinosato
Atsugi, Kanagawa 243-01
tel. 0462-40-3990
Tsukuba Engineering Development Center
(Tsukuba Gijutsu Kaihatsu Senta)
1-7-1 Hanabatake, Daihocho
Tsukuba, Ibaraki Pref. 305
tel. 0298-52-2511
Kokusai Denshin Denwa Co. Ltd.
2-3-2 Nishi-Shinjuku
Shinjuku-ku, Tokyo 163
tel. 03-3347-7111
fax 03-3347-7000
Y 14 billion
KDD Research Institute
(KDD Kankyujo)
2-1-23 Nakameguro
Meguro, Tokyo
staff: 180

Research companies
Mitsubishi Kasei Institute of Life Sciences
11 Minami-Oya
Machida, Tokyo 194
tel. 0427-26-1211
staff: 180
Mitsubishi Kasei Institute of Toxicological and Environmental Sciences
2-1-30 Shiba
Minato-ku, Tokyo 105
tel. 03-3454-7571
staff: 105
Yokohama Research Institute
(Yokohama Kenkyujo)
1000 Kamoshida-cho, Midori-ku
Yokohama, Kanagawa Pref. 227

tel. 045-962-1211
staff: 25
Kashima Research Institute
(Kashima Kenkyujo)
14 Sunayama, Hazakicho
Kashima, Ibaraki Pref. 314-02
tel. 0479-46-2871
staff: 58
NRI life Sciences
(Nomura Seibutsu Kagaku Kenkyujo)
4-7-1 Kajihara
Kamakura, Kanagawa Pref. 247
tel. 0467-47-1881
staff: 126
Toray Research Centre Inc.
(Tore Risachi Senta)
3-1-8 Nihonbashi-muromachi
Chuo-ku, Tokyo 103
tel. 03-3245-5633
staff: 250
Hayashibara Biochemical Laboratories Inc.
1-2-3 Shimoishii
Okayama 700
tel. 0862-24-4311
staff: 160
Shiraishi Central Laboratories Co. Ltd.
(Shiraishi Chuo Kenkyujo)
4-78 Motohamacho
Amagasaku, Hyogo 660
tel. 06-417-3131
staff: 50
NHK Spring R&D Centre Inc.
(Nippon Hatusjo Gurupu Chuo Kenkyujo)
1 Shin-isogo
Isogo-ku, Yokohama 235
tel. 045-751-1800
staff: 31
Nikkin R&D Co. Ltd.
(Nikkin Soken)
4-10-1 Funado
Itabashi, Tokyo 174
tel. 03-3968-6419
staff: 14
Nikkei Techno Research Co. Ltd.
(Nikkei Gi Ken)
3-13-12 Mita
Minato-ku, Tokyo 108
tel. 03-3456-9336
staff: 300
Ebara Research Co. Ltd.

(Ebara Sogo Kenkyujo)
4720 Fujisawa
Fujisawa, Kanagawa Pref. 251
tel. 0466-81-1121
staff: 150
Inoue Japax Research Inc.
(Inoue Japakkusu Kenkyujo)
5289 Nagatsuda
Midori-ku, Yokohama 227
tel. 045-922-3121
Fujitsu Laboratories Ltd
(Fujitsu Kenkyujo)
1015 Kamikodanaka, Nakahara-ku
Kawasaki, Kanagawa Pref. 211
tel. 044-777-1111
staff: 1280
  Kawasaki Research Institute
  (Kawasaki Kenkyujo)
  1015 Kamikodanaka, Nakahara-ku
  Kawasaki, Kanagawa Pref. 211
  tel. 044-777-1111
  Atsugi Research Institute
  (Atsugi Kenkyujo)
  10-1 Wakamiya, Morinosato
  Atsugi, Kanagawa Pref. 243-01
  tel. 0462-48-3111
Fuji Electric Corporate Research and Development Ltd.
2-2-1 Nagasaka
Yokosuka, Kanagawa Pref. 240-01
tel. 0468-56-1191
staff: 750
Matsushita Research Institute Tokyo Inc.
(Matsushita Giken)
3-10-1 Higashi-mita, Tama
Kawasaki, Kanagawa Pref. 214
tel. 044-911-6351
staff: 260
Honda R&D Co. Ltd.
(Honda Gijutsu Kenkyujo)
1-4-1 Chuo
Wako, Saitama Pref. 351-01
tel. 0484-61-2511
  Wako Research Institute
  (Wako Kenkyujo)
  1-4-1 Ehuo
  Wako, Saitama Pref. 351-01
  tel. 0484-61-2511
  Asaka Research Institute
  (Asaka Kenkyujo)
  3-15-1 Sensui

Asaka, Saitama Pref. 351
tel. 0484-64-2511
Asaka East Research Institute
(Asaka Higashi Kenkyujo)
3-15-1 Sensui
Asaka, Saitama Pref. 351
tel. 0484-66-2411
Tochigi Research Institute
(Tochigi Kenkyujo)
4630 Shimotokanezawa, Haga-machi
Haga, Tochigi 321-33
tel. 0286-77-3311
Toyota Central Research and Development Laboratories Inc.
(Toyota Chuo Kenkyujo)
41 Nagakuta
Aichigun, Aichi Pref. 480-11
tel. 05616-2-6111
staff: 820

Universities

National universities

The following is a complete listing of national universities according to *A Guide to Institutions of Higher Education in Japan*, Tokyo: Maruzen Co. Ltd., 1987.
Each entry gives the name and address. The following two lines give information on:
- total enrollment (graduate students only)
- number of professors, if available

Aichi University of Education
1 Hirosawa, Igaya-cho, Kariya-shi, Aichi 449
4320 (117)
128
Akita University
1-1 Tegata Gakuen-cho, Akita City, Akita Pref. 010
4024 (190)
116
Asahikawa Medical College
4-5 Nishikagra, Asahikawa-shi, Hokkaido 078
809 (54)
37
Chiba University
1-33, Yayoi-cho, Chiba-shi, Chiba Pref. 260
11256 (816)
351
Ehime University
10-13, Dogo-Himata Matsuyama-shi, Ehime Pref. 790
2237 (358)
Fukui Medical School
23 Shimoaizuki, Matsuoka-cho, Yoshida-gun, Fukui 910-11
635 (23)
37
Fukui University
3-9-1 Bunkyo, Fukui-shi, Fukui Pref. 910
3079 (173)
94
Fukushima University
2 Sugumichi, Asakawa, Matsukawa-machi, Fukushima-shi, Fukushima 960-12
3727 (34)
111

Fukuoka University of Education
729 Akama, Munakata-shi, Fukuoka Pref. 811-41
3759 (87)
94
Gifu University
1-1 Yanagido, Gifu-shi, Gifu Pref. 501-1
4551 (303)
188
Gunma University
4-2 Aramaki-machi, Maebashi-shi, Gunma Pref. 371
4115 (243)
180
Hamamatsu University School of Medicine
3600 Handa-cho, Hamamatsu-shi, Shizuoka Pref. 431-31
696 (64)
35
Hirosaki University
1, Bunkyo-sho, Hirosaki City, Aomori Pref. 036
5045 (264)
137
Hiroshima University
1-1-89, Higashi-Senda-Machi, Naka-ku, Hiroshima-shi, Hiroshima 730
12892 (1600)
469
Hitotsubashi University
2-1 Naka, Kunitachi City, Tokyo 186
4344 (327)
144
Hokkaido University
Nishi 5, Kita 8, Kita-ku, Sapporo-shi, Hokkaido 060
12104 (1937)
520
Hokkaido University of Education
Minami-24, Nishi-13, Chuo-ku, Sapporo-shi, Hokkaido 064
5325 (5)
176
Hyogo University of Teacher Education
942-1 Shimokume, Yashiro-cho, Kato-gan, Hyogo Pref. 673-14
1321 (482)
77
Ibaraki University
2-1-1, Bunkyo, Mito-shi, Ibaraki Pref. 310
6224 (287)
197
Iwate University
3-18-8, Ueda, Morioka-shi, Iwate Pref. 020
5285 (158)
161
Joetsu University of Education
1 Yamayashiki-machi, Joets-shi, Niigata Pref. 943

1232 (423)
70
Kagawa Medical School
1750-1 Ikenobe-oaza, Miki-cho, Kita-gun, Kagawa Pref. 761-07
Kagawa University
1-1, Saiwai-cho, Takamatsu-shi 760
4222 (54)
142
Kagoshima University
21-24, Kourimoto, 1-chome, Kagoshima-shi 890
9016 (444)
288
Kanazawa University
1-1, Marunouchi, Kanazawa City, Ishikawa Pref. 920
7771 (769)
310
Kitami Institute of Technology
165 Koen-cho, Kitami-shi, Hokkaido 090
1395 (21)
32
Kobe University
1-1 Rokkodai-cho, Nada-ku, Kobe-shi, Hyogo Pref. 657
11522 (1241)
372
Kobe University of Mercantile Marine
5-1-1 Fukaeminami-machi, Higashinada-ku, Kobe-shi, Hyogo Pref. 658
891 (31)
34
Kochi Medical School
Kohasu, Oko-cho, Nankoku-shi, Kochi 781-51
696 (71)
36
Kochi University
2-5-1 Akebono-cho, Kochi-shi, Kochi 780
3506 (146)
164
Kumamoto University
40-1 Kurokami 2-chome, Kumamoto-shi, Kumamoto Pref. 860
8088 (599)
265
Kyoto Institute of Technology
Hashigami-cho, Matsugasaki, Sakyo-ku, Kyoto-shi, Kyoto-fu 606
2648 (271)
78
Kyoto University
Yoshida Honmachi, Sakyo-ku, Kyoto-shi, Kyoto 606
15281 (3728)
680
Kyoto University of Education
1 Fukakusa-Fujinomori-cho, Fushimi-ku, Kyoto-shi, Kyoto-fu 612

1770 (no graduates)
53
Kyushu Institute of Design
4-9-1 Shiobaru, Minami-ku, Fukuoka-shi, Fukuoka Pref. 815
629 (58)
24
Kyushu Institute of Technology
1-1 Sensui-cho, Tobata-ku, Kitakyushu-shi, Fukuoka Pref. 804
3031 (252)
70
Kyushu University
6-10-1 Hakozaki, Higashi-ku, Fukuoka-shi, Fukuoka Pref. 812
12220 (2242)
510
Medical College of Oita
1-1506 Idaigaoka, Hazama-cho, Oita-gun, Oita Pref. 879-56
701 (75)
36
Miyagi University of Education
Aramaki-Aza Aoba, Sendai-shi, Miyazi Pref. 980
1797 (11)
66
Mie University
1515, Kamihama-cho, Tsu-shi, Mie 514
5639 (512)
209
Miyazaki Medical College
5200 Kihara, Kiyotake-cho, Miyazaki-gun, Miyazaki Pref. 889-16
719 (65)
35
Miyazaki University
7710, Oaza Kumano, Miyazaki-shi, Miyazaki Pref. 889-21
3420 (93)
Muroran Institute of Technology
27-1 Mizumoto-cho, Muroran-shi, Hokkaido 050
2662 (198)
74
Nagasaki University
1-14, Bunkyo-machi, Nagasaki-shi, Nagasaki 852
6615 (310)
214
Nagoya Institute of Technology
Gokiso-cho, Showa-ku, Nagoya-shi, Aichi Pref. 466
5082 (371)
120
Nagoya University
Furo-cho, Chikusa-ku, Nagoya-shi, Aichi Pref. 464
9380 (1822)
456
Nara University of Education

Takabatake-cho, Nara-shi, Nara 630
1342 (85)
63
Nara Women's University
Kitauoyahigashi-machi, Nara-shi, Nara Pref. 630
1795 (168)
73
Naruto University of Teacher Education
Takashima, Naruto-shi, Tokushima 772
497 (294)
59
National Institute of Fitness and Sports in Kanoya
1 Shiromizu-cho, Kanoya-shi, Kagoshima 891-23
458 (no graduates)
14
Niigata University
850 Ikarashi 2-nocho, Niigata-shi, Niigata Pref. 950-21
9433 (534)
332
Obihiro University of Agriculture and Veterinary Medicine
Nishi 2-11, Inada-cho, Obihiro-shi, Hokkaido 080
1221 (135)
46
Ochanomizu University
1-1, Otsuka 2-chome, Bunkyo-ku, Tokyo 112
2064 (398)
80
Oita University
700 Dannoharu, Oita-shi, Oita Pref. 870-11
3995 (127)
99
Okayama University
1-1-1 Tsushimanaka, Okayama-shi, Okayama 700
2032 (913)
340
Osaka Kyoiku University
4-88 Minami-Kawahori-cho, Tennoji-ku, Osaka-shi, Osaka 543
4656 (203)
129
Osaka University
1-1 Yamadaoka, Suita-shi, Osaka 565
12752 (2848)
488
Osaka University of Foreign Studies
2734 Aomadani, Minoo-shi, Osaka 562
3768 (58)
66
Otaru University of Commerce
3-5-21 Midori, Otaru-shi, Hokkaido 047
1600 (40)

38
Saga Medical School
Nabeshima-Sanbonsugi, Nabeshima-machi, Saga-shi, Saga 840-01
647 (22)
38
Saga University
1 Honjo-machi, Saga City, Saga Pref. 840
Saitama University
255, Shimo-Okubo, Urawa City, Saitama Pref. 338
6357 (301)
176
Shiga University
1-1-1, Banba, Hikone-shi, Shiga Pref. 522
3085 (11)
80
Shiga University of Medical Science
Seta-Tsukinowa-cho, Otsu-shi, Shiga 520-21
691 (66)
35
Shimane Medical University
89-1 Enya-cho, Izumo-shi, Shimane 693
Shimane University
1060, Nishikawatsu-cho, Matsue-shi, Shimane Pref. 690
3826 (82)
133
Shinshu University
3-1-1 Asahi, Matsumoto-shi, Nagano Pref. 390
7992 (672)
305
Shizuoka University
836 Ooya, Shizuoka-shi, Shizuoka Pref. 422
7435 (430)
275
The Technological University of Nagaoka
1603-1 Kamitomioka-machi, Nagaoka-shi, Niigata 940
1315 (525)
58
Tohoku University
2-1-1, Katahira, Sendai-shi, Miyagi Pref. 980
12160 (2085)
626
Tokyo Gakugei University
4-1-1 Nukuikita-machi, Koganei-shi, Tokyo 184
5437 (419)
139
Tokyo Institute of Technology
12-1, O-Okayama 2-chome, Meguro-ku, Tokyo 152
5567 (1999)
227
Tokyo Medical and Dental University

5-45, Yushima 1-chome, Bunkyo-ku, Tokyo 113
1231 (238)
56
Tokyo National University of Fine Arts and Music
12-8 Ueno Koen, Taito-ku, Tokyo 110
2453 (562)
76
Tokyo University of Agriculture and Technology
1-8, Harumi-cho 3-chome, Fuchyu-shi, Tokyo 183
4231 (575) 121
Tokyo University of Fisheries
4-5-7 Konan, Minato-ku, Tokyo 108
1247 (80)
54
Tokyo University of Foreign Studies
4-51-21 Nishigahara, Kita-ku, Tokyo 114
2842 (127)
89
Tokyo University of Mercantile Marine
2-1-6, Etchujima, Koto-ku, Tokyo 135
685 (16)
43
Toyama Medical and Pharmaceutical University
2630 Sugitami, Toyama-shi, Toyama 930-01
1216 (163)
60
Toyama University
3,190 Gofuku, Toyama City, Toyama Pref. 930
5509 (162)
134
Toyohashi University of Technology
1-1 Hibarigaoka, Tenpaku-cho, Toyohashi-shi, Aichi 440
1354 (510)
55
The University of Electro-communications
1-5-1, Chofugaoka, Chofu-shi, Tokyo 182
3124 (300)
79
University of Library and Information Sciences
1-2 Kasuga, Tsukuba-shi, Ibaraki Pref. 305
593 (36)
24
University of the Ryukyus
1 Senbaru, Nishihara-cho, Okinawa 903-01
5438 (134)
208
University of Tokushima
24, Shinkura-cho 2-chome, Tokushima-shi, Tokushima Pref. 770
4630 (342)
181

The University of Tokyo
7-3-1 Hongo, Bunkyo-ku, Tokyo 113
19644 (5265)
868
University of Tottori
4-101, Koyama-cho, Minami Tottori City, Tottori Pref. 680
4504 (423)
176
University of Tsukuba
1-1-1, Tennodai, Tsukuba-shi, Ibaraki Pref. 305
9770 (2312)
443
University of Wakayama
930 Sakaedani, Wakayama-shi, Wakayama Pref. 640
2498 (4)
73
Utsunomiya University
350, Mine-machi, Utsunomiya-shi, Tochigi Pref. 321
4217 (207)
140
Yamagata University
4-12, Kojirakawa, 1-chome, Yamagata City, Yamagata Pref. 990
7449 (302)
198
Yamaguchi University
1677-1, Yoshida, Yamaguchi-shi, Yamaguchi 753
8642 (438)
249
Yamanashi Medical College
1110 Tamaho, Nakakoma-gun, Yamanashi 409-38
38
Yamanashi University
4-37 Takeda 4-chome, Kofu-shi, Yamanashi Pref. 400
3384 (180)
110
Yokohama National University
156 Tokiwadai, Hodogaya-ku, Yokohama-shi, Kanagawa Pref. 240
8026 (613)
220

Local public colleges and universities

The following is a complete listing of public colleges and universities according to *A Guide to Institutions of Higher Education in Japan*, Tokyo: Maruzen Co. Ltd., 1987.

Each entry gives the name and address. The following two lines give information on:

– total enrollment (graduate students only)
– number of professors, if available
Aichi Prefectural University
3-28 Takada-cho, Mizuho-ku, Nagoya-shi, Aichi Pref. 467
1532 (undergraduates only)
50
Aichi Prefectural University of Fine Arts
1-1 Sagomine, Yazako, Nagakute-cho, Aichi-gun, Aichi Pref. 480-11
682 (77)
31
Fukushima Medical College
5-75 Sugitsuma-cho, Fukushima-shi, Fukushima Pref. 960
Fukushima Women's University
1-1-1 Kasumigaoka, Higashi-ku, Fukuoka-shi, Fukuoka Pref. 813
659 (undergraduates only)
23
Gifu Pharmaceutical University
5-6-1 Mitahora-higashi, Gifu-shi, Gifu 502
Gunma Prefectural Women's College
1395-1 Kaminote, Tamamura-machi, Sawa-gun, Gunma Pref. 370-11
Himegi Institute of Technology
2167 Shosha Himeji-shi, Hyogo 671-22
1486 (112)
44
Hiroshima Women's University
1-1-71 Ujina-higashi, Minami-ku, Hiroshima-shi, Hiroshima Pref. 734
920 (undergraduates only)
27
Kanazawa College of Art
5-11-1 Kodatsuno, Kanazawa-shi, Ishikawa 920
581 (35)
21
Kitakyushu University
4-2-1 Kitagata, Kokuraminami-ku, Kitakyushu-shi, Fukuoka Pref. 802
3737 (37)
71
Kobe City University of Foreign Studies
9-1 Gakuen-higashi-machi, Nishi-ku, Kobe-shi
1490 (12)
35
Kobe University of Commerce
4-3-3 Seiryodai, Tarumi-ku, Kobe-shi, Hyogo Pref. 655
1969 (56)
45
Kochi Women's University
5-15 Eikokuji-cho, Kochi-shi, Kochi 780
709 (undergraduates only)
35
Kumamoto Women's University
2432-1 Mizuarai, Kengum, Kumamoto-shi, Kumamoto Pref. 862

Kyoto City University of Arts
13-6 Kutsukake-cho, Ooe, Nishikyo-ku, Kyoto-shi, Kyoto-fu 610-11
848 (94)
47
Kyoto Prefectural University
1-5 Shimogamo-Hangi-cho, Sakgo-ku, Kyoto-shi, Kyoto-fu 606
1442 (46)
46
Kyoto Prefectural University of Medicine
465 Kajii-cho, Kawaramachi-dori, Hirokoji-agaru, Kamigyo-ku,
Kyoto-shi, Kyoto 602
752 (113)
38
Kyushu Dental College
2-6-1 Manazuru, Kokurakita-ku, Kita Kyushu-shi, Fukuoka 803
801 (56)
27
Nagasaki Prefectural University of International Economics
123 Kawashimo-cho, Sasebo-shi, Nagasaki 858
933 (undergraduates only)
18
Nagoya City University
1 Kawasumi, Mizuho-cho, Mizuho-ku, Nagoya, Aichi Pref. 467
1843 (132)
75
Nara Medical University
840 Shijo-cho, Kashihara-shi, Nara 634
672 (53)
40
Okinawa Prefectural College of Fine Arts
1-4 Tonokura-cho, Shuri, Naha-shi, Okinawa 903
Freshmen Enrollment 65
Osaka City University
3-3-138, Sugimoto, Sumiyoshi-ku, Osaka-shi, Osaka-fu 558
6849 (712)
233
Osaka Women's University
2-1 Daisen-cho, Sakai-shi, Osaka 590
707 (26)
30
Sapporo Medical College
Nishi 17 chome, Minami 1-jo, Chuo-ku, Sapporo-shi, Hokkaido 060
692 (80)
42
Shimonoseki City College
2-1-1 Daigaku-cho, Shimonoseki-shi, Yamaguchi Pref. 751
1336 (undergraduate only)
22
Shizouka College of Pharmacy
2-2-1, Oshika, Shizuoka-shi, Shizouka Pref. 422

547 (77)
21
Shizouka Women's University
409 Yata, Shizouka-shi, Shizouka Pref. 422
603 (undergraduates only)
15
Takasaki City University of Economics
1300 Kaminamie-machi, Takasaki-shi, Gunma 370
2159 (undergraduates only)
31
Tokyo Metropolitan Institute of Technology
6-6 Asahigaoka, Hino-shi, Tokyo 191
720 (undergraduates only)
27
Tokyo Metropolitan University
1-1-1, Yakumo, Meguro-ku, Tokyo 152
4446 (655)
168
Tsuru University
3-8-1 Tohara, Tsuru-shi, Yamanashi Pref. 402
2375 (undergraduates only)
36
University of Osaka Prefecture
804, Mozu-Umemachi 4 chome, Sakai-shi, Osaka-fu 591
4809 (551)
148
Wakayama Medical College
9 Kyuban-cho, Wakayama City, Wakayama Pref. 640
391 (29)
44
Yamaguchi Women's University
3-2-1 Sakurabatake, Yamaguchi-shi, Yamaguchi Pref. 753
675 (undergraduates only)
28
Yokohama City University
22-2 Seto, Kanazawa-ku, Yokohama-shi, Kanagawa Pref. 236
3032 (72)
103

Selected private universities

The following is a highly selective list of private universities. The selection criteria have been good reputation, large enrollment or regional significance, or a combination of these factors.

Each entry gives the name and address. The following two lines give information on:
– total enrollment (graduate students only)
– number of professors
The information is taken from *A Guide to Institutions of Higher Education in*

Japan, Tokyo: Maruzen Co.Ltd., 1987.

Aoyama Gakuin University
4-4-25, Sibuya, Shibuya-ku, Tokyo 150
17690 (317)
248
Chuo University
742-1, Higashinakano, Hachioji City, Tokyo 192-03
31299 (554)
386
Doshisha University
Imadegawa-dori, Karasuma-Higashiiru, Kamikyo-ku, Kyoto-shi, Kyoto
602
19824 (447)
280
Gakushuin University
1-5-1 Mejiro, Toshima-ku, Tokyo 171
6950 (323)
128
Hosei University
2-17-1 Fujimi, Chiyoda-ku, Tokyo 102
26428 (399)
373
International Christian University
10-2, Osawa 3-chome, Mitaka-shi, Tokyo 181
2193 (183)
60
Jichi Medical School
3311-1 Yakushiji, Minami Kawachi-machi, Kawachi-gun, Tochigi Pref. 329-04
652 (28)
52
Jikei University School of Medicine
3-25-8 Nishi-shinbashi, Minato-ku, Tokyo 105
836 (74)
93
Kansai University
3-3-35 Yamate-cho, Suita-shi, Osaka 564
22244 (581)
339
Keio University
15-45, Mita 2-chome, Minato-ku, Tokyo 108
24604 (1775)
458
Komazawa University
1-23-1 Komazawa Setagaya-ku, Tokyo 154
17305 (205)
192
Kwansei Gakuin University
1-1-155, Uegahara, Nishinomiya-shi, Hyogo Pref. 662
13882 (277)

229
Meiji University
1-1, Kanda Surugadai, Chiyoda-ku, Tokyo 101
31868 (677)
390
Nansan University
18 Yamazato-cho, Showa-ku, Nagoya-shi, Aichi Pref. 446
5024 (77)
93
Nihon University
4-8-24 Kudan-Minami, Chiyoda-ku, Tokyo 102
79486 (1936)
866
Nippon Medical School
1-1-5 Sendagi-cho, Bunkyo-ku, Tokyo 113
758 (127)
54
Rikkyo University
(St Paul's) 3-34-1 Nishi-Ikebukuro, Toshima-ku, Tokyo 171
12488 (361)
232
Ritsumeikan University
56-1 Kitamachi, Tojiin, Kita-ku, Kyoto-shi, Kyoto-fu 603
19305 (201)
255
Science University of Tokyo
1-3, Kagurazaka, Shinjuku-ku, Tokyo 162
17195 (972)
274
Senshu University
3-8 Kanda, Jinbo-cho, Chiyoda-u, Tokyo 101
19309 (141)
227
Sophia University
(Jochi) 7-1 Kioicho, Chiyoda-ku, Tokyo
10310 (747)
256
Tokai University
2-28, Tomigaya, Shibuya-ku, Tokyo 151
30751 (526)
606
Tokyo College of Pharmacy
1432-1, Horinouchi, Hachioji-shi, Tokyo 192-03
2145 (145)
34
Tokyo Electrical Engineering University
Kanda-Nishiki-cho, Chiyoda-ku, Tokyo
9045 (144)
112
Tokyo Medical College

6-1-1 Shinjyuku, Shinjyuku-ku, Tokyo 160
Tokyo Women's Medical College
8-1 Kawada-cho, Shinjuku-ku, Tokyo 162
709 (36)
98
Toyo University
5-28-20 Hakusan, Bunkyo-ku, Tokyo 112
18523 (209)
234
Tsuda College
2-1-1, Tsuda-machi, Kodaira-shi, Tokyo 187
2544 (81)
43
Waseda University
6-1, Nishiwaseda 1-chome, Shinjuku-ku, Tokyo 160
43364 (2832)
769

Appendix IV

Directory of projects within major national R&D programmes

National Research and Development Programme (Large Scale Projects)

New Energy and Industrial Technology Development Organization (NEDO) – Agency for Industrial Science and Technology (AIST), MITI

Name	Amount Y million	Period
Super/high performance electronic computer	10,100	1966-1971
Desulfurisation process	2,700	1966-1971
New methods of producing olefin	1,200	1967-1972
Sea water desalination and by-product recovery	7,000	1969-1977
Remotely controlled undersea oil drilling rig	4,500	1970-1975
Electric car	5,700	1971-1977
Pattern information processing system	22,100	1971-1980
Jet engines for aircraft		
1st phase	6,900	1971-1975
2nd phase	12,900	1976-1981
Comprehensive automobile control technology	7,400	1973-1979
Direct steelmaking process using high temperature reducing gas	14,000	1973-1980
Resource recovery technology		
1st phase	1,300	1973-1975
2nd phase	11,400	1976-1982
Olefin production from heavy oil as raw material	14,200	1975-1981
Flexible manufacturing system complex provided with laser	13,500	1977-1984
Subsea oil production system	17,200	1978-1985
Optical measurement and control system (Optoelectronics)	15,700	1979-1985

Name	Amount Y million	Period
C$_1$ chemical technology	10,500	1979-1985
High-speed computing system for scientific and technological uses		1981-1989
Manganese nodule mining system		1981-1991
Automated sewing system	10,000	1982-1990
Advanced robot technology	20,000	1983-1990
Observation system for earth resources satellite	10,900 (until 1988)	1984-1990
New water treatment system	11,800	1985-1990
Interoperable database system	15,000	1985-1991
Advanced material processing and machining system	15,000	1986-1993
Fine chemicals from marine organisms		1988-1996
Super/hyper-sonic transport propulsion system		1989-1996
Underground space development technology		1989-1996

Future Industries (Jisedai)

New Energy and Industrial Technology Development Organization (NEDO)

Name	Period
New Materials:	
High performance ceramics	1981-1992
Synthetic membranes for new separation technology	1981-1990
Synthetic metals	1981-1990
High performance plastics	1981-1990
Advanced alloys with controlled crystalline structures	1981-1988
Advanced composite materials	1981-1988
Photoreactive materials	1985-1992
Biotechnology	
Bioreactor	1981-1990
Large scale cell cultivation	1981-1989
Utilization of recombinant DNA	1981-1990
New electronic devices	
Superlattice devices	1981-1990

Name	Period
Three dimensional ICs	1981-1990
Bioelectronic devices	1986-1995
Superconductivity	
Superconducting materials and superconducting devices	1988-1997
High performance materials for severe environments	1989-1996
Non-linear photonics materials	1989-1998
Technology for application of functional protein complexes	1989-1998

Medical and Welfare Equipment Technology

New Energy and Industrial Technology Development Organisation (NEDO)

Name	Period
Hyperthermia system for cancer therapy	completed
Prosthetic socket processing system	completed
Automated differential blood cell analyzer	completed
Multi-channel automated biochemical analyzer	completed
Positron computer tomography equipment	completed
Modular-type motorized wheelchair	completed
Training equipment for function recovery of the physically handicapped	completed
Braille copying machine	completed
Multi-functional bed for severely handicapped	completed
Speech training machine for aphasics	completed
Wheelchair capable of 3-dimensional movement	completed
Automatic HLA typing system	1987-1990
Anti-ducubitus mechanical mattress	1987-1990
Laser angioplasty system	1988-1991
Three-dimensional imaging system for medical diagnosis	1988-1991
Laser osteotomy system	1989-1992
Evacuation care system	1989-1993
Three-dimensional display for the blind	1989-1992

Engineering Research Associations (ERA) (Gijutsu Kenkyu Kumiai) – MITI

The following contains a complete list of Engineering Research Associations (ERA) at the end of March 1990. The full translation is Technological Research Associations in Mining and Industry (Kokogyo Gijutsu Kenkyu Kumiai) although often referred to as Engineering Research Associations (ERA). The provisions for the ERAs are formulated in a law which was promulgated in 1961 (Kokogyo Gijutsu Kenkyu Kumiai Seido no Kaisetsu) The costs for projects are shared between the government (MITI) and the participating companies. The listing provides the English official name of the ERA (or a translated equivalent), the Japanese name (in romaji), date of establishment, address and fax number

The list is arranged chronologically on the basis of the date of establishment.

Some of the ERAs continue to exist although all research has been completed. This is true for the VLSI ERA which now has a responsibility for repaying government grants from profits flowing from the commercialization of research results.

1. **Research Association for Automobile Appliances**
(Jidosha Kiki Gijutsu Kenkyu Kumiai)
February 24, 1971
c/o Hitachi Sanwa Factory
2520 Takaba Oaza
Katsuda-city 312
tel. 0292-73-2461
fax: 0292-73-2467

2. **Automotive Safety and Anti-Pollution Technology Research Alliance**
(Sogo Jidosha Anzen Kogai Gijutsu Kenkyu Kumiai)
November 27, 1971
c/o Mitsubishi Denki
1-5-15 Tsuchiyama
Himeji-city, Hyogo Pref. 670
tel. 0792-93-1251
fax: 0792-98-8857

3. **Automatic Measurement Technology Research Association**
(Jido Keisoku Gijutsu Kenkyu Kumiai)
May 21, 1974
c/o Yokogawa Denki
2-9-32 Nacho-machi
Musashi-shi, Tokyo 180
tel. 0422-54-1111
fax: 0422-55-0461

4. **VLSI Technology Research Association**
(Cho Eru Esu Ai Gijutsu Kenkyu Kumiai)
March 1976
Mita Kokusai Bldg.
1-4-28 Mita
Minato-ku, Tokyo 108

tel. 03-3452-4815
fax: 03-3451-6103
5. Technology Research Association of Medical and Welfare Apparatus
(Gijutsu Kenkyu Kumiai Iryo Fukushi Kiki Kenkyujo)
October 1, 1966
Kikai Shinko Kaikan
3-5-8 Shibakoen
Minato-ku, Tokyo 105
tel. 03-3459-9584
fax: 03-3459-6887
6. Engineering Research Association of Flexible Manufacturing System Complex Provided with Laser
(Reza Oyo Fukugo Seisan Shisutemu Gijutsu Kenkyu Kumiai)
April 1, 1978
Yayoi Bldg.
4-2-2 Ginza
Chuo-ku, Tokyo 104
tel. 03-3561-8241
fax: 03-3567-7285
7. Research Association for Residual Oil Processing
(Jushitsuyu Taisaku Gijutsu Kenkyu Kumiai)
June 18, 1979
Kojima Bldg.
1-4-2 Uchi Kanda
Chiyoda-ku, Tokyo 101
tel. 03-3233-3531
fax: 03-3233-3530
8. Computer Basic Technology Research Association
(Denshi Keisanki Kihon Gijutsu Kenkyu Kumiai)
July 31, 1979
Mita Kokusai Bldg.
1-4-28 Mita
Minato-ku, Tokyo 108
tel. 03-3451-6361
fax: 03-3451-6103
9. Research Association for Petroleum Alternatives Development
(Shin Nenryoyu Kaihatsu Gijutsu Kenkyu Kumiai)
June 5, 1980
Kojima Bldg.
1-4-2 Uchi Kanda
Chiyoda-ku, Tokyo 101
tel. 03-3233-3531
fax: 03-3233-3530
10. Research Association for Gas Engine Heat Pump System
(Kogata Gasu Reibo Gijutsu Kenkyu Kumiai)
May 9, 1981
c/o Tokyo Gas Technology Research Institute
1-16-25, Shibaura
Minato-ku, Tokyo 105
tel. 03-3452-2211

fax: 03-3437-4695
11. Synthetic Paint Technology Research Association
(Gosei Toryo Gijutsu Kenkyu Kumiai)
July 10, 1981
Toryo Kaikan
5-18-17 Roppongi
Minato-ku, Tokyo 106
tel. 03-3585-3375
fax: 03-3589-4236
12. Engineering Research Association for High Performance Ceramics
(Fuain Seramikkusu Gijutsu Kenkyu Kumiai)
September 8, 1981
No 10 Mori Bldg.
1-18-1 Toranomon
Minato-ku, Tokyo 105
tel. 03-3595-2472
fax: 03-3503-3484
13. Research Association for Biotechnology
(Baiotekunoroji Kaihatsu Gijutsu Kenkyu Kumiai)
September 2, 1981
Saruda Bldg.
1-4-10 Akasaka
Minato-ku, Tokyo 107
tel. 03-3583-8291
fax: 03-3589-3785
14. Research Association for Basic Polymer Technology
(Kobunshi Kikan Gijutsu Kenkyu Kumiai)
August 31, 1981
Kotobuki Bldg.
2-5-21 Toranomon
Minato-ku, Tokyo 105
tel. 03-3595-0861
fax: 03-3595-0863
15. Technology Research Association of High Speed Computer System for Scientific and Technological Application
(Kagaku Gijutsuyo Kosoku Keisan Shisutemu Gijutsu Kenkyu Kumiai)
December 18, 1981
Yayoi No 2 Bldg.
4-1-21 Toranomon
Minato-ku, Tokyo 105
tel. 03-3434-1310
16. Technology Research Association of Manganese-Nodules Mining-System
(Gijutsu Kenkyu Kumiai Mangan Dankai Saiko Shisutemu Kenkyujo)
January 14, 1982
New Tokyo Bldg
5-11-13 Ginza
Chyo-ku, Tokyo 104
tel. 03-3542-6091
fax: 03-3541-6840
17. The Japan Industrial-Furnace Manufacturers Association

(Gijutsu Kenkyu Kumiai Kogyoro Gijutsu Kenkyujo)
September 10, 1982
Yamasa Bldg.
2-21-10 Yoyogi
Shibuya-ku, Tokyo 151
tel. 03-3370-6236
fax: 03-3320-3115
18. **Research Association for New Smelting Technology**
(Seisei Shin Kiban Gijutsu Kenkyu Kumiai)
September 9, 1982
Keidanren Kaikan
1-9-4 Otemachi
Chiyoda-ku, Tokyo 100
tel. 03-3241-8287
fax: 03-3245-0144
19. **Research Association of Enriching Oxygen Membrane and Combustion**
(Koso Fuka Maku Nensho Gijutsu Kenkyu Kumiai)
September 10, 1982
Toyobo Bldg.
17-9 Koami-cho
Nihonbashi Chuo-ku, Tokyo 103
tel. 03-3662-4798
fax: 03-3660-4829
20. **Technology Research Association for Paper Production**
(Seishi Gijutsu Kenkyu Kumiai)
September 11, 1982
KamiParupu Kaikan
3-9-11 Ginza
Chuo-ku, Tokyo 104
tel. 03-3546-1466
21. **Japan EOR Research Association (Oil Fraction Recovery)**
Genyu Ni-Sanji Kaishu Gijutsu Kenkyu Kumiai)
November 5, 1982
No 39 Mori Bldg.
2-4-5 Ayabudai
Minato-ku, Tokyo 106
tel. 03-3434-0290
fax: 03-3434-1847
22. **Technology Association of Automated Sewing System**
(Jido Hosei Shisutemu Gijutsu Kenkyu Kumiai)
January 6, 1983
Shinbashi Kikuei Bldg.
5-13-1 Shinbashi
Minato-ku, Tokyo 105
tel. 03-3434-8934
fax: 03-3434-8938
23. **Technology Research Association for Open-cal Coal Extraction**
(Sekitan Rotenbori Kikai Gijutsu Kenkyu Kumiai)
March 28, 1983
Kikai Shinko Kaikan

3-5-8 Shiba Koen
Minato-ku, Tokyo 105
tel. 03-3434-3599
24. **Research Association for Utilization of Light Oil**
(Keishitsu Ryubun Shin Yoto Kaihatsu Gijutsu Kenkyu Kumiai)
June 1, 1983
Shiba YS-Bldg.
2-16-9 Shiba
Minato-ku, Tokyo 105
tel. 03-3455-6011
fax: 03-3457-7508
25. **Technology Research Association for High Efficiency Synthetic Fibres**
(Ko-Koritsu Gosen Gijutsu Kenkyu Kumiai)
September 22, 1983
Osaka Kagaku Seni Kaikan
4-6-8 Kamara-machi
Cyuo-ku, Osaka-city 541
tel. 06-231-6563
26. **Technology Research Association of New Production Methods for Chemicals by Applying Organic Functions**
(Seitai Kino Riyo Kagakuhin Shin Seizo Gijutsu Kenkyu Kumiai)'
September 27, 1983
Mitsubishi Denki Bldg.
2-2-3 Maronouchi
Chiyoda-ku, Tokyo 100
tel. 03-3218-2167
fax: 03-3218-2188
27. **Research Association of Electronic Conductivity in Organic Compounds**
(Du Densei Muki Kagobutsu Gijutsu Kenkyu Kumiai)
October 6, 1983
Shinbashi Sumitomo Bldg.
5-11-3 Shinbashi
Minato-ku, Tokyo 105
tel. 03-3436-8888
fax: 03-3436-8734
28. **Research Association for New Technology Development of High Performance Polymers**
(Koseino Jushi Shin Seizo Gijutsu Kenkyu Kumiai)
September 26, 1983
c/o Sekuriru K.K.
2-12-8 Shinkawa
Chuo-ku, Tokyo 104
tel. 03-3297-3010
fax: 03-3297-2759
29. **Research Association of Aluminium Powder-Metallurgy**
(Aruminium Funmatsu Yakin Gijutsu Kenkyu Kumiai)
September 24, 1983
Nihonbashi Asahi Seimei Kaikan
2-1-3 Nihonbashi
Chuo-ku, Tokyo 103

tel. 03-3281-8012
fax: 03-3213-2918
30. **Engineering Research Association of Shape-Memory Alloys**
(Keijo Kioku Gokin Gijutsu Kenkyu Kumiai)
September 26, 1983
Furukawa Denki Kogyo
2-4-3 Okano Nishi-ku
Yokohama-city, Kanagawa Pref. 220
tel. 045-316-8356
fax: 045-316-6374
31. **Fuel Alcohol Research Association**
(Nenryoyo Arukoru Kaihatsu Gijutsu Kenkyu Kumiai)
November 10, 1983
Dowa Bldg.
5-10-5 Shinbashi
Minato-ku, Tokyo 105
tel. 03-3459-6387 3
fax: 03-3459-1440
32. **Advanced Robot Technology Research Association**
(Kyokugen Sagyo Robotto Gijutsu Kenkyu Kumiai)
February 4, 1984
Kikai Shinko Kaikan
3-5-8 Shibakoen
Minato-ku, Tokyo 105
tel. 03-3434-0532
fax: 03-3434-0217
33. **Technology Research Association of Super Heat Pump Energy Accumulation System**
(Supa Hito Ponpu Enerugi Shuseki Shisutemu Gijutsu Kenkyu Kumiai)
April 24, 1985
Takara Bldg.
1-6 Ogawa-cho
Kanda Chiyoda-ku, Tokyo 101
tel. 03-3255-4624
fax: 03-3255-4708
34. **Research Association of Advanced Housing Technology**
(Shugo Jutaku Shin Zairyo, Kiki Shisutemu Kaihatsu Gijutsu Kenkyu Kumiai)
July 9, 1985
No 23 Mori Bldg.
1-23-7 Toranomon
Minato-ku, Tokyo 105
tel. 03-3592-1681
fax: 03-3503-4540
35. **Advanced Nuclear Equipment Research Institute**
(Gijutsu Kenkyu Kumiai Genshiryoku-Yo Jisedai Kiki Kaihatsu Kenkyujo)
October 14, 1985
Terayama Pacific Bldg.
1-23-11 Toranomon
Minato-ku, Tokyo 105

tel. 03-3504-2831
fax: 03-3504-2836
36. Toyama Foundation for Development of Local System Technology
(Toyama-ken Chiiki Shisutemu Kaihatsu Gijutsu Kenkyu Kumiai)
October 30, 1985
Toyama Technology Exchange Koryu Center
529 Takada
Toyama-city 930
tel. 0764-33-6402
fax: 0764-33-6170
37. Aqua Renaissance Research Association
(Akua-Runesansu Gijutsu Kenkyu Kumiai)
December 23, 1985
Toranomon Takagi Bldg.
1-7-2 Shinbashi
Nishi Minato-ku, Tokyo 105
tel. 03-3503-2131
fax: 03-3503-2139
38. Research Association for Hydrogen-from-Coal Process Development
(Sekitan Riyo Suiso Seizo Gijutsu Kenkyu Kumiai)
June 16, 1986
Seishin Kudan Bldg.
3-4-15 Minami Kudan
Chiyoda-ku, Tokyo 103
tel. 03-3261-7281
fax: 03-3261-7320
39. Integrated Coal-Gasification Combined-Cycle Power-Generation Technology
(Sekitan Gasu-ka Fukugo Hatsuden Gijutsu Kenkyu Kumiai)
June 10, 1986
Matsumoto Ginza Bldg.
3-11-13 Ginza
Chuo-ku, Tokyo 104
tel. 03-3546-2260
fax: 03-3546-2266
40. Technology Research Association of Improving Gas Turbine
(Gasu-Tabin Jitsuyo Seino Kojo Gijutsu Kenkyu Kumiai)
July 12, 1986
c/o Ishikawajime Harima Jukogyo
3-2-6 Toyosu
Koto-ku, Tokyo 135
tel. 03-3534-2287
fax: 03-3534-2288
41. Technology Research Association for Higher Utilization of Hokkaido Wood Resources
(Hokkaido Mokuzai Kodo Riyo Gijutsu Kenkyu Kumiai)
September 11, 1986
Rakuno Kaikan
9-chome 6 jo Minami
Nishi Obihiro-city, Hokkaido 080

tel. 0155-24-5951
fax: 0155-24-8451

42. Research Association of Fabric Production System
(Seni Seihin Seizo Shisutemu Gijutsu Kenkyu Kumiai)
November 7, 1986
Fukui Industrial Technology Center
10 Kitaimada Aza
61 Washizuka-cho
Kawai, Fukuishi-City, Fukui Pref. 910
tel. 0766-55-0695
fax: 0776-55-1552

43. Technology Research Association for Very Advanced Processing Systems
(Cho Sentan Kako Shisutemu Gijutsu Kenkyu Kumiai)
January 12, 1987
1-1, Kyo-machi
Tenman, Chuo-ku
Osaka-city 540
tel. 06-947-5151

44. Laser Atomic Separation Engineering Research Association of Japan
(Reza Noshuku Noushuku Gijutsu Kenkyu Kumiai)
April 16, 1987
2-76 Shirane Aza Shirakata Tokai-mura
Naka-gun, Ibaraki Pref. 319-11
tel. 0292-87-0812
fax: 0292-83-2206

45. Advanced Cogeneration Technology Research Association
(Adobansu Kojienereshiyon Shisutemu)
June 9, 1987
No 4 Sumitomo Higashi Shinbashi Bldg.
6-9-6 Shinbashi
Minato-ku, Tokyo 105
tel. 03-3578-8621
fax: 03-3578-8622

46. Engineering Research Association for Super Conductivity Electricity Generation Equipment and Materials
(Cho Dendo Hatsuden Kanren Kiki Zairyo Gijutsu Kenkyu Kumiai)
October 1, 1987
Umeda UN Bldg.
5-14-10 Tenma Nishi
Kita-ku, Osaka-city 530
tel. 06-361-1141
fax: 06-361-1437

47. Technology Research Association for Developing Production Systems for Compound Materials
(Fukugo Zairyo Seihin Kaihatsu Shisutemu Gijutsu Kenkyu Kumiai)
December 3, 1987
3-4-20 Jinzan Nishi Yakata-ku
Kita Kyushyu-city 806
tel. 093-671-0865
fax: 093-671-0867

48. Technology Research Association for Molten-Carbonate Fuel-Cell Power-Generation-System
(Yoyu Tansanen Nenryo Denchi Hatsuden Shisutemu Gijutsu Kenkyu Kumiai)
January 21, 1988
Nihon Seimei Minami Otsuka Bldg.
3-10-10 Otsuka Minami
Toshima-ku, Tokyo 170
tel. 03-3590-7251
fax: 03-3590-7265

49. Japan Pottery Manufacturers Federation
(Jinko Nendo Gosei Gijutsu Kenkyu Kumiai)
May 26, 1988
Nihon Tojiki Centre Bldg.
39-18 Daikan-cho
Higashi-ku, Nagoya-city 461
tel. 052-435-7231
fax: 052-935-7254

50. International Laboratory for Fuzzy Engineering Research
(Gijutsu Kenkyu Kumiai Kokusai Fuajii Kogaku Kenkyujo)
March 3, 1989
89-1 Yamashita-cho
Naka-ku, Yokohama-city, Kanagawa Pref. 231
tel. 045-212-8211
fax: 045-212-8256

51. Research Association of Technology Development for New Industrialized Housing Production
(Shin Kogyoka Jutaku Seisan Gijutsu Shisutemu Kaihatsu Gijutsu Kenkyu Kumiai)
September 25, 1989
1-20-9 Toranomon
Minato-ku, Tokyo 105
tel. 03-3597-0181
fax: 03-3597-0160

52. Engineering Research Association for Super-Sonic Transport Propulsion System
(Cho Onsoku Yunyu Kikiyo Suishin Shisutemu Gijutsu Kenkyu Kumiai)
February 2, 1990
Sumitomo Kaijo Asagaya Bldg.
3-1-30 Asagaya Minami
Setagaya-ku, Tokyo 166
tel. 03-5397-1821
fax: 03-5397-1820

Japan Key Technology Centre (JKTC)

R&D companies under capital investment scheme – Ministry of International Trade and Industry (MITI) and Ministry of Posts and Telecommunications (MPT)

The Japan Key Technology Centre (JKTC) was established in 1985 with funds provided from the sale of the stock from the privatized Nippon Telegraph and Telephone Corporation (NTT). JKTC has several functions of which investing in R&D companies is the most significant one. The list provides name, address, telephone and telefax numbers for R&D companies which have been established during the period 1986-90. The list also provides information about the date of establishment, approximate length of research project and funds provided by JKTC, if available. Generally, JKTC provides 70 per cent of the investment funds, with the remainder invested by the participating companies. The R&D companies are themselves incorporated stock companies with a formal expectation of yielding return on investment – which is only likely to materialize in a limited number of cases.

1. **Protein Engineering Research Institute** (PERI)
(Tanpaku Kogaku Kenkyujo K.K.)
6-2-3 Furuedai
Suita-city 565
tel. 06-872-8200
fax: 06-872-8210
April 23, 1986; 10 years
Y million 12000
2. **Optoelectronics Technology Research Laboratory** (OEIC)
(Hikari Gijutsu Kenkyu Kaihatsu K.K.)
5-5 Higashi Hikaridai
Tsukuba-city 300-26
tel. 0298-47-4331
fax: 0298-47-4180
June 3, 1986
Y million 7000
3. **Japan Electronic Dictionary Research Institute Ltd.** (EDR)
(Nihon Denshika Jisho Kenkyujo K.K.)
Mita Kokusai Bldg. Annex
1-4-28 Mita
Minato-ku, Tokyo 108
tel. 03-798-5521
fax: 03-798-5335
4. **Non-Oxide Glass Research Development Company Ltd.**
(Hi Sankabutsu Garasu Kenkyu Kaihatsu K.K.)
Shinbashi Sumitomo Bldg.
5-11-3 Shinbashi
Minato-ku, Tokyo 105
tel. 03-3436-8884
fax: 03-3798-5335

April 25, 1986; 5 years
Y million 500
5. Space Technology Corporation (STC)
(Uchu Kankyo Riyo Kenkyujo K.K.)
Kudan New Central Bldg.
1-4-5 Kita Kudan
Chiyoda-ku, Tokyo 102
tel. 03-3221-7901(-4)
fax: 03-3221-2095
April 28, 1986; 7 years
Y million 3916
6. Interactive Basic Information System Development Corporation (IBIS)
(Kiso Joho Shisutemu Kaihatsu K.K.)
Funaba Center Bldg 2, 2F
1-4 Chuo Funaba
Higashi-ku, Osaka 541
tel. 06-236-1181
fax: 06-263-1018
May 30, 1986; 5 years
Y million 2480
7. Optical Measurement Technology Development Company (OMTEC)
(Hikari Keisoku Gijutsu Kaihatsu K.K.)
2-11-13 Naka-machi
Musashino-city, Tokyo 180
tel. 0422-54-3336
fax: 0422-55-8080
May 26, 1986; 6 years
Y million 3000
8. Research Institute for Metal Surface of High Performance Ltd.
(Raimuzu (= Limes) K.K.)
Toranomon Takagi Bldg. 2F
1-7-2 Nishi-Shinbashi
Minato-ku, Tokyo 105
tel. 03-3592-0187
fax: 03-3592-1285
February 27, 1986; 6 years
Y million 2800
9. M&D Research (MD)
(Emu Mitsui K.K.)
Dei Risachi Toranomon Bldg.
3-8-1 Kasumigaseki
Chiyoda-ku, Tokyo 100
tel. 03-3507-3249
fax: 03-3507-3159
April 25, 1986; 5 years
Y million 1200
10. Sortec
(Sorutekku K. K.)
16-1 Wadai
Tsukuba-city 300-42

tel. 0298-64-4550
fax: 0298-64-4589
June 3, 1986; 10 years
Y million 10000

11. Auditory and Visual Perception Research Laboratories (ATR)
(ATR Shichokaku Kiko Kenkyujo K.K.)
5 Koji Sanpeidani Daiji Inuidani
Seika-cho, Soraku-gun, Kyoto 619-02
tel. 07749-5-1411
fax: 07749-5-1408
April 26, 1986; 7 years
Y million 9600

12. Interpreting Telephony Research Laboratories
(ATR Jido Honyaku Denwa Kenkyujo K.K.)
5 Koji Sanpeidani, Daiji Inuidani
Seika-cho, Soraku-gun, Kyoto 619-02
tel. 07749-5-1311
fax: 07749-5-1308
April 26, 1986; 7 years
Y million 1160

13. Communication Systems Research Laboratories
(ATR Tsushin Shisutemu Kenkyujo)
5 Koji Sanpeidani, Daiji Inuidani
Seika-cho, Soraku-gun, Kyoto-hu 619-02
tel. 07749-5-1211
fax: 07749-5-1208

14. Optical and Radio Communications Research Laboratories
(ATR Hikari Denpa Tsushin Kenkyujo K.K.)
5 Koji Sanpeidani, Daiji Inuidani
Seika-cho, Soraku-gun, Kyoto-hu 619-02
tel. 07749-5-1511
fax: 00749-5-1508
April 26, 1986; 10 years
Y million 11600

15. Callnet Inc.
(Korunetto K.K.)
Nishi Shinjuku 6-chome Bldg.
16-24-6 Shinjuku
Shinjuku-ku, Tokyo 160
tel. 03-3205-6891
fax: 03-3205-9325
April 28, 1986; 6 years
Y million 2400

16. Japan Database Network Laboratory Company Ltd. (JDNL)
(Nihon Datebesu Nettowaku Kenkyujo K.K.)
Hosei Bldg. No 2
1-6-54 Suizenji Kami
Kumamoto-city 862
tel. 096-385-7007
fax: 096-385-7018

April 28, 1986; 6 years
Y million 300
17. **Future Building R&D** (FBS)
(Mirai Biru Kenkyu Kaihatsu K.K.)
Nishi Shinbashi Bldg.
3-13-3 Shinbashi Nishi
Minato-ku, Tokyo 105
tel. 03-3459-6919
fax: 03-3547-7629
May 23, 1986; project finished
Y million 372
18. **Colloid Research Institute** (CRI)
(Koroido Risachi K.K.)
c/o Nippon Steel
350-1 Ogura Ohaza Higashi-ku
Yahata, Kita Kyushu-city, Fukuoka Pref. 805
tel. 093-681-5610
fax: 093-681-5656
February 2, 1987; 5 years
Y million 1050
19. **Plant Cell Culture Technology** (PCC)
(PCC Tekunoroji K.K.)
2-8-7 Shibuya
Shibuya-ku, Tokyo 150
tel. 03-3409-3925
fax: 03-3409-3747
February 14, 1987; 6 years
Y million 1960
20. **Bio Material Research Institute Co. Ltd.**
(Baiomateriaru Kenkyujo K.K.)
c/o Japan Automobile Research Institute
1 Taya-machi
Sakai-ku, Yokohama-city, Kanagawa Pref. 244
tel. 0298-56-1801
fax: 045-851-9270
February 14, 1987; 7 years
Y million 1960
21. **Advanced Combustion Engineering Institute Co.Ltd.** (ACE)
(Shin Nensho Shisutemu Kenkyujo K.K.)
2530 Karima
Tsukuba-city 305
tel. 0298-56-1801
fax: 0298-55-1801
February 14, 1987; 6 years
Y million 1050
22. **Frontier Aircraft Basic Research Centre Co.Ltd.** (FARC)
(Jisedai Kokuki Kiban Gijutsu Kenkyujo K.K.)
3-12-33 Shin-machi
Hoya-city, Tokyo 202
tel. 0424-64-6311

fax: 0424-64-5353
March 31, 1986; 6 years
Y million 2800
23. Food Product Machinery Basic Technology Research Institute
(Shokuhin Kikai Kiban Gijutsu Kenkyujo K.K.)
c/o Japan Food Product Machinery Industry Association
Window Building 2F
7-4-8 Roppongi
Minato-ku, Tokyo 106
tel. 03-3796-4391
fax: 03-3796-4392
March 19, 1987; 4 years
Y million 700
24. Telematique International Research Laboratories
(Teremateikku Kokusai Kenkyujo K.K.)
Koramu Aoyama Bldg. 7F
7-1-5 Aoyama
Minato-ku, Tokyo 107
tel. 03-3495-7241
fax: 03-3498-7517
February 27, 1987; 5 years
Y million 2000
25. Conditional Access Technology Inc. (COATEC)
(Kondeishiyonaru Akusesu Tekunoroji Kenkyunjo K.K.)
1-20-7 Toranomon
Minato-ku, Tokyo 105
tel. 03-3595-3401
fax: 03-3435-0125
Febaruary 16, 1987; 4 years
Y million 1400
26. Space Communication Research Corporation (SCR)
(Uchu Tsushin Kiso Gijutsu Kenkyujo K.K.)
Hayekawa Tonaka Bldg, 5F
2-12-5 Iwamoto-cho
Chiyoda-ku, Tokyo 101
tel. 03-3865-8761)
fax: 03-3865-8765
February 20, 1987; 8 years
Y million 4000)
27. Graphics Communication Technologies Ltd. (GCTEC)
(Garafuikusu Komiyunikeshiyon Tekunorojizu K.K.)
Kuramu Minami Aoyama, 6F
7-1-5 Minami Aoyama
Minato-ku, Tokyo 107
tel. 03-3498-7141
fax: 03-3498-7543
February 26, 1987; 4 years
Y million 1200
28. Reotec Ltd. (Semi-solid processing)
(Reotekku K.K.)

Toranomon Takagi Bldg, 2F
1-7-2 Nishi Shinbashi
Minato-ku, Tokyo 105
tel. 03-3592-1986
March 25, 1988; 7 years
Y million 2100

29. Three-D Composites Research Co.
(Suri Dei Konpori, K.K.)
Tsukuba Research Support Centre C-B3
2-1-6 Sengen
Tsukuba-city 305
tel. 0298-58-6217
fax: 0298-58-6218

30. AI Language Research Institute Ltd. (AIR)
(AI Gengo Kenkyujo K.K.)
Sakunai Bldg
3-15-15 Shiba
Minato-ku, Tokyo 105
tel. 03-3456-0454
fax: 03-3456-4418
March 29, 1988; 4 years
Y million 1610

31. Amorphous Magnetic Device Laboratories
(Amorufuasu Denshi Debaisu Kenkyujo K.K.)
c/o Electrical Magnetic Material Research Institute
2-1-1 Minami Yagiyama
Taihaku-ku, Sendai-city 982
tel. 022-245-1711
fax: 022-245-9095
March 29, 1988; 6 years
Y million 1610

32. Small Power Communication System Research Laboratories
(Sho Denryoku Kosoku Tsushin Kenkyujo K.K.)
c/o Handotai Kenkyu Shinkokai
Mubanchi, Sennai
Aoka-ku, Sendai-city 980
tel. 022-266-6811
fax: 022-266-6815
March 31, 1988; 5 years
Y million 1400

33. CATV Key Technology Research Corporation
(CATV Kiban Gijutsu Kenkyujo)
Reo Shinjuku Bldg. 4F
1-2-3 Kabuki-cho
Shinjuku-ku, Tokyo 160
tel. 03-5273-8555
fax: 03-5273-8554
March 23, 1988
Y million 2600

34. Advanced System Research Organization Ltd. (ASRO)

(Adobansudo Shisutemu Kenkyujo K.K.)
CSK Information Education Center, 5F
2-5-1 Suma
Tama-city 206
tel. 0423-72-5051
fax: 0423-72-4577
March 24, 1988; 5 years
Y million 1400
35. **Robotech Laboratory Co.Ltd.**
(Robotekku Kenkyujo K.K.)
3-1848-1 Ono-cho
Ichikawa city 272
tel. 0473-381650
fax: 0473-38-1659
February 28, 1988; 5 years
Y million 1500
36. **Alithium (AL-Li Alloys)**
(Arishiumu K.K.)
Toranomon Takagi Bldg, 2F
1-7-2 Nishi Shinbashi
Minato-ku, Tokyo 105
tel. 03-3595-1482
fax: 03-3592-1285
March 24, 1989; 7 years
Y million 1400
37. **Giant Electronics Technology Co.** (GTC)
(Ji Tei Shi K.K.)
Higashi Nihonbashi Sato Bldg., 6F
1-6-5 Higashi Nihonbashi
Chuo-ku, Tokyo 103
tel. 03-3865-7621
fax: 03-3865-7645
March 23, 1989; 6 years
Y million 1960
38. **Space Communication Laboratory**
(Eisei Tsushin Shisutemu Gijutsu Kenkyujo K.K.)
Kuramae Sakai Bldg, 3F
3-15-7 Kuramae
Dai Koto-ku, Tokyo 111
tel. 03-5687-5585
fax: 03-5687-4477
March 29, 1989; 6 years
Y million 1470
39. **High Definition Television Engineering Co.** (HDTEC)
(Kodo Eizo Gijutsu Kenkyujo K.K.)
Sanseido Shinjuku Bldg., 4F
4-15-3 Nishi Shinjuku
Shinjuku-ku, Tokyo 160
tel. 03-5371-0311
fax: 03-5371-0310

March 31, 1989; 5 years
Y million 2400
40. **Super Conducting Sensor Laboratory**
(Cho Dendo Sensa Kenkyujo K.K.)
Higashi Nihonbashi Sato Bldg., 5F
1-6-5 Higashi Nihonbashi
Chuo-ku, Tokyo 103
tel. 03-865-0541
fax: 03-865-9876
March 23, 1990; 6 yars
Y million 3990
41. **Advanced Intelligent Communication System Laboratories**
(Kodo Tsushin Shisutemu Kenkyujo K.K.)
c/o NTT
1-8-8 Taihara
Aoba-ku, Sendai-city 981
tel. 022-275-1871
fax: 022-275-1877
March 30, 1990; 6 years
Y million 2211
42. **Mobile Communication Technology Development Co.Ltd.**
(Ido Tsushin Shisutemu Kaihatsu K.K.)
Izumi Ningyocho Bldg, 5F
2-33-8 Ningyo-cho Nihonbashi
Chuo-ku, Tokyo 103
tel. 03-663-2791
fax: 03-663-0905
February 3, 1990; 5 years
Y million 2020

Exploratory Research for Advanced Technology (ERATO)

Research Development Corporaton of Japan (JRDC), Science and Technology Agency (STA)

Completed and ongoing projects

Name	*Duration*
Ultra-Fine Particle Project (Hayashi)	81-86
Amorphous & Intercalation Compounds Project (Masumoto)	81-86
Fine Polymer Project (Ogata)	81-86
Perfect Crystal Project (Nishizawa)	81-86
Bioholonics Project (Mizuno)	82-87
Bioinformation Transfer Project (Hayaishi)	83-88
Superbugs Project (Horikoshi)	84-89

Name	Duration
Nano-Mechanism Project (Yoshida)	85-90
Solid Surface Project (Kuroda)	85-90
Quantum Magneto Flux Logic Project (Goto)	86-91
Molecular Dynamic Assembly Project (Hotani)	86-91
Biophoton Project (Inaba)	86-91
Terahertz Project (Nishizawa)	87-92
MorphoGenes Project (Furusawa)	87-92
Molecular Architecture Project (Kunitake)	87-92
Quantum Wave Project (Sakaki)	88-93
Micro Photoconversion Project (Maduhara)	88-93
Plant Ecochemical Project (Mizutani)	88-93
Electron Wavefront Project (Tonomura)	
Atomcraft Project (Aono)	
Genosphere Project (Ikeda)	
Metamelt Project (Kimura)	90-95
Protein Array Project (Nagayama)	90-95
Nutrient-stasis Project (Torii)	90-95
Chemirecognics Project (Shinkai)	90-95

Bio-oriented Technology Research Advancement Institution (BRAIN)

Capital investment in research projects – R&D companies – Ministry of Agriculture, Forestry and Fisheries (MAFF), ongoing projects

Name	Period
Research for the development of cold-resistant plant resources by biotechnology Hokkaido Green-bio Inst. Inc.	1987-1993
Studies on biotechnological breeding of florihorticultural bulbs and on their high-volume and high-speed culture systems Okinoerabu Bulb Bio-research Inst. Inc.	1987-1993
Research and development of mass production systems for seeds and seedling Nursery Technology Inc.	1987-1993
Studies on effective utilization of wooden biomass materials for use as animal feeds and other purposes Iwate Bio-research Centre Ltd.	1987-1993

Name	*Period*
Developmental research on genetic resources of brewing microorganisms Research Inst. of Brewing Resources	1987-1993
Developmental research on feed for fish aquaculture Marine Culture Centre	1987-1992
Developmental research on marine culture systems for "high class" fish yet to be developed Seatex Co.Ltd.	1987-1991
Developmental research on new types of processed rice Processed Rice Breeding Research Inst.	7 years
Establishment of hydrocultures of green plants Environmental Green Resource Development Centre	7 years
Developmental research on production of experimental animals NT Science Co.	7 years